DOCTORING THE MEDIA

The Reporting of Health and Medicine

Anne Karpf

Routledge: London

First published in 1988 by Routledge
11 New Fetter Lane, London EC4P 4EE

Published in the USA by Routledge
in association with Routledge, Chapman and Hall, Inc.
29 West 35th Street, New York, NY 10001

Set in 10/11 pt Palatino
by BookEns, Saffron Walden
and printed in Great Britain
by Cox & Wyman Ltd, Reading

British Library Cataloguing in Publication Data
Karpf, Anne
  Doctoring the media: the reporting of
  health and medicine.
  1. Medicine. Reporting by media
  I. Title
  610

ISBN 0-415-00250-8

For me,
but also for Josef and Natalia

REF:

KARPF, A. (1988) Doctoring The Media:
The Reporting of Health and Medicine.
London: Routledge.

Contents

Acknowledgments

I've always wanted to challenge the convention of humility in prefaces by starting a book with the claim that all its virtues should be credited to me, and its flaws to others. But here I am, forced to follow tradition because of the generous help I've received from so many people, who unfortunately can't be held accountable for my arguments or shortcomings.

The book's (distant) origins lay in a part-time M.Sc. in the Sociology of Health and Illness I took at the Polytechnic of the South Bank: thanks to some stimulating lecturers and especially to Jean Seaton for so ably nurturing my dissertation on medicine and television. This was based on a participant–observation study of Yorkshire TV's 'Where There's Life' series: thanks to Duncan Dallas and his team for the access they so liberally allowed me, and to the late Health Education Council, and its former Research Officer David St George in particular, for a travel grant.

I also intended to break with tradition by listing the many funding organisations who refused me grants, but I found better ways to use three pages. This book was written mostly in financial hardship, but I'd like to thank the Joseph Rowntree Charitable Trust for a grant which was invaluable in the research's early stages, and my only income through a difficult period. Thanks also to the British Council, and Sandy Eddington in particular, for a grant to visit the United States to do research, and to the British Sociological Association Support Fund for a small grant covering my research expenses in the BBC's Written Archives Centre. My parents generously helped me out with hardware and software – including a video and an Apricot computer – which immeasurably eased the task.

I'm grateful to the BBC for permission to use copyright material from the BBC Written Archives Centre, Caversham, in Chapters 2 and 10, and thanks to Jacqueline Kavanagh, Chief Archivist, for her help, and to Amanda Mares for her enthusiastic assistance there. I'm grateful to Dr Charles Fletcher for permission to quote from his first 'Your Life in Their Hands' script. Mallory Wober and Peter Dannheiser of the IBA, Robin McCron and David Paterson of the BBC, and Anne-Marie Bernon of Paris, were also helpful, and so was Nicholas Dorn. Sue Woodman in New York helped me set up my American trip and tracked down obscure articles I asked for, and thanks to her and Michael Matthewson for their warm hospitality in Manhatten. For theirs in San Francisco, thanks to Jerry Mander, Ani Vesel Mander, and Yari and Kai Mander.

Alison Macfarlane, Jill Rakusen, Paddy Scannell, and Helena Sheiham read chapters and made valuable comments. Wendy Farrant read all but the drama chapters: the book has profited hugely from her many stimulating suggestions and the always perceptive connections she made, and her unflagging enthusiasm was more important than she'll ever realise. Talia Rodgers reduced its bulk with intelligence, skill and sensitivity.

My friends have been encouraging and their high boredom thresholds impressive. Thanks especially to Corinne Pearlman, a loving and sustaining friend, and to Barbara Rosenbaum for her insight, love, and friendship through hard times.

To Esther Green, without whom none of it would have been possible, thanks beyond words.

And finally, Peter M. Lewis read the whole manuscript closely. His rigorous criticisms (I now grudgingly concede) have significantly improved the book. He has tolerated my absences and watched more TV programmes on medicine than anyone should have to. His encouragement, humour, cooking, and love have been enriching.

Anne Karpf
London, June 1987

Introduction

The media's longstanding interest in health and medicine has swelled in recent years into an obsession. Pages and programmes are crowded with patients offering up their illnesses, physical and emotional, for the viewers' gaze; doctors parading their novel skills and micro instruments; philosophers pondering medico-ethical conundrums; and testimonials from ex-hedonists renouncing their former ways and flaunting their healthy new routines.

One survey found, in a randomly selected fortnight, thirty-four British radio and television programmes or items (fictional and non-fictional) devoted to reproduction and childcare alone.[1] An American study of all daytime serials found that nearly half of all characters were involved in health-related occurrences.[2] And Jane Fonda's aerobics 'Workout' is the best-selling home video of all time.

Audiences respond eagerly to the media's offers of health information: a local radio health and fitness programme attracts 200 letters a day,[3] while the BBC received a quarter of a million requests for a booklet on healthy eating, part of its Food and Health Campaign.[4] And by all accounts, the public is greedy for more. In America, an NBC study of radio news found that 81 per cent of the general population wanted more news about health and medicine (while only 31 per cent wanted more political news, and 29 per cent more show business news).[5]

Despite their close dealings, the medical and broadcasting professions don't invariably minuet together in harmony. On the contrary, their relationship has been regularly riven by crises. Over the past decade controversies about the induction of labour (1975), whooping-cough vaccine and vaccine-damaged children

1

(1976/7), and organ transplants and brain-death (1980), have provoked hostile salvoes from both sides and wracked the relationship to snapping-point. The BBC was so stung by criticism of its medical coverage that it published a report on the subject in 1976.[6] The medical profession thinks television and radio so important that since 1978 the *British Medical Journal* has carried a regular 'Medicine and the Media' page. And government and industry have entered the fray, lambasting TV reports on mental hospitals (1981), asbestos (1982), and nuclear power and leukaemia (1983).

This book's central argument is that, in spite of greater diversity in the media's reporting of health and medical issues over the past decade, medical definitions and perceptions still prevail, and squeeze out more contentious, oppositional viewpoints which take an environmental approach and look at the politics of health. These are especially significant since, as we'll see, it isn't generally medical treatment which crucially determines how healthy we are.

By excluding or marginalising other perspectives – notably, a more explicitly political analysis of the origins of illness – the media play a significant part in narrowing public debate about health, illness and medicine. This approach is an analysis of the ways in which medicine as a social and ideological force is fortified and amplified by the mass media, among other cultural institutions.

I'm mindful of the significant gaps here: there's little on media coverage of mental health, for instance, or of how the health issues of the Third World are reported. Though partly a problem of time and space, my omissions also reflect those of the media itself, and this is a problem of media analysis: what I've lingered on is what the media itself lingers on, and is consequently just as partial.

Mirrored or framed?

In spite of decades of media studies, the idea is still rife that the mass media simply and neutrally reflect events and debates which happen 'out there'. Many people still believe that there's a 'natural fit' between an event or process and its media representation, which is unmediated by the production team. 'The camera never lies' remains a potent maxim (albeit a rather battered one). Its proponents argue that media coverage of medicine is more extensive and crisis-ridden these days because of the unprecedented problems which medicine is confronting, new developments in technology bringing in train new ethical problems.

But this view obscures the fact that it's impossible to make a programme on any subject without articulating ideas about that subject. Even if you're a fence-sitting liberal, who swears never to have knowingly held an opinion, the very way that you define your subject, and mark out the scope of your programme, speaks and conveys meaning. It establishes a way for the subject to be considered. It invites the viewer to ask certain questions about the subject, and discourages them from raising other ones.

This isn't an indictment of journalism, or something which the ideologically-kosher broadcaster would avoid. As any journalist who's wrestled with intractable lumps of information will testify, material and data can't be managed and processed into an accessible form (like an article or a programme) without using a 'frame', angle or a peg. Frames have been described as 'principles of selection, emphasis, and presentation composed of little tacit theories about what exists, what happens, and what matters'.[7] The question I'll be asking is whether the persistent frames (or approaches, as I'll be calling them) used in the media coverage of health and illness permit a healthy debate, and why and how alternative frames or approaches are regularly excluded.

A difference in diagnosis

Medical opinion about the media isn't either homogeneous or static. At any one time there are differing views about the media among doctors, and even the dominant beliefs have changed over time. Few today, even among the most camera-shy doctors, would go along with the opinion of the famous surgeon William Osler when, in a lecture to nurses and medical students in 1907, he declared: 'In the life of every successful physician, there comes the temptation to toy with the Delilah of the Press – daily and otherwise. There are times when she may be courted with satisfaction but beware: Sooner or later she is sure to play the harlot and has left many a man shorn of his strength, viz the confidence of his professional brethren.'[8]

Yet even when 'Your Life in Their Hands' began in 1958, the majority of doctors, as we'll see, believed that it was wrong to submit medicine to television's gaze in any way, that a little public learning was a dangerous thing, and that anxiety and hypochondria would ripple through the audience. But the medical profession has learned to live with, and even in some cases to love, 'the box' and doctors have wised up about popularising. Indeed, 'how to' writings represent a major proportion of medical literature about the media: how to prepare for an interview, how to present your self to your best advantage, how to retain editorial control, etc.

The main contemporary medical criticism of the media is that it's alarmist and sensationalist, fanning controversy. Typical is an American doctor who berates the media for

> sounding alarums and heightening public anxiety whenever evidence, no matter how tenuous or unconfirmed, is presented linking a commonly available substance with cancer .... Allegations against artificial sweeteners, atomic energy plants, food colorings and preservatives, pharmaceutical products, and industrial chemicals are made almost daily and keep the public in a state of fear that borders on hysteria.[9]

The media are also thought to be gunning for the medical profession itself and the medicine it practises, conducting a 'trial by television'. According to another American doctor, some journalists and broadcasters seem determined

> to frighten people with the potential dangers of careless and indifferent doctors; to provoke malpractice suits and generally to portray physicians as an overpaid, inadequately trained, selfish, union-card-carrying group whose chief purpose is to play golf on Wednesday, split fees, drive expensive, flashy cars, and refuse to make house calls.[10]

And the media's inaccuracy is a common target of doctors, apparently corroborated by a succession of American 'accuracy studies' which record the error-rate in articles about science as judged by scientists who acted as the articles' sources.[11]

Many scientists and medical researchers believe that there's a fundamental incompatibility between themselves and the media: between their own unpressurised timetables and copiously-documented research, and the media's '500 words by yesterday' orientation, in thrall to the deadline. Reporters are seen as almost wilfully distorting medicine for their own base ends (scoops, ratings, and newspaper sales), and misleading the public into wanting a new drug or giving up an old one, routinely creating panics through their biases.

It isn't hard to fathom the kind of reporting which many in the medical profession (along with most other professions) would ideally like. The British Medical Association's evidence to the Pilkington Committee on Broadcasting in 1960 was revealing (and perhaps not so very dated) when it declared that

> nothing but good can come from the acceptance of the idea, encouraged by good medical broadcasts, that the doctor has a scientific and logical basis for his actions, and does his best to carry them out with compassion for the sick and suffering.[12]

In general, the medical establishment is hostile to images of medicine which differ significantly from its own, and deviations are likely to be branded as 'distortions' and 'bias' (see Chapter 10), part of a recurring medical chorus on the media's irresponsibility.

Medical critics of broadcasting are generally in agreement with non-medical critics in their opposition to the media's infatuation with breakthroughs and 'miracle cures', with doctors arguing that patients' hopes are often unreasonably and mis-leadingly raised.

But at the same time the medical establishment generally wants the media to reproduce medical values and ideology. I'll be suggesting that it's (partly) because journalists have so enthusiastically adopted a belief in the efficacy of medicine that they're attracted to stories of breakthroughs and cures. In other words, the medical orientation favoured by doctors has itself, to some extent, generated the media excesses which doctors deplore.

How do the makers of medical programmes see their own practice? Generally, they argue that they're reporters who cover the subject objectively, and not polemicists and dogmatists peddling one line or other. They dismiss those who discern recurring patterns in representations either by adopting the 'transparent' view of the media described above (i.e., we're simply reflecting the most important things happening in medicine now) or by reproducing journalistic ideology: that they balance competing views, and act as conduits for rival opinions to reach the public, taking pains to avoid seepage of their personal beliefs. They see themselves as mediators between the lay public and the increasingly specialised world of science, bridging two cultures.

They also argue that, if their programmes are faulted for their inaccuracy and sensationalism, the medical profession itself is partly to blame. It's too elitist and prolix, with a predilection for complicated syntax and passive constructions. As a former science correspondent of CBS News in America put it:

> Before I begin an interview, I ask the expert to use lay terms. Unfortunately, often the explanations still sound as if they are being offered to a colleague and not the average person. The language gap is one of the most vexing problems encountered in medical reporting.[13]

Broadcasters want doctors to defer to them on how best to communicate with the audience, and a joust of professionals sometimes results: which will prevail?[14] Al Byrne, maker of a weekly Irish radio medical programme 'Discovery', explains that

> For a subject to get an airing on 'Discovery' it's not sufficient that, in the medical field . . . doctors may think a subject is of sufficient importance to be presented. It has to meet . . . other requirements as well. And it's a broadcaster who has the training, knowledge and expertise to decide that and not the doctor.[15]

Broadcasters repeatedly argue that they're thwarted by the jargon and scientific nitpicking of the medical profession, which doesn't appreciate the fervid public interest in certain treatments and illnesses, and doesn't realise that entertainment and gloss aren't necessarily the enemies of substance and information.

But it would be misleading to depict medico–journalist relations as predominantly rocky. On the contrary, as we'll see, the relationship is more often symbiotic. And a major theme in the writings of both sides is the need for cooperation. Dr Charles Fletcher, the first presenter of 'Your Life in Their Hands', argued that 'Every doctor should now be willing to collaborate with the media today in public education about what medicine has to offer in prevention and cause of disease.'[16] And an American doctor succinctly suggested, 'It's easier if all doctors understand something about communication, than if all journalists study medicine.'[17]

The collaborative approach is favoured by health educators too: they often want to join with broadcasters in using the media to disseminate health information. Their ideas will be examined more fully in Chapters 3 and 13, but generally their campaigns draw on ideas from social psychology and communication research: they seek ways of making their messages more persuasive, and they're especially interested in how people absorb, comprehend, retain and act on information. They see the problem with the media as one of developing better methods of communication, and not of venal and hopelessly populist broadcasters.

There's another, less common approach to media coverage of medicine which doesn't originate in either camp, and which explicitly addresses issues of institutional power and ideology, but in a fatalist and monochrome way. Its adherents believe that broadcasting yields without resistance to the imperatives of the state and private capital, which they consider anyway indistinguishable. Censorship, direct or indirect, sieves out dissenting opinion. Broadcasters and doctors alike are merely apparatchiks, they say, bearers of ideology, whose knee-jerk conservatism ensures programmes which uncritically reinforce state and professional power, in this case medical authority.

Such a summary is a little unfair, partly because it's rare to find (at least in print, and beyond the pages of the party political broadsheet) such a crude example, and partly because there's something in it. It does, at least, go beyond the claims of both parties. But it's altogether too simplistic a position, which doesn't acknowledge the contradictions and complexities, and gives us no way of understanding how and why dissenting programmes get made. Programmes are produced by real people who aren't simply the victims of false consciousness or institutional lackeys who suspend all critical impulses for promotion's sake. They do exercise an autonomy of sorts, though within limits. Our task, as media researchers have suggested, is to discover those limits.[18]

This book starts from a different position to the four (of

doctors, broadcasters, health educators, and critics of the mass media) outlined above. It rejects the idea that all medical programmes are similarly and inevitably uncritical of medicine. Nor does it see media representations of medicine as a problem located either in the media or in medicine, as if either broadcasters should represent medicine more accurately and curb their scoop-hunger, or doctors should flush out the jargon and learn demotic speech, or both. Each of these strategies assumes that there's an unproblematic and scientific thing called medicine, which the media should reflect or convey. Each ultimately takes the medical profession's own definition of itself and its practice as benchmark.

But if we give up the idea that the medical profession's view of medicine is necessarily and invariably the only authentic one, and treat its definitions instead as only one among a number of other, competing accounts of medical practice, we're able to get beyond questions of distortion and bias. We can then examine a variety of different approaches to medicine in the media, and ask why particular images dominate at certain times, and why media representations change. Now we're no longer obliged to swing between the two poles (media and medicine) with their two inevitable responses. On the contrary, both the medical and media response are now available as subjects to be examined: we can try to trace the connections between two powerful professions, each with their own traditions and ideologies. With medical definitions no longer the arbiter of the 'correctness' of media images, we're freer to try to unravel media medicine.

1

Doctoring the Box

If we're a therapeutic society, nowhere is it more evident than in the media. Medico-dramas jostle with science and medical documentaries, medical news stories are followed by medical phone-ins, and cholesterol conscious food programmes preceed health obsessed soap operas. How can we generalise about so many different programmes? For all their peculiarities, programmes are rarely one-off originals, but share assumptions and form discernable patterns.

This chapter identifies four different types of radio and TV health and medical programmes: the medical approach, celebrating medicine's curative powers; the consumer approach, criticising the doctor–patient relationship; the look-after-yourself approach, appealing for changes in individual behaviour; and the environmental approach, stressing the social origins of illness. It also discusses their different ideologies, and examines which type predominates. Producers get understandably fractious when media analysts try to impose rigid frameworks on their programmes, but these four types aren't meant to be an exhaustive compendium of all medical programming. They're skeletons which individual programmes flesh out in their own way, with cross-breeds and hybrids aplenty. And organising medical programmes in this way shouldn't be taken to mean that the media originate their underlying conceptions of health and medicine. On the contrary, the four approaches are all current in the wider culture.

The medical approach

When we think of tele-medicine, it's the icons of the medical approach which come to mind: the white-coated male doctor, the stethoscope, the heartbeat, the ambulance, the test-tube, the pill, the injection, the operating theatre, the drip – images of medicine so powerful, yet so naturalised, that they've penetrated every corner of our thinking. This is the approach that seems so self-evident and taken-for-granted that it's almost invisible to us.

The medical approach is organised around diseases, perceived as disrupters of the body's normal functioning: as abnormal and pathological. We 'get it', 'catch it', 'get rid of it', 'shake it off' – it's discontinuous from our normal life. The illness itself is considered unproblematic; cancer or measles, bronchitis or a broken leg, are seen as discrete physical entities, no matter in which culture or individual they occur, or who has the power to diagnose them. Illnesses in this approach are pre-existing categories, discovered but not invented by human beings: they have a life independent of social structure and social organisation.

The medical approach is largely uninterested in the causes of disease. In a sense it subscribes to a 'pigeon-dropping' view of illness: illness strikes an individual by chance or accident, with no more reason or logic than a pigeon uses in selecting the unfortunate victim of its droppings.[1] A major aspect of the medical approach is the cure, effected by the doctor applying medical treatment to the patient's body. It's an approach variously characterised as a 'gee-whizz' or Eureka! line, with a belief in the 'magic bullet' or 'technological fix'. It's also been called an instrumental, mechanistic, or engineering model, premissed on a mind–body split (commonly dated back to Descartes), with the body serviceable like a car.

Programmes using the medical approach usually feature acute disease (an episode of illness which leads to a crisis), rather than chronic, degenerative disease. The medical programme emphasises sophisticated, high-technology, hospital-based treatments (although primary and community care are increasingly getting a medical approach from the media). It favours biological explanations, locating the source and solution to health problems in individual biology, the body's cells and biochemistry. It invokes genetic or physiological explanations for phenomena which could also be explained socially or psychologically, from alcoholism and crime to postnatal depression. For instance, a programme describes research suggesting a chemical defect in the brains of suicidal people (and a possible chemical antidote),[2] a newspaper story reports on a study arguing that earning power is an inherited trait,[3] and an American TV two-hour block-buster on depression discusses possible chemical and physiological origins and treatments without a nod to possible social causes.[4]

'They'll find a cure for it' is an integral part of the medical approach, which sees the history of medicine as a soaring graph of progress, with successive scientific discoveries and break-throughs extending human knowledge and curative powers, and replacing primitive nostrums and folk remedies. (Disease in the Third World, with its 'natural' causes, and the possibility of a Western medical technological cure, fits this thesis snugly.) The bad old days are contrasted with the better todays, and the promise of even better tomorrows. As one book puts it, the history of medicine is expressed in triumphalist terms.[5]

Indeed, we use a whole vocabulary of combat to talk about illness in which healing is a pitched battle between doctor and disease.[6] Patients are urged to fight their illness, to conquer it: if they die, the disease is said to have 'claimed another victim'. In turn, the language of illness has furnished us with a metaphor for evil and aggression: as one writer said, 'To describe a phenomenon as a cancer is an incitement to violence.'[7]

The medical approach also equates health with medicine: better health has come from better medicine: more medicine (more hospitals, more medical technology, more doctors, and more spending on health services) will create more health.[8] The effectiveness of medicine is taken as read: the strapping health of today's youngsters and the staunch longevity of old people is considered undeniable proof. At the same time, because the National Health Service is part of the public sector of the economy, better health (i.e., more services) is thought to result only from the creation of more 'wealth' in the market or private sector of the economy. To afford the NHS, an unproductive 'drain on the economy', therefore requires growth in the productive part of the economy (the goods or services that can be sold).[9]

At the heart of the medical approach lies the doctor, con-sidered the legitimate authority on what constitutes disease and how it should be treated. Doctors' views of health and illness are accorded a unique value, far beyond that of other health professionals such as nurses or paramedics. Not that the medical approach gags all criticism of medicine. Medical programmes often advocate more public spending on medicine, debate the cuts in medical services, or criticise Britain's low expenditure on the National Health Service. But such discussions are largely quantitative: more medicine or less medicine, publicly-funded or private medical care are the issues, and not the sort of qualitative questions raised in some of the other approaches. And though these programmes sometimes air differences between doctors or take issue with a medical treatment, the criticisms mostly come from other doctors, thereby gaining legitimacy.

For above all, the medical approach validates experts, especially the expertise of the doctor, and the visual grammar of medical programmes tends to reinforce the doctor's centrality and authority. The camera is often positioned so that we see the patient through the doctor's eyes: it's situated in the doctor's surgery or in a medical meeting before the patient walks in. We viewers, like the doctor, are already there when the patient enters. The medical gaze prevails.

The prototype of the medical approach is BBC TV's 'Your Life in Their Hands' (YLITH) (Chapter 2 describes its birth). It has a mythical quality. It celebrates surgery, high-technology curative medicine, and pharmaceutical therapies. It tells us that we can be made whole again. Each 'YLITH' programme shows an individual undergoing hospital treatment. At the start they're sick. In the course of the film, doctors in distinguished teaching hospitals operate on them. (In many of the programmes, the surgeon after probing locates a malign growth and cuts it out, visibly vanquishing evil – not for nothing has this been called heroic surgery.) By the end of the film the patient is well, or well on the road to recovery. (Encouraging progress reports are often voiced-over the closing credits.) Medical treatment appears largely successful and rational. Operations are almost never shown to fail. (A 'YLITH' where the patient has died has never been transmitted. Although this is partly through courtesy to the relatives, in one case relatives gave permission but the producer nevertheless decided not to transmit.[10]) And non-surgical treatments are almost never shown, except as adjuncts to, or unsuccessful therapies en route to, the operation.

The only major change to the programme since its inception in 1958 is that since 1981 it's begun before there's a clear diagnosis of the patient's illness, then followed the patient through the diagnostic procedure and returned to them at the end of their treatment. The change is significant: a response to the new spirit of the consumer approach (see below), so that the patient wouldn't be seen simply as a slab of meat, awaiting the surgeon's knife. But it doesn't substantially alter the programme: the diagnosis acts as a kind of question, to which the operation is the answer.

The series is presented by a doctor, since 1981 an obstetrician and gynaecologist specialising in microsurgical treatment of infertility. But he ventures into medical worlds alien to him as well as to us, the viewers. He is our guide. He mediates medical knowledge to us, getting the surgeons to explain their techniques. The programme is compelling and hugely successful, notching a regular audience of six million. It's almost impossible to watch it without declaring – no matter how strong your initial cynicism or resistance – 'marvellous what they can do these days'. The series is a guided tour to the other side of the ether, displaying medical practice to an audience which can never have seen it like that, since we're never sentient at the time of our own operations. 'Your Life in Their Hands' offers us the chance to become medical voyeurs, and it's irresistible.

Although 'YLITH' has been uniquely successful among British medical programmes, some of its narrative conventions are shared by similar series, like the prestigious BBC science and medical series 'Horizon' and its American sister programme, WGBH's 'Nova', both of which report primarily on medical and scientific research. Programmes using the medical approach are made by general features or science departments and are broadcast in peak evening or later evening slots, but this approach also recurs in educational programmes, broadcast in the afternoon or late at night. They address an audience of individuals, potential patients, implicitly telling us 'this is what medicine could do for you'. They describe a world largely rational and ordered, where science increasingly dominates nature, where medical knowledge is incremental, cumulative, and systematic. They invite us to feel confident in a knowable and caring world; they make us feel better.

The consumer approach

If the doctor has the starring role in the medical programme, the patient is the leading player in the consumer programme. And where the operation or clinical investigation is the climax of the medical approach, at the heart of the consumer approach is the consultation.

The doctor is no longer seen in isolation, or in relation to his panoply of medical technology. The doctor is seen by the patient, and the doctor–patient relationship held up for scrutiny. The medical approach took a 'doctor knows best line': the patient was shown gratefully acquiescing to the superior knowledge of the doctor, their interests identical – the well-being of the patient. But the consumer approach introduces the thorny issue of power, and suggests a conflict of interest: the doctor exercises his power, the patient struggles to empower herself. At best, it's negotiation; at worst, it's war.

Gender isn't accidental in the consumer approach: often it's central. The doctor's authority is seen as deriving partly from his social power as a man, while the passivity and powerlessness of the patient is attributed to some extent to her socialisation as a woman. (See also Chapter 3 for a discussion of this.) Indeed, the consumer approach found its most perfect expression in media coverage of childbirth (the subject of Chapter 4). Consumer programmes question the organisation of medical care. They criticise doctors for being uncommunicative, arrogant and patronising, for not explaining diagnoses and prognoses sufficiently and for not listening to the patient.

This theme has generated a huge literature, with many publications and groups articulating the view that it's only when the patient wrests back some power, when the relationship between doctor and patient becomes more equal, that the patient will improve. The College of Health was formed in 1983 because of

> the present imbalance between medical professionals and their patients. The former have power, the latter do not . . . . It is . . . due to the large gap between the knowledge and information of the two parties. Information (as always) is power. The best way of putting professionals and patients on more level terms is therefore to endow patients with more of it.[11]

A Patients' Charter, drawn up in 1982 by the National Consumer Council, declared that 'consumers will get the best of the health service only when they know what is reasonable to expect of it and what their rights and responsibilities are, and when they have the confidence and skill to assert them'.[12] Others are more assertive: 'Your body belongs to you and only you should decide what to do with it and what to have done with it.'[13]

To this end, many consumer programmes give information, the sort which the doctor rarely gives but which could help the patient make choices. They compare different kinds of treatment, report on self-help groups for people with particular diseases or disabilities, recommend sources of health information, spell out the consequences of various drugs, and suggest ways of avoiding them. Doctors sometimes decry them as 'trial by media', but such programmes aren't necessarily hostile to medical technology, sometimes calling for *more* technology or *better* technology.

When the consumer programme looks into the causes of illness, it usually lays the blame at the door of medical treatment itself: so-called 'iatrogenesis', illness resulting from drugs prescribed by doctors.[14] It campaigns against the long-term, addictive use of GP-prescribed tranquillisers, or investigates harmful contraceptives such as the Dalkon Shield.

Above all, consumer programmes introduce the patient's experience of illness, and often have a confessional feel – patients 'telling it like it is' in human interest stories elicited by the presenter with 'what does it feel like?' questions. They validate the patient's perception of disease, and often powerfully advocate self-help. It's consumer medical programmes and writings which have been pejoratively labelled 'doctor-bashing'. Doctors are often the baddies of these programmes and, as with the medical approach, they're assumed to be uniquely powerful, their inadequacies held accountable for the inadequacies in medical care.[15]

The consumer approach is common in afternoon or early evening radio and television slots, aimed specifically at a female audience, addressed as mothers and carers as well as patients. It's often found in radio phone-ins and TV and radio 'social action' programmes recruiting volunteers and putting viewers and listeners in touch with social welfare agencies. Consumer programmes are often studio-based discussions, frequently within magazine or education programmes, and some of their arguments can be heard regularly in the American media. They rarely come from science departments.

The look-after-yourself approach

Another set of images has now joined, and often supplanted, the medical and consumer ones. Where once the camera lingered lovingly on an operation, it's now just as likely to track along supermarket shelves. The patient is no longer photographed only in the GP's surgery: now we see her cooking in her kitchen, as a track-suited jogger, or in a leotard, working out in an aerobics or dance studio. Preventive health has arrived on the public agenda.

The new approach appears to challenge medicine, by looking outside biology for the causes of illness and not seeing medicine as a solution. If there was any theory of causality in the medical approach it was that illness resulted from biological aberration – a defective organism, a limb gone awry. The look-after-yourself approach, on the other hand, reinstates the mind and will of the patient: illness is the result of harmful individual habits or a 'lifestyle' undertaken voluntarily – eating the wrong foods, drinking too much, smoking, lack of exercise, and stress. Where the consumer programme saw patients as innocent victims, the look-after-yourself programme sees them as active, though perhaps unwitting, self-harmers.

This was in part a response to research and debate about the limits of medicine (the title of a key book by Ivan Illich published in 1976) which popularised research demonstrating the relative unimportance of medical services in producing the past century's changes in life expectancy, and suggesting that a vast amount of contemporary clinical care was incidental to the curing of disease. In tandem ran a belief that medicine, though effective, had done all the curing it was able to, and that 'curative medicine may be increasingly subject to the law of diminishing returns'.[16] It was becoming evident that infectious diseases (such as TB, measles, whooping-cough, diphtheria, and pneumonia), the main cause of death in Western societies in previous eras, had been replaced by new chronic and degenerative diseases (such as cancer, heart disease, stroke, mental illness) which were proving alarmingly intractable to the arsenal of curative medical treatments.

Indeed, these diseases had causes quite unlike the idea of 'defective biology' so favoured hitherto. Their origins could be traced back to eating unhealthy foods, smoking and drinking, etc. One doctor contrasted the old orthodoxies with the new assertions in this way: 'It is assumed we are ill and are made well, whereas it is nearer the truth to say that we are well and are made ill.'[17] Illness is no longer pathology or a deviation from the norm. On the contrary, it's our personal norms – most people's lifestyle – which make us sick. But if illness is caused by individual habits it can also be prevented, and it's here that the look-after-yourself approach diverges so dramatically from the medical one. No longer can the medical profession reassuringly hold out the prospect of a cure. Instead, it's the individual who's credited with the ability to prevent their illness.

A series of government reports, consultative documents and White Papers embodied the new beliefs. The very title of the first, 'Prevention and health: everybody's business', published in 1976, seemed to challenge the conventional view that health was only doctors' business. The 1979 DHSS discussion booklet 'Eating for Health' argued that to reduce the 'diseases of affluence', each individual should modify their diet. The Health Education Council also entered the fray, making its message plain by calling its campaign 'Look After Yourself'. And medical organisations too uninhibitedly backed the new approach, offering medical evidence of the consequences of unhealthy personal habits.

Implicit in all their arguments is a cluster of beliefs about human behaviour examined more fully in Chapter 3. Essentially, an unhealthy lifestyle was primarily put down to ignorance and irresponsibility: with more accurate information and motivation to take responsibility, people would change their lives and become healthier. In this approach, individuals are accorded almost unqualified powers to shape their lives, with their future physical well-being their priority.

The media took up the new approach with unbounded enthusiasm. Where Victorian public health campaigners had railed against germs, twentieth-century tele-doctors cautioned darkly against cholesterol. The perils of sugar were expounded, the benefits of fibre extolled, and it sometimes seemed as if, alongside the five giant evils which Beveridge urged social policy to attack – Want, Disease, Ignorance, Squalor, and Idleness – were now two more: Fat and Flab. TV presenters gamely got into the hot seat, demonstrating arduous fitness regimes to achieve the fashionably lean, spare look. Doctors were recruited into health education, paunchless GPs filmed with their families at breakfast happily eating fibrous bran out of hand-thrown pottery bowls. And chain-smoking human guinea-pigs attempted to quit their bad habit before millions of weekly onlookers. Advice and information about avoiding illness poured out of the media, often in concert with medical organisations and the Health Education Council. All these programmes dispensed information, like consumer programmes, but they told the audience how to avoid illness, not what to do when they had it. They showed viewers how to stay away from the doctor, not how to get more from him or her. They spoke of responsibilities, not rights.

While almost no part of the media refused the new approach, it surfaced especially in programmes made by continuing education departments and magazine programmes, often presented by tele-doctors like Dr Miriam Stoppard and Dr Alan Maryon-Davis. In the United States it's also ubiquitous, especially in news segments and morning television, with 'medical anchors' like Dr Art Ulene and Dr Timothy Johnson dispensing health education while the nation breakfasts. Indeed, the involvement of doctor–presenters in media health education is striking, suggesting a symbiotic relationship between medicine and health education discussed in Chapter Three.

Perhaps the most telling illustration of the triumph of the look-after-yourself approach is a programme proposed in 1982 (although never actually made) by the producer of 'Your Life in Their Hands' – the classic medical programme – which was intended as a successor to 'YLITH' but devoted to the prevention of ill-health. Its working title was 'Your Life in Your Hands'.

The environmental approach

Environmental programmes leave the hospital and gymnasium far behind. The camera is more likely to be panning along a factory conveyor-belt where unhealthy foods are being processed, or collaring workers outside a factory gate to quiz them about their firm's health and safety record. A TV series about health using the environmental approach only ventured inside a hospital for one out of its eight programmes, and that was to examine the poor conditions in which the hospital staff worked.[18] We've abandoned the world of consumption, and entered that of production.

Not that the environmental approach is wholly dissimilar to the look-after-yourself one. Both reject the notions of pathology and cure endemic to the medical programme, and turn instead to the preventable causes of illness. Both believe that there are limits to medicine. Like the look-after-yourself advocates, the environmentalists draw on research demonstrating that the impact of medical advances in the nineteenth and twentieth centuries was significantly less than generally assumed. When the mortality data of those centuries were juxtaposed with the dates when techniques like vaccination and inoculation were first developed and applied, infectious diseases were found to have declined long before effective medical measures were introduced to combat them. Researchers argued that, with the notable exceptions of streptomycin and polio vaccine, medical techniques had been less important than better nutrition, and purification of water and sewage disposal which improved hygiene and sanitary arrangements.

But though the environmentalists' and look-after-yourselfers' diagnosis was similar, they advanced different solutions. Where look-after-yourselfers maintained that current diseases resulted from individual human behaviour or lifestyle rather than social conditions, the environmentalists believe today's chronic and degenerative diseases to be as environmentally or socially-caused as the diseases of the past. They challenge the belief that a wealthier society is a healthier one, and implicate the social structure itself. For example, more indiscriminate production and consumption means producing and using more cars which, they argue, leads to more accidents, more injury and ill-health.

Similarly more industrial production causes more occupational disease, necessitating more costly medical care, paid for by more production and economic growth, which then creates more disease – and the cycle continues.[19]

Drawing on ideas from political economy, the environmentalists suggest that we can't separate patterns of health and illness from the mode of production in which they occur. They argue that the health needs of the mass of the population conflict with the imperatives of the production process and the quest for profits, making health a relatively low social priority, and distributing ill-health along class lines. Bad housing, poverty, the policies of the food and tobacco industries, sexism and heterosexism, racism, discrimination against people with disabilities – all combine to produce illness and stress. And if illness is largely socially caused, then it can be only socially – and not medically or individually – prevented.

Unlike the look-after-yourself approach, the environmental approach to health is explicitly political. It was medically endorsed in the summer of 1980 with the publication of the Black Report, 'Inequalities in Health', commissioned by the DHSS and written by a working group chaired by the President of the Royal College of Physicians. This suggested that the so-called diseases of affluence were in fact diseases of poverty. It traced the differences in patterns of illness and death between the different social classes from the cradle to the grave, and examined their unequal access to medical facilities. It rejected biological explanations, medical solutions, and look-after-yourself notions, and was followed up in 1987 by a Health Education Council report 'The Health Divide: Inequalities in Health in the 1980s'. Such reports in themselves generate media coverage, but they're rarely incorporated into journalists' framework, and used to shape subsequent media coverage of health.

What I've called the environmental approach contains various bedfellows. Marxists see the origins of illness in *social relations* within capitalist societies. They argue that health needs are commodified, turned into pills and medical consultations which essentially don't disturb the production process or existing social relations.[20] Liberals, on the other hand, focus on single issues and *social conditions* which, though socially created, can be improved through more commodities (services, equipment) or less (the reduction of environmental hazards, etc), i.e., still a movement of commodities.[21] The media rarely sing the full-throated Marxist refrain. When they adopt an environmental approach they opt rather for the liberal critique, with its single issues and incremental solutions.

The environmental approach to health developed as part of growing public disquiet about science in general, with technological solutions no longer seen as unquestionably safe panaceas. The nineteenth-century view of science and technology as essentially neutral and progressive was increasingly challenged by protests against thalidomide, pollution, nuclear weapons and energy, and other environmental and occupational hazards. Programmes using the environmental approach to health tend to tease out one specific occupational or environmental hazard, and trace its origins and effects. They originate more often in current affairs than science departments, where there's a symbiotic relationship between broadcasters and the medical profession. Current affairs journalists on 'World in Action', 'TV Eye' or 'Panorama' are more likely to treat science and medicine as political issues, and their environmental programmes are often investigative and campaigning reports, presented by named reporters heard in interviews and voice-over, and sometimes seen delivering a piece to camera, unlike the medical programme (such as 'Horizon') where the interviewer is generally edited out. They report on issues like toxic waste, the excesses of the pharmaceutical industry, and environmentally-caused cancer. Their programmes appeal not for individual but political solutions.

'Panorama's 1983 two-part series on the anti-arthritic drug Opren, whose licence was suspended after sixty linked deaths, was called 'The Opren Scandal'. It's hard to imagine a 'Horizon' or another programme from a science department called 'The . . . Scandal', unless it referred to something which occurred 100 years ago, or in another country, or had been certified as scandalous by the medical profession itself.[22] A major, controversial attempt to introduce an environmental perspective into the medical debate came in the BBC's 1980 Reith Lectures, where Ian Kennedy argued that any significant improvement in people's health would only come through major political, social and economic changes. In America, the environmental approach is found in programmes like CBC's '60 Minutes' series, investigating issues such as the health effects of herbicide sprays. But such stories appear less commonly on the three major commercial networks than on the Public Broadcasting System (PBS), and are always rare, partly because of American broadcasting's news orientation and its comparative lack of documentaries, but also because (even on PBS) they require sponsorship, and commercial sponsors for contentious subjects are hard to find.

Beyond Belief

Broadcasters often react bullishly to the idea that their theoretical positions can be analysed in this way, ridiculing the notion that they sit and ponder over which approach to adopt. On the contrary, they insist, when they've chosen their subject, they adopt the approach they think will interest the audience, satisfy the boss, and perhaps glean them some respectable audience ratings, a good review, and a dash of personal satisfaction. They're astonished when others read so much into such an innocent and relatively straightforward undertaking.

Certainly, most broadcasters experience their work as proceeding in an *ad hoc* fashion, making individual pragmatic editorial decisions to deal with technical, institutional, and (occasionally) political problems as they arise. Their programmes, they claim (sometimes wistfully) are made 'on the cutting-room floor', that is, the producer's line only really emerges in the editing, and I've personal experience of this. BBC TV's Head of Science and Features Department in 1976 declared that 'We do not sit down at Television Centre and draw up a list of objectives, then devise medical programmes to achieve them. It is programmes that make policy, not policy that makes programmes.'[23] Nor do the commercial television companies have a common, expressed medical programme policy as such. And all that the Independent Broadcasting Authority enjoins, in its programme guidelines, is that TV medical programmes should be based on competent professional advice, and give a hearing to more than one opinion on matters of potential controversy.

But just because producers or researchers, when embarking

on a programme, don't consciously or intentionally choose one theoretical position or another, doesn't mean that their practice is totally apolitical or non-ideological. It's strange that there's so much resistance to this idea within the mass media (among producers of all kinds, not just medical ones) when it's a commonplace of literary or stage criticism. No one shudders in disbelief when we analyse a Shakespeare play or a poem by Keats and see in it things of which their authors weren't aware and perhaps didn't intend. And when critics categorise a novel or painting as belonging to the classical or modernist tradition (which the artist may not have heard of), no one squeals at the illegitimacy of the enterprise (though they may dispute the category). So why the hostility with the broadcast media?

It can't be just because the authors of the mass media 'text' are (mostly) still alive. For an adequate explanation, we'd need to inquire more deeply into the ideology of broadcasting, and indeed the ideology of everyday life. As one writer on culture put it, 'what seems obvious and natural is not necessarily so, but . . . on the contrary the "obvious" and the "natural" are not *given* but *produced* in a specific society by the ways in which that society talks and thinks about itself and its experience'.[24] The 'obvious' and 'natural' approaches which makers of medical programmes adopt have been produced in our society from taken-for-granted beliefs. It's only when we start to examine another society's 'naturals' (or our own past ones) that their theoretical underskirt shows: we see a set of beliefs invisible to those who hold them. In a sense, when examining our ideas about medicine and the media, we need to become the anthropologists of our own culture.

So when producers and researchers devise programmes, they don't somehow bypass their culture, nor can any of us do so, however much we might fantasise about being professional noble savages. Suggesting that programme makers draw on social habits and meanings isn't a criticism but an explanation. To those who completely refuse the idea that their practice is underpinned by theories of any kind, one can only reply, as one critic has, 'Hostility to theory usually means an opposition to other people's theories and an oblivion to one's own.'[25]

There's another argument sometimes advanced by broadcasters. A particular subject, they suggest, offers up its own approach: there's something intrinsically 'environmental' about an industrial disaster like that at Bhopal in India in 1984, where thousands of people died after a leak of the lethal gas methyl isocyanate from the Union Carbide plant. To cover that subject with a look-after-yourself approach would have been inappropriate and irrelevant. Similarly other subjects, like the doctor–patient relationship, demand a consumer approach, and so on.

There's some truth in this argument. Obviously, with Bhopal and other major industrial accidents like those at Flixborough in 1974 and Seveso in 1978, journalists will be expected to report on their industrial origin and try to discover who was responsible and how a repetition can be avoided. But even subjects like these can be treated in a variety of ways. An American study compared coverage of occupational hazards in the mainstream and alternative press, and found significant differences: while the alternative press stressed the structural causes of occupational hazards (American socio-economic values, the profit motive, government/industry links, etc.), the mainstream press emphasised bureaucratic and technical causes (red tape, scientific and technical problems, etc.).[26]

Moreover, most medical programmes – and even news stories – aren't major accidents like Bhopal. More usually, they're events or processes which have to compete with others for the media's attention. Their selection depends on editorial judgments which, as I've argued, involve using a frame or an approach. So it won't wash for journalists to claim that a subject invites its own approach, since they need a frame in order to choose a subject as interesting and worth covering in the first place. In other words, the approach or frame preceeds the choice of subject.

Another reason for broadcasters' antipathy to media analysis is that it often represents journalists and producers as cultural automata, robotically reproducing social values and producing programmes from pre-existing packages of ideas. But programme makers play an active role in making programmes and making meaning: they amplify, modify, and sometimes contest current ideas. And approaches and programmes aren't things, with an existence independent of their thinkers. Producers, in drawing on ideas and reproducing them, also help to constitute them. Marx wrote that men make history, though not in conditions of their own making. We shouldn't forget that people also make medical programmes, though not in conditions (or departments) of their own making.

Very occasionally, broadcasters consciously analyse the existing range of programmes, and set out to enlarge them. One such occasion was the establishment of Channel 4. Its commissioning editor of health and medical programmes started by compiling a document called 'Health and Channel Four – New Channel, New Challenges', where she categorised existing health programmes into three types, similar to those here (with the consumer and environmental types merged). Her 'manifesto' included a commitment to broaden the range of health programmes by using all the approaches available.

Just what the doctor ordered

Contrary to the belief of many doctors, the medical approach is alive and well and deeply embedded in most parts of the British and American media. There's a decent body of research (British and American, ranging across different media and different periods) to substantiate this, and for over twenty-five years critical scientists and doctors themselves have been faulting science and medical reporters' over-enthusiastic attention to medicine's milestones.

Already in 1961, a Nobel Prize-winning physicist was claiming that the public was bombarded by news of triumphs in science.[27] In 1963, the laboratory director at the Carnegie Institution and editor of 'Science' argued that 'the material which is printed is usually gee-whiz, Buck Rogers distortions of the facts. Science writers for the wire services, wanting their copy to be used, tend to seek the more glamorous items.'[28]

The authors of recent, more systematic studies of the media agree. A content analysis of BBC TV medical programmes over twelve weeks in 1982 found the medical approach clearly predominating. Ninety-four per cent of the programmes were oriented towards doctors and hospitals, and the use of technology (both drugs and machines) figured prominently. Issues of social class, safety at home and at work occupied only a small percentage of programmes. Medical TV's leading characters were doctors, far more abundant than their real proportions warranted, and far outnumbering other health workers. Doctors comprised 40.5 per cent of the total number of health workers shown, while nurses, who make up 92 per cent of medical staff working in English hospitals, comprised only 7.5 per cent of on-screen health workers. The majority of doctors, moreover, were consultants and hospital doctors, with very few GPs – no relation to the actual proportions of GPs and hospital doctors in practice in the UK. Other health workers, such as health visitors, administrators, and ancillary workers, hardly figured at all.[29]

When the Unit for the Study of Health policy monitored the press and television in 1976, they too found the medical approach prevailing, to the virtual exclusion of significantly different interpretations. They were baffled by the fact that, during the whole of their monitoring period, they didn't see any articles or programmes questioning the notion that better health derives from unselective economic growth and a wealth-producing economy.[30] A 1981 study of British newspapers also discovered a preponderance of stories about disease and medical advances, but very few on class inequalities in health, or the health of minority groups and unemployed people.[31]

A content analysis of coronary heart disease in American magazines (*Ladies Home Journal, Reader's Digest,* and *Time*) for the period 1959 to 1974 also found a combined medical and look-after-yourself approach predominating. The articles saw heart disease as either a mechanical defect or an isolated physical effect, citing 'physiological malfunction' most of all as its cause, and social, environmental, occupational, familial and stress factors least of all. The reports were enthusiastic about technological advances for treating coronary heart disease, even those later discredited. Medical hardware, drugs and surgery featured prominently and were rarely criticised. Few articles suggested that government policy was connected with the diagnosis, treatment, or prevention of heart disease, but many gave 'the general impression . . . that the individual was to blame . . . for causing his or her own heart failure or disease'.[32] Channel 4's commissioning editor of health and medical programmes, surveying British media coverage of the subject, also noted

a heavy bias towards existing medical values and priorities, and although these may be challenged on specific issues they are rarely questioned in any fundamental way .... They ... perform the function of informing the public about current practice or new frontiers in predominantly main-line 'curative' medicine.[33]

Most of these researchers would acknowledge that medicine has a significant, if circumscribed role to play in treating illness, and few would seek to *exclude* the medical approach from broadcasting. They would argue rather that, despite major changes in orientation (see Chapter 3), and individual programmes and very occasionally series from an environmental perspective, contemporary media coverage of health and illness continues to overemphasise the significance of medicine, and seriously neglect social, political, and economic factors.

Medical news: the same old story?

The medical approach finds its most powerful expression in news bulletins. It provides reporters working to tight deadlines with the powerful icons and proven stories they need, even if caveats and qualifications get lost in the process, often generating complaints about inaccuracy. Medical news reports are brief (the average BBC medical story runs for 1½ minutes), but reporters must also make their stories 'hard', by using material which seems incontrovertible and not conjectured. Figures are favoured since they have the feel of facts about them. Graphs, maps and percentages also give an aura of 'facticity'.

Reporters seize on the exceptional rather than the typical, on glamorous, life-threatening diseases rather than the commonest ones. Between 1971 and 1981, American nightly TV news reported on diabetes 32 times, compared with 215 stories about heart disease, and 925 on cancer.[34] Ordinary people, or Unknowns, feature much less often than elite people, or Knowns (political or social figures),[35] and the same goes for their illnesses – Elton John's throat operation or Barbara Woodhouse's stroke.

Because of the 24-hour cycle in which broadcasting and newspapers operate, reporters are also preoccupied with events rather than issues – disasters and dramatic events reaching a climax, rather than slowly-developing processes. So operations are particular favourites, and bad news about health and medicine tends to take the form of scandals, one-off outrages with specific origins and solutions.

News reports also focus on deaths or side-effects from a particular drug, as if they're individual rogue drugs and the others are implicitly safe. The campaign to ban Debendox (prescribed in pregnancy) had to isolate this drug to gain media attention, although the campaigners wanted *all* drugs prescribed in pregnancy monitored and followed up. Occupational illnesses from pesticides and other chemicals are also reported as sudden and unforeseeable disasters, rather than the result of the organisation and priorities of the industry.[36] Even 'running stories' such as a persistently leaky nuclear plant are reported largely as re-enactments of a single event (another leak) or as a new episode in the story (a new report, a debate in the House) rather than as issues with roots.

One feature of news which keeps the medical approach in circulation is its predictability. To criticisms about the superficiality of news, its focus on the dramatic, single, and sudden incident, journalists often respond that news by definition is about what's new and different. Yet, as media researchers have argued, 'news' are actually 'olds', 'because they correspond to what one expects to happen – and if they are too far away from the expectation, they will not be registered'.[37] An editor will reject a story on a new subject before it's reached the public agenda because they've no meaningful way of understanding it, but once it's been certified as newsy and they're sensitised to the subject, it recurs over and over again in different guises, with what made it newsy in the first place accentuated.

News are olds partly because of news-gatherers' organisational needs and routines, but also because reporters have to use a shorthand immediately understandable to viewers and readers, and therefore they constantly reproduce dominant ideas and values. As a result, news gives the feeling of 'novelty without change',[38] and conveys the impression of 'eternal recurrence'.[39] In medical news, this means that reporters work with a limited number of familiar stories: *the breakthrough* (an operation or new treatment, often connected with hearts or babies, or better still, both); *the disaster* (health consequences of earthquakes, fires, explosions, accidents); *the ethical controversy* (currently surrogate mothers, test-tube babies); *the scandal* (deaths from prescribed drug, drug withdrawn from sale, mental hospital stories); *the strike* (National Health Service dispute); *the epidemic* (its course and treatment); and *the official report or speech* – government or medical – on a health problem. The breakthrough or miracle cure, in particular, is often a human interest story, used to end news bulletins, and send viewers away into the night comfortable, reassured that all's ultimately well with the world.

Most news reporters reject such classifications, insisting on their objectivity and impartiality. At the same time, they claim that the news-gathering process isn't available for scrutiny: it's a matter of journalistic flair, seat-of-the-pants, rule of thumb. Certainly, the relatively high incomes and prestige enjoyed by national journalists encourage a feeling of being above the fray: they're likely to have limited personal experience of industrial disputes, and to hold liberal values which apparently attract little dissent and seem universal.

Their own ideology being invisible, they tend to associate ideology with extremism. BBC News' Science Correspondent, who covers medicine, says:

> There's been a great anti-science feeling in the media over many years .... There's a temptation by people who don't know much about science to always be suspicious of science, and to accept stories from politically-motivated lobby groups. I'm not suggesting that the Friends of the Earth group haven't got some good arguments, but on energy, they're against nuclear power .... You don't give emphasis to the anti-science side.[40]

Coverage of NHS strikes is shaped by both these characteristics of news reports and the medical approach. A leader is identified and often scapegoated, most infamously the National Union of Public Employees (NUPE) spokesman, Jamie Morris, in the 1975 Westminster Hospital dispute over the existence of private paybeds in a NHS hospital. The tabloids went for crude vilification, with full-page headlines like 'Jamie You're A Bastard'. Behind much of the coverage was journalistic indignation that hospital porters and other ancillary workers were intervening in areas considered medical or clinical. What most reporters missed was the story behind the story: the growing unionisation of NHS staff and especially ancillary workers, as a response to the new managerialism in the NHS. But that was an ongoing, invisible issue, unlike the tale of malign Morris.

Stories about striking hospital workers tend to either downplay their success ('many hospitals are running normally') or emphasise their dire effects on patients, sometimes straining simultaneously to do both. Strike coverage also concentrates on which services are running, since journalists are generally more interested in the disruptive results of disputes than their causes. Workers who don't participate in strikes generally receive sympathetic coverage: still-working ambulance drivers in the 1982 strike over low NHS pay were sought out and interviewed, often disproportionately to their numbers. Reporting on the dispute focussed on the provision of emergency cover, and the possibility of patient deaths, with a typical television discussion returning repeatedly to the possibility of fatalities, and pressing a consultant to confirm them.[41] (Hospital workers often complain that journalists wait like vultures for patients to die so that they can headline it in the papers and news bulletins.)

Reporters, like Governments, often pit patients' interests against workers, as if gains to NHS staff were somehow at the expense of patient care. Patients who support NHS strikers, though they're common and often highly appreciative, are rarely interviewed on radio and TV, and journalists repeatedly turn to doctors for authoritative comments on NHS strikes, as if scientific objectivity obtained even over industrial disputes. If strikers manage to gain medical support, they're in a far stronger position: legitimated by the medical profession, to reporters their cause becomes valid. On the rare occasions when doctors themselves strike, media coverage is generally much more sympathetic.[42] And striking nurses (still portrayed as 'angels') are also usually exempt from media attacks: coverage of the 1982 pay dispute differentiated between striking nurses who were good and had a valid case, and other striking NHS staff, who weren't and didn't.

Reporters' concern for patients is admirable, but selective. When a hospital consultant blamed a staff shortage for the death of a 62-year-old woman in a busy hospital ward, because she bled to death when a tube became disconnected from her ankle, the Press Association (PA) sent out a 13-paragraph story.[43] But there were no 'Stop This Slaughter' headlines, and neither the

Sun, the *Daily Express,* the *Daily Mail,* national BBC News, or national ITV News reported it.[44] The PA Associate Editor said, 'If it had been because of a strike, I'm quite sure it would have been widely used', though he added 'It also depends on what else was available.'[45]

The NHS cuts were clearly a non-event. Yet a year later, in early 1988, the media were saturated with stories about the death of patients because of staff shortages and the fatal effects of a cash-starved NHS. What had changed? The medical profession as a group had intervened.

Their impact was remarkable. When, in December 1987, a 1200-signature Save-The-NHS petition signed by doctors and professors from throughout Britain was handed in to Downing Street by five NHS consultants, it captured the headlines. And once the story had taken hold there was no stopping it, with daily reports of the dire state of the NHS. Though the cuts had been taking effect for several years, and staff and patient opposition to them had been vocal, the subject only seriously joined the media agenda after receiving the medical imprimatur.

What also happened, along with (and partly because of) medical endorsement, was a shift in reporting style. The cuts changed from being a story about a strike (though some nurses did strike) or an official report or speech, and became instead a scandal. There was a series of headline stories about hole-in-the-heart children at risk of death because of a shortage of intensive care nurses. Hospitals willingly helped parents go public, and the combination of hearts and babies – more commonly features of the breakthrough – and scandal made powerful human interest stories. Patient deaths were no longer caused by irresponsible strikers but by a heartless government. Only the medical establishment could have achieved such a substantial shift in coverage.

2

Health Talk 1928-1962

Fitness and fibre first time round

Leotarded health zealots, anxiously charting their daily fibre intake, seem the very epitome of modernity – the result of recent knowledge about health and illness. So it's chastening to cast back to the 1920s, 1930s, and 1940s and see a fitness craze and a preoccupation with nutrition almost identical. People were exhorted to exercise their way to fitness, and great stress was placed on diet as an agent for improving health. Even the language was the same – the talk over the airwaves was of 'positive health'. The look-after-yourself approach in the media, which we tend to think succeeded the medical approach, actually preceded it.

From the earliest days of the BBC, radio was seen as a powerful tool for health. Hilda Matheson, Director of Talks until 1931, believed that

> broadcasting can do a great deal to make effective the modern campaign for preventive medicine. It is obviously unsuitable to attempt to prescribe treatment by wireless ... but men and women may be interested in the whole problem of keeping well, of avoiding things liable to cause ill-health, of managing problems of diet, of exercise, of growing old, of sedentary lives.[1]

A thoroughly topical agenda. The BBC Talks Department was implicitly educational in orientation, its aim – in keeping with the Reithian ethic of edifying the audience – to develop public consciousness. As early as 1927, Friday morning radio talks were given under the auspices of the Ministry of Health, on Health in Autumn, How to Keep Fit at Fifty, How to Avoid Infection. From their inception they were seen as an unqualified success: the first quarter's broadcasts in 1929 garnered 20,000 letters from a listener population of approximately 10 million. In 1935, the papers were full of 'the BBC-reared baby', Gerald Addyman, who had been brought up strictly according to the advice given in broadcast talks, and apparently thrived on it.

But there was one national health obsession which the BBC resisted for as long as it could, and that was mass calisthenics. In 1929, the United States (on NBC), Denmark, and Germany were broadcasting early morning physical exercises, but Matheson was sceptical: 'Psychologically, I doubt whether we are a nation which likes to be dragooned in intimate matters of personal habit.'[2] To boot, the Ministry of Health was mistrustful of 'indiscriminate broadcast exercises'.[3] But as the Depression and unemployment grew, so too did body fetishism. Physical culture became an obsession, and groups dedicated to cultivating bodies fit and beautiful mushroomed. The Women's League of Health and Beauty, founded in 1930, its aim 'Racial Health Leading to Peace' bearing more than a passing resemblance to the eugenic ideas of Marie Stopes and Nazi beliefs about the body, had over 90,000 members by 1936. They hankered to get their Bagot Stack Stretch and Swing System and other exercises onto the air. Such groups put pressure on the BBC to change its policy, but the Corporation replied to one inquirer, 'we have the very definite impression that the British character neither welcomes nor appreciates any form of entertainment or education which forces it from its bed at an earlier hour than is absolutely essential'.[4]

Public pressure intensified, and after further press lobbying the BBC was deluged by aspiring presenters. By 1934, even the African Broadcasting Company was doing it, and in America, WOR's daily physical jerks sponsored by a meat packing company were getting a remarkable audience response – over 50,000 letters received in 1936 alone. Questions were asked in the House of Commons about why the BBC still desisted. Finally in 1939, ten years after the idea had first been mooted, and after what had amounted to a campaign by fitness afficionados, they capitulated. One reason may have been the imminence of war. The health of recruits was dubious and a 1935 newsreel, 'The March of Time', even suggested that the undernourishment and physical underdevelopment of potential recruits to the British army might jeopardise the country's safety.

The BBC fitness programme, optimistically entitled 'Up In the

Morning Early', started in December 1939. Exercises were done to the sound of almost continuous and cheerful music, like Merry Widow tunes and Spanish guitar music – 'and sometimes the broadcaster even breaks into song'.[5] In the first eight days, over 11 per cent of the male and female population listened and, so the BBC claimed, 40 per cent of the listeners actually did the exercises daily, though the figures dropped in later months, and additional programmes were added for the 'over forties'.[6] The series ran until September 1945. By the late 1950s, Eileen Fowler's television 'Keep Fit', with her wholesome aertex shirts and cheerful talk of 'flattening the seat', was all the rage. In the 1980s we got the Green Goddess, but it had all started back in 1939.[7]

Why was the country and the BBC so preoccupied with health and not medicine? One reason was that doctors weren't in a position to offer the population medical care on a mass scale, so there was little point in fostering public interest in medicine. The success of medical care and access to it also varied considerably from one area to another. And though in places the friendly societies still arranged cheap care for working-class people, in 1939 married women (who suffered higher than average ill-health) had no access to free state medical attention unless they were expecting, or had recently given birth to, a baby. So, in the words of one of them, a woman would not 'start a doctor's bill if she could possibly stand on her feet'.[8] Even workers covered by the 1911 National Health Insurance Act often couldn't get satisfactory medical care, and got by with the most basic medical treatment from their 'panel' doctor.

There was also very little confidence in the effectiveness of medicine.[9] Deaths from water and food-borne diseases (such as cholera, dysentery, typhoid and typhus) fell continuously from the second half of the nineteenth century because of improvements to hygiene, especially purification of water and sewage disposal, but the trend owed nothing to medicine. Immunization and medical therapies introduced from the mid-1930s to the 1940s (especially the sulphonamides) did help reduce deaths from airborne diseases (TB, pneumonia, whooping cough, scarlet fever, and diphtheria), but mortality from these illnesses was declining anyway long before they became available, so they weren't the main influence on the nation's improving health.

Another reason for the BBC's health orientation was a prevailing view within the medical profession that medicine was not for lay people to meddle in. It took six years of medical training to become a doctor, and broadcasting medical information to people with anything less would lead to hopeless misunderstandings or hypochondria, while doing so to an undifferentiated audience, which might include the frail and the neurotic, was anathema. There were rare exceptions, like the 1930 series of talks, arranged in collaboration with the Chief Medical Officer at the Ministry of Health, Sir George Newman, on 'The Future of Medicine', in which 'seven of our most eminent doctors' explained their branch of medicine and its likely future achievements. But generally, broadcasters were enjoined to confine themselves to prevention, and 'not (to) touch on cure',[10] and a proposal in 1932 for a talk on cancer was abandoned because 'there is no useful preventive work to be done'.[11] There were plenty of radio talks on science, but this was treated as a separate sphere from health and health education, whose claims rested more on empirical observation than scientific experiment, in spite of being mediated by doctors.

But perhaps the most important reason for the obsession with health lay in the period of austerity that the country was experiencing. I'll be arguing in Chapter 3 that the recent recurrence of 'healthism' signals a return to a punitive individualism, where each citizen has a moral duty to make themselves fit. The notion of individual responsibility for health was also rampant in the 1930s and 1940s. Superficially, the resemblance between then and now is striking: just as the healthy image is used to sell anything from Coca-Cola to chocolate bars today, so in the 1930s ads for Ovaltine, calling itself 'The National Beverage for National Fitness', demanded 'Mother, how many in *your* family are 100 per cent fit?' while Hovis claimed that it 'radiates health'. Health became a buzz word and healthy eating a cherished concept. Nutrition research was widespread, with nutritionists arguing that many ailments could be eliminated by a proper diet. The official British position was that malnutrition derived from female 'ignorance of food values and unwise spending'.[12] Sir George Newman claimed that malnutrition was 'due directly or indirectly to our faulty habits and customs'[13], and also attributed infant mortality to maternal ignorance, which required not direct economic assistance but maternal education.[14] This line, redolent of 1980s ideology, placed responsibility squarely on individual women and faulty working-class culture.

But there's an important difference between the dominant ideas and media coverage of nutrition in the 1930s and in the 1980s. In the 1930s there was also a raging and often bitter public debate about the role of poverty in causing malnutrition and ill-health. A key intervention came in 1936 with the publication of John Boyd Orr's 'Food, Health, and Income', based on a study of the food intake of over 1000 families, which argued that 9½ million people had inadequate diets, one-tenth of the population (including a fifth of all children) were chronically ill-nourished, half suffered from some sort of deficiency, and only one-third of the population enjoyed a healthy diet.

Orr's findings were criticised on methodological grounds and for applying too high a standard of nutritional good health, but were corroborated by other studies, like an important survey by Dr G. C. M'Gonigle (Medical Officer of Health for Stockton-on-Tees) and John Kirby, called 'Poverty and Public Health'. And in 1939, a major and devastating account of the ill-health of 'Working-Class Wives' was published, logging in grisly detail their illnesses, a typical day's work, their slum housing and poverty-line diets, and testifying to their fortitude.

In 1936, the Grierson-led documentary film movement took up the subject. Edgar Anstey, maker of a powerful film on slum housing, *Housing Problems* (1935), directed what was to become a classic film on nutrition, *Enough to Eat?* Financed by the British Gas Corporation and with a commentary by Julian Huxley, the film was based on Orr's research, and was a radical condemnation of poverty-caused malnutrition. It didn't blame women, it talked of class (comparing the weight and height of public school and state school boys), and called for a national food policy. *Housing Problems* and *Enough to Eat?* created a public stir, generating whole pages in the *Daily Herald* and *Daily News*. When first shown, *Enough to Eat* was branded as 'subversive', though the Minister of Health later expressed his gratitude for it, and it was thought to have influenced Britain's official nutrition policy.[15]

Other British independent films on the theme included the 1934 drama *Bread*, directed by a Communist Party member, in which an unemployed man denied relief by the Charity Commissioners (because of his wife's small income from cleaning) steals a loaf of bread from a baker's shop, but gets caught and sentenced to jail. And Ivor Montagu's *Peace and Plenty* (1939), which powerfully compared the 3s. an unemployed family got for a child's food, clothes and upkeep, with the 5s. 3d. which the British Medical Association reckoned necessary to provide a minimally adequate diet.

Social accounts of the causes of ill-health and malnutrition were clearly on the public agenda and, controversial though they were, the BBC couldn't avoid them.[16] The task fell to Janet Quigley, the gifted producer responsible for most health talks. In 1937, she proposed a series on nutrition and physical culture, 'Towards National Health'. It was a difficult undertaking since, as the Assistant Director of Talks noted, there was a popular tendency 'to regard Nutrition as the Left Wing's pigeon, and physical training [as] the Right Wing's', something he urged her to discourage.[17]

Consulting with the Ministry of Health over the series, Quigley immediately encountered hostility to its very idea: 'In fact, they practically admitted that the Government would like the soft pedal put down on the whole subject of Nutrition at the present moment.'[18] She'd lined up ten speakers, including Sir John Boyd Orr and Dr M'Gonigle. The Ministry objected to all but two, considering the others were 'all what they term "left wing" ', and Orr and M'Gonigle were 'advertisers'. They proposed instead someone whom Quigley saw as an old-fashioned crank. But the BBC, resolute, went ahead, and 'Towards National Health' proved a major and radical series, breaking new ground in programmes for a national audience, and in places uncannily modern: Sir Robert McCarrison's prescription of a healthy diet, butter and cheese excepted, could have come from any 1980s teledoctor, wholemeal bread, lentils, and all. M'Gonigle and Boyd Orr's contributions uncompromisingly stressed the economic root of malnutrition, and were critical of government policy.

They're an early example of an environmental approach, but they weren't the only BBC programmes to take a radical line on nutrition. 'The Classic Soil',[19] a feature on poor people's inadequate diet and housing, compared examples of hardship from Engels' 1844 *The Condition of the Working-Class* with contemporary women's accounts of making little go far, citing instances of people on largely bread-and-marge diets. Compared with

'The Classic Soil', 'Towards National Health' was more muted and BBC in tone, and in retrospect Quigley felt they'd wrongly avoided controversy and regretted the format of talks, instead of discussions. Yet 'Towards National Health' was a significant achievement, outspoken even today, and represented a major BBC success in resisting government pressure at a time when there was barely a tradition of broadcasters' independence.

Maybe, Minister: the BBC and the Ministry of Health

While the BBC was instructing the nation on how to stay healthy, its relations with the Ministry of Health were far from harmonious, with recurring struggles for control and autonomy. Despite stabs at independence, the BBC had largely acquiesced to government fiat and ideology in the 1926 General Strike. But in its dealings with the Ministry of Health, it didn't tamely capitulate, exercising instead skilful resistance and polite conciliation.

BBC Radio's social and political role in national life before the war, it's been argued, was shaped by a process of continual struggle and negotiation, through which its aspirations were modified, readjusted, or thwarted. Its independence was always a *relative* autonomy: 'It was the government who set the terms for the Corporation, whose subsequent history was in part an accommodation to and acceptance of those terms.'[20] This was certainly true of the BBC's engagement with the Ministry of Health. As early as 1928, the minutes of the BBC's Controversy Committee noted that

Sir George Newman [Chief Medical Officer at the Ministry of Health] took great interest in talks by medical men and on medical subjects, and ... in addition to supervising all questions of broadcasts by medical men he often asked to see the manuscripts of talks on medical or semi-medical subjects to be given by non-medical men. In spite of this the Ministry ... refused to admit that it acted in an advisory capacity to the BBC or had any say in the question of what talks were suitable or unsuitable. This attitude puts the BBC in a very difficult position.[21]

The skirmish was ominous: major confrontations lay ahead. In the 1930s and 1940s the BBC was constantly re-contesting and re-negotiating its relative autonomy on medical matters, trying to resist government pressure while recognising the need for a working relationship. The Ministry of Health, for its part, started off by policing the BBC's medical programmes, and then tried to influence them – a subtle but important change, producing a generally workable and mutually welcomed *modus vivendi*. But when the Ministry's influence (periodically) ceased to be effective – or as effective as it wished – it resorted once again to direct control, against which the BBC chafed. The breakdown of informal influence, and the attempts by the Ministry to directly take over the reins, generated two major crises in BBC–government relations.

Crisis no.1: 'We are reaching the point of breakdown'

The first was inadvertently caused by Mrs Pallis of Sunderland, the wife of an unemployed man who, in 1934, gave a talk on 'the woman's side of unemployment'.[22] Mrs Pallis graphically described her family's scanty meals, which fell laughably short of the recommendations of the health educationalists of the day. Her talk was followed by a doctor's on the hot topic of whether unemployed people could maintain their health. Broadcasting anonymously (as was the rule for doctors), Dr Waller argued that in spite of Mrs Pallis' skills as cook and manager, there was no way that her family could survive healthily on their meagre diet.

It was relatively novel for practising doctors to broadcast on health and medical topics. The General Medical Council (GMC) had banned them from doing so until 1932, when they agreed that on subjects concerning medicine and public health, broadcasters (who should be registered medical practitioners) and scripts should be approved by a GMC nominee. This turned out to be none other than Chief Medical Officer at the Ministry of Health, Sir George Newman, who vetted all scripts prior to recording. But when the producer duly sent the script of Dr Waller's talk to the Ministry, Newman questioned the doctor's suitability for the broadcast, and suggested alterations to his talk which the producer was advised by his boss to disregard, since they were literary and had nothing to do with medicine. Bristling with pique at the BBC's failure to oblige, Newman reminded them that he could have rejected Waller's script altogether and that Waller, in ignoring his recommendations, was infringing GMC regulations. Worst of all, Waller had been implicitly and incorrectly critical of central and local government in Sunderland. Beneath the billows of righteous indignation, could Newman have been raging against a rare criticism of the Government and the Ministry of Health by a doctor on the radio?

Waller's talk must have been especially irksome since only a year earlier the Ministry of Health had declared 'there is at present no available medical evidence of any increase in physical impairment, sickness, or mortality as a result of the depression or unemployment',[23] and here was a medical man roundly assert- ing the opposite. What's more, Waller had suggested that Mrs Pallis, like most women in her position, was probably anaemic, and he was supported by extensive studies indicating that a disproportionate number of women suffered from anaemia and debility due to poor diet and their tough lives. But in 1931 Newman had said that anaemia in women was 'more closely associated with sickness, pregnancy, post-confinement, lactation, etc' than with unemployment and malnutrition.[24] And while Waller claimed that Mrs Pallis was seriously underfed, Newman had argued that there wasn't 'any excess in malnutrition or incapacity in women'.[25] The publicity given to the high maternal mortality rate in the 1930s was politically embarrassing, and Newman sought to dampen public interest in the issue, privately admitting that it could create a demand for State action which could cost money.[26].

As the conflict raged, BBC Director-General Sir John Reith intervened, defending the 'autonomous position of the Corporation'.[27] but Newman was unsoothed, warning that 'we are reaching the point of breakdown'[28] and issuing thinly-veiled threats ('I still remain convinced of the importance and utility of medical broadcasting, and I should regret if it is found necessary to restrict it unduly'[29]). The row was resolved when the BBC turned to the GMC, who'd only ever been interested in prevent- ing doctors from advertising, and with relief agreed to the BBC taking full responsibility for selecting medical speakers.

The BBC seemed to have won, but in reality, consultation with the Government on medical talks simply became more informal and the controls became internalised, rather than exter- nal. Three years later, the BBC was reminding staff to consult the

BMA and the Ministry of Health about the suitability of medical speakers and their subjects. After all the fireworks and bullish displays of independence, little had really changed.

Crisis no.2: infiltration

Institutions have short memories. In 1942, a second crisis erupted, bearing an uncanny resemblance to the first. This time it was launched by Wilkinson, the pushy Chief Public Relations Officer at the Ministry of Health. Where Newman had vetoed, Wilkinson initiated. He didn't merely respond to the BBC, he harried them with ideas for programmes and series. When Wilkinson wrote to the Director of Talks, suggesting 'infiltration of health matter into existing programmes',[30] he clearly had two kinds of infiltration in mind. One was simply smuggling into popular programmes information about coughs and sneezes, diphtheria immunisation, and the shortage of nurses. But the other was institutional: he would furnish BBC producers with a list of the work of the Ministry, so that Ministry specialists could be interviewed whenever medical news broke. In return, he'd get a list of medical producers at the BBC, to whom Ministers could suggest programme ideas.[31]

Sir Richard Maconachie, Controller (Home), wasn't misled by the coughs-and-sneezes line, and clearly saw to the heart of Wilkinson's suggestion. In a memo bluntly headed 'Ministry of Health Infiltration', he railed, 'Mr Wilkinson seems to me to be under a misapprehension. We are not in the least interested . . . in publicising the activities of any Department or Ministry . . . . It does not seem to me that this policy of infiltration is likely to be either practicable or, if it was practicable, acceptable.'[32] Undaunted, a few months later Wilkinson tried again, this time going further by arguing that since Health Ministers were responsible for the dissemination of information about health and disease, and couldn't delegate the responsibility to any outside body, the BBC should arrange health broadcasts with the Ministry. In one bound, they were back to 1934.

Maconachie was apoplectic, pencilling over Wilkinson's letter 'NO. We have got along for 10 years without doing this.'[33] The issue was finally resolved by hammering out a new agreement, strikingly similar to the old. As Maconachie put it, 'The principle is that the BBC will treat the Ministry with frankness, telling them in advance of proposals for Health talks, and the Ministry will *comment*, from the policy angle, without any wish to *control*.'[34]

The crisis had arisen because Wilkinson had demanded external control of the BBC; it was resolved when the BBC wrested back internal control. The Ministry was once again allowed to influence. Both these crises had served to reassert the social and political reality: they were a way of policing the BBC, of reminding it of the limits to its freedom. At the same time, the BBC had drawn itself up to its full height, reaffirming its need for relative autonomy, and renegotiating the terms by which it could exercise it.

Why was the Ministry of Health so hell-bent on dominating the BBC? The Ministry was in a difficult position. Despite the improvement of average life expectancy and the decline in infectious diseases, the Depression and mass unemployment caused high maternal and infant mortality in the depressed areas, and 'deficiency diseases' were widespread. The extent and causes of maternal mortality, and the question of whether malnutrition was rampant or not, became the key controversial health issues of the 1930s, and an ideological war was fought over the data. Newman and the Ministry came down heavily on anyone who opposed his department's glowing image of satiety. Dr G. C. M'Gonigle was threatened with removal from the medical register for ethical misconduct when he made it known that he intended to participate in a broadcast on the problem of malnutrition. He was later visited by Ministry inspectors who leaned on him to correct his 'freak' reports.[35]

By 1935, two-thirds of households owned radio sets. No wonder Newman was anxious to control such a powerful means of communication which might gainsay the rosy picture he worked hard at creating. It was only at the beginning of the war, and when its attempt to bully statistics into submission had clearly collapsed, that the Government admitted that its data were unreliable and conceded the extent of malnutrition. Nutrition came to be seen as a national rather than a political issue.

Ministering to the BBC

I've argued that the State came to substitute indirect for direct means of control over the BBC's health and medical programmes.

As the BBC had proved itself responsible in its exercise of power, it was entrusted with the right to police itself. To go further, the Ministry of Health not only moved from *control* to *influence*, it also attempted to become a *source* for the BBC.

When health talks and health and medical news stories began, there were no press officers or press conferences – no pre-existing mechanisms for Ministry output to get onto the air. The Chief Medical Officer wrote tentative letters to the Director of Talks asking if the Ministry could explain the provisions of a new Act over the wireless, or give details of a new report. It seems extraordinary today that such an arrangement had to be renegotiated by the Chief Medical Officer and the Director of Talks for each report. But the notion of the Ministry of Health not just policing the news but supplying it, was novel. Soon, however, they were even specifying in which news bulletin their report should be publicised. By 1935, the Ministry of Health had press officers and press notices. In the 1940s, the Chief Medical Officer started to hold press conferences to which the BBC was invited along with the newspapers, and by the early 1950s there were even telexes flowing between Ministry press officers and the BBC.

A news system was being set up. At first, there were few expectations and each side was grateful for what the other granted. By the 1950s, a fully developed symbiotic relationship was in operation. It wasn't unique to the Ministry of Health: in the 1930s, all major state departments installed Publicity and Press Officers, part of a systematic attempt by the State to control publicity and manage information for the media. But it also signalled a developing media awareness in the Ministry of Health, which came to recognise the problems of leaning directly on broadcasters, and began instead to establish itself as a major news source. After first policing the BBC, they learnt how to capture its headlines.

The Radio Doctor: biology without tears

Wartime broadcasting, like the war years in general, has been drenched in nostalgia. The over-fifties' eyes moisten at the mention of 'ITMA', and convulse over the memory of Band Waggon. With wry prescience, a wartime cartoon depicting queuing chaos bore the words, 'I suppose that in about thirty years' time people will insist on describing these as the good old days.' Yet it's hard to overestimate broadcasting's role in Britain during the last world war as a morale-raiser and a force for social integration. In 1939 there were over 9 million wireless licences, and BBC Radio – even if it homogenised the nation's cultural life and reflected a southern, upper-middle-class bias – became the hearth of the nation. Charles Hill, the Radio Doctor, played a major role in pumping up the morale of the Home Front, and became a totem of British resilience and pragmatism. If he hadn't existed, the BBC would have had to invent him – and in a sense, they did.

One event played a double role in catapulting Hill into broadcasting. In 1933, as secretary of the committee which drafted the BMA Nutrition Report, he was invited by the BBC to give a series of four radio talks on it. He'd already been enraged by inaccurate press coverage of the Report, but believed 'that the form and language of the findings were largely responsible for this reaction'.[36] Hill had awoken to the power of popularisation.

He gave other talks, but it was the 'Kitchen Front' which first established him as an institution. The series 'on what to eat and how to cook it' began in June 1940. It was aimed at housewives and commanded an audience of well over 5 million. Hill became a regular contributor. He attempted to stimulate the nation's taste-buds at a time of rationing, assuring them that liver and kidneys were 'very solid organs stuffed full of food',[37] extolling the virtues of the dandelion leaf as a salad vegetable, trying to tempt them with Purée of Stinging Nettles, Sorrel Turnover, Hawthorn Jelly and Elderberry Ketchup, and denouncing sugar as 'a menace'. With the Ministry of Food's encouragement, he set upon traditional English cooking, decrying the Sunday joint ('Hot on Sunday – cold on Monday – and if there's anything left, hashed or murdered on Tuesday') and protesting against the 'assassination' of vegetables by over-boiling. Hill had perfected the art of Home Front radio.

He also gave some of the regular Friday morning health talks which Janet Quigley was fostering in the belief that the subject was under-exposed. And when in 1941 a series of evening health talks was proposed for the first time, Hill had a clear idea of what they should contain.

I believe that simple, descriptive talks on the human body, how it is constructed and how it works, can be made both informative and fascinating. It is a subject which interests every human being. Such knowledge must be the basis of all genuine health education. Breathing, walking, eating, sleeping, yes even reproduction – all are capable of sane and exciting treatment.[38]

For its part, the BBC was interested in grooming him as a star. Quigley, pondering methods of presenting the evening talks, suggested that 'one way of holding the series together would be to build up a Radio Doctor who would broadcast frequently himself and would always be in the background as consultant in the actual broadcast, as compere, chairman, what-you-will'.[39]

Hill's first evening series, 'The Human Body – How It Works', was broadcast in 1942. Its success prompted a new series of ten-minute evening talks on 'positive health' called 'Doctors Agree', which Hill dominated, and thereafter he became a regular evening presenter. Although he broadcast anonymously, under the soubriquet – dreamed up by a Ministry of Food official – of Radio Doctor, Hill knew it deceived no one: his voice and style were familiar to listeners. What distinguished him as a broadcaster was his fondness for the demotic. He made an art – and a career – out of plain speaking. In an era without the time or inclination for the niceties of circumlocution, Hill was a bespoke hero.

Where others talked of food, he referred to grub. To him, a child was a nipper. Blokeish, his vowels on the flat side, he had an extraordinary affinity with the audience. According to his new producer, 'as a self-made man, he can speak to the people from among whom he came with great certainty of touch'.[40] Hill breached the chasm between the BBC's Reithian notions of self-improvement, and its role as entertainer. He was both serious and popular. In December 1944 the *Daily Mail* said he could be 'as broadly entertaining as Tommy Handley and as lucidly erudite and brilliant as Professor Joad'. He made health into something jocular – important, but never solemn, as in his favourite talk, 'Hallo Children', given on Boxing Day, 1949: 'This is stomach speaking. Yes, I mean it, *your* stomach. In fact, I'm the shop-steward of the Society of Suffering Stomachs. Stomachs don't often speak. As a rule I get on with my work without as much as a murmur or rumble.'[41]

Until the Radio Doctor and the Brains Trust, 'serious' broadcasting tended to mean turgid talks by pompous, stentorian speakers about intellectual abstractions, or stressing their own superior wisdom, as if the radio talk was simply a lecture. Hill dictated his scripts tramping around his office, and believed that some of his best broadcasts were drafted in a hurry, 'the less meticulous the preparation, the more easily do the words seem to slip off the tongue when in front of the microphone'.[42] He understood the particular strengths of the medium, and addressed the audience not as an aggregated mass but a constellation of individuals positioned in families, gathered around the hearth.

The first post-war BBC research survey revealed that the average listener understood only 30 per cent of the average BBC talk and had difficulty with the language. Hill, on the other hand, used breezy idioms and humour ('Now for tripe, that tasty morsel of the North. No, the comedians are wrong. It is not liver struck by lightning, or even boiled knitting'[43]) and eschewed euphemism, so acquiring a reputation for coarseness and vulgarity. He called prunes 'black-coated workers', and 'I admit I did once define a pathologist as a man who sits on one stool and examines others. Following one broadcast I was publicly censored for indelicacy.'[44] Quigley, especially prizing his skills in the shorter five-minute talk, helped to build him up as a radio personality, and the audience loved him: in peak weeks his postbag contained 500 letters, many listing symptoms (he dubbed them 'organ recitals') and asking for free medical advice.

Hill's position in broadcasting was uniquely powerful: he had carte blanche 'within the limits of policy, [to] talk about anything he likes in the medical field'.[45] But as the Director of Talks noted,

> There is also danger in the fact that Charles Hill is our chief medical speaker . . . and at the same time, as secretary of the BMA, our chief adviser on medical matters. If Hill wishes to go further than the Corporation, the Corporation at present has to take its expert advice from Hill and that is an impossible position.[46]

The Director of Talks was keen to groom an understudy, but Hill wielded his power discreetly, and his doubly entrenched position in the medical establishment (now as Secretary of the BMA and Chairman of the Central Council of Health Education) was precisely what made the BBC feel safe and secure from medical and Ministerial criticism. It also gave the BMA an unrivalled influence on broadcasting. As the Director of Talks said, 'On health matters Hill speaks with the authority of the British Medical Association. The views he puts forward on health matters are those of the BMA.'[47]

What Hill said was less novel than the way in which he said it. Generally he spoke the medical orthodoxies of the time. Health and national fitness were seen as a contribution to the war effort, so he spread the philosophy of positive health ('No one who's interested in health only when it's gone is really healthy'[48]).

His chief medical originality was probably his belief in the importance of the public learning about biology, and his rejection of medical reticence, obfuscation and self-importance – there was nothing *de haut en bas* about him. He bridged the worlds of medicine and broadcasting, contributing simultaneously to the democratisation of medical knowledge and to the spread of the idea that doctors were uncontestable experts on health. Since he frequently broadcast with the authority of a doctor on subjects about which medicine had no special knowledge, his talks are also an early example of medicalisation.[49]

Hill's conservatism, medical and political, protected his privileged position in broadcasting. When, in the 'Brains Trust', the socialist scientist Julian Huxley attacked patent medicines and called for a National Health Service, the Tories complained. And when J. B. Priestley in his radio talks criticised the Government, the BBC removed him, questioning 'whether any single person should be given the opportunity of acquiring such influence [in broadcasting]'.[50] Hill was, and retained it because his views were politically uncontentious.

The Radio Doctor played a powerful mythical role in British culture, both at the time and subsequently. If the nation shared a doctor, it could also be said to share the same illness and treatment. Mass health interventions and broadcasts directed at the whole population implied that all were similarly wanting. After the raging public debates about malnutrition, unemployment, and poverty, the Radio Doctor reconstituted everyone as equal citizens and patients, equally affected by the difficulties of the war – adieu health differences by class, region, or gender. He also became an emblem of Englishness, representing the stalwart British character, uncomplainingly resilient. It's this image of a united, hardy and equal society ('a siege economy [where] the perils were immense, and we all had a feeling that we belonged to one another'[51]) which is invoked when the Radio Doctor in wartime is nostalgically recalled.

The NHS is coming

A subtle change in health broadcasting began in the middle of the war. At the repeated request of the Ministry of Health, the BBC started running talks on diphtheria immunisation, and by 1944 was broadcasting Ministry-prepared 'flashes' on the subject. Other talks – on the maternity, child welfare, and school medical services – asked 'are you sure you're taking full advantage of them and getting value for your money?'[52] Public health programming like this for the first time encouraged listeners to use the state medical and health services which were forerunners of the NHS.

When a National Health Service seemed likely and then inevitable, the BBC broadcast general discussions on the issue, asking 'Should All Doctors Be State-Employed?' and, in 'The State and the Doctor', featuring the contrasting viewpoints of Charles Hill and a doctor from the Socialist Medical Association. But the NHS also presented them with something of a problem. The fourteen-day rule prevented the Corporation from broadcasting any discussions on issues about to be debated in either House of Parliament for a fortnight before the debates took place. The Director of Talks tried and failed to have it waived in the case of the NHS. This meant that the introduction of the NHS was never fully discussed in the country at the appropriate time through the biggest single medium of communication.[53]

Then there was the problem of how to cover it when they were allowed to. Lay listeners, the BBC imagined, would be bored by turgid controversies about administrative detail, and they didn't want to use dull doctors lacking in broadcasting flair. They were also lobbied by the BMA to give more space to the opinion of the medical profession. (The BMA made its own propaganda film, *Family Doctor*, to show how cherishable GPs were.) Hill himself was in an ambiguous position. As secretary of the BMA, he was masterminding the medical profession's fight to wring concessions out of Minister of Health Nye Bevan (principally to avoid a full-time salaried service). But he also continued to broadcast. His producer worried that his radio popularity was being exploited by the BMA,[54] while Hill's suggestion that broadcast discussion about the NHS White Paper be deferred until negotiations were more advanced seemed to owe more to the needs of the BMA than the listeners.

In the late 1940s and early 1950s the form of health and medical programmes was also changing. There were now three radio networks, and a growing number of debates and discussions with more spontaneous speech, though almost all featured doctors and medical experts, and avoided polemics or criticisms of medicine. And although there was a greater variety of voices, all articulated points of view more or less acceptable to the BMA.

Operation success: 'Your Life in Their Hands'

It would be hard to overstate the magnitude of the shift in media thinking about health which occurred in the late 1950s. The orthodoxies of the previous thirty years were pulverised, and within a few years what had once been thought wholly irresponsible was established as the new orthodoxy. The medical approach had arrived.

The change is strikingly illustrated in a letter written by Bill Duncalf, the first producer of 'Your Life in Their Hands', in 1961.

> I feel that if we went over to the positive approach and made concrete suggestions for the prevention of certain diseases and suggested and encouraged our millions of viewers actively to follow such advice, then ... the general practitioners of the country would have a justifiable complaint that we were cutting across them .... It seems to me that there is a great difference between telling the viewers what medical science knows about the formation of gallstones and their removal and suggesting what they might do to prevent their appearance. We could indeed be accused in the latter instance of trying to influence people to follow a certain course of action.[55]

Cure had utterly replaced prevention on the BBC agenda, all recollection of the fitness and fibre obsession erased from producers' minds.

The shift started quietly enough, with the first BBC television medical series, 'Matters of Life and Death' (1949–52), followed by five live outside broadcast television programmes from St Mary's Hospital, Paddington (1954 and 1956), the uncontroversial forerunners of 'Your Life in Their Hands'. And in a 1957 BBC TV series about mental illness, 'The Hurt Mind', demonstrating electric convulsive treatment (ECT), insulin treatment and (by diagrams) leucotomy, ex-patients joined specialists on screen to describe their experiences and 'to testify to their perfect recovery. It was not only a deeply interesting programme', reported the *Listener*, 'it was also completely reassuring as to the nature of the various treatments.'[56]

Commercial television had arrived in 1955, so the BBC now had to compete in winning an audience. ITV's fictional series, 'Emergency Ward 10' (which started in 1957) focussed on life-threatening conditions and the heroic interventions of doctors (see Chapter 11). 'Your Life in Their Hands' (its very title marking a break with past attempts to foster self-reliance) was dreamt up by Duncalf as a weekly outside broadcast of an operation or other medical procedure from regional hospitals throughout the country. Transmission began on 11 February 1958, with a programme from Oxford about polio, followed by 'the latest methods of cancer treatment' from Manchester, a mitral valvotomy (a heart operation) in Birmingham, and seven other procedures.

The series was presented by Dr Charles Fletcher, an old broadcasting hand, who topped and tailed the opening programme with jolly Blue Peterish optimism:

> Now there's absolutely no need to feel squeamish about seeing these people breathing this way. As you will see for yourselves they are extremely happy and getting on well. Of course they can't talk because there is no air passing over their vocal chords.[57]

But no amount of soothing commentary could deflect the uproar which followed the transmission of the first programme. The medical profession led the onslaught, with the *British Medical Journal* in the forefront. In an editorial ironically entitled

'Disease Education By The BBC', it asserted that doctors and nurses were appearing as 'mummers' to provide entertainment for the British public, that the series would heighten anxiety and that, by pandering to interest in the morbid, it would increase hypochondria and neurosis.

Fletcher, though he broadcast anonymously, was told that his appearance would prejudice his medical future, and the BBC was obliged to appease his employers by saying that he wasn't the TV equivalent of the Radio Doctor. And before the transmission of the third programme, the announcer suggested that anyone who didn't like watching an operation should turn down the vision and listen to the explanation. But the opposition was implacable. The Council of the BMA debated the programme with speakers articulating their own, as well as public, distress over it. Their final resolution asked the BMA 'to place on record its great regret that the BBC did not, before the production of the series, avail itself of the cooperation and advice which the Association has offered freely in such matters ever since 1951'.[58] As the row brewed, the BMA seemed motivated as much by a sense of exclusion as by genuine concern.

The Press also played a major role in fanning the controversy. Though many of the provincial papers roundly defended the series, newspapers eagerly reported cases of suicide among worried viewers. Meanwhile, the correspondence columns of the *BMJ* were buzzing with attackers and defenders, some questioning how much the patient should know, others railing against the 'obscurantist criticism' of their colleagues. The antis pitched in with examples of their patients fainting while watching the programmes (and of a dog vomiting his dinner). They also protested that 'the privacy of the surgical insult to a human body, even a consenting one, should be inviolable, and should never be made the basis of a Roman holiday for the titillation of the public's demand for thrills'.[59] Others thundered

> It has been suggested that prospective hospital patients need to be reassured about the skill and care with which they will be treated. What cant! Do they need to see engineers immersed in their calculations before they can cross a bridge confidently?[60]

Sarcasm was a popular channel for their rage: 'Let us not be blinded by old-fashioned prejudice. There is still the gynaecological out-patients to be viewed. Having seen the heart, are we to be denied the cervix?'[61]

The medical profession's allegations of sensationalism, audience squeamishness, hypochondria, and morbid interest, were all a reaction to the novelty of the medical approach. In retrospect, and in the light of its subsequent effects, what's surprising is how few doctors awoke to the potential public relations role it would play for the medical profession, garnering them extra prestige and not diminishing it.

And what of the audience? The BBC had prudently commissioned audience research to ward off the criticisms, and testify to the programmes' benign effects, which it duly did.[62] Three-quarters of the sample audience praised the series, agreeing that it was 'an ideal way of "keeping the public informed" about "the wonderful things hospitals can do for us"; of increasing confidence in the medical profession; of allaying unnecessary fears'.[63] The audience varied between 7½ and 10¼ million, and by mid-April the BBC had received 909 letters from the viewing public praising the programmes, and only 37 against.

What had caused the shift from the Radio Doctor to 'Your Life in Their Hands', from the dominance of the look-after-yourself approach (both inside and outside the media), to the medical perspective?[64] The 1950s bubbled with therapeutic optimism. It was the era of the Sputnik: the development of space technology seemed to exemplify Macmillan's 'you've never had it so good' credo. To many in the public, scientists' invention of the H-bomb represented the pinnacle of technological achievement, and they'd even discovered the structure of DNA. 'Big science' was now the thing, with the production of pharmaceuticals and chemicals forming the basis of major industrial complexes. 1950s Britain was a time of affluence and economic growth, a place of drip-dry shirts and Formica, when the wartime's cheerful stoicism and the post-war rationing mentality gave way to a belief in the unbounded potential and efficacy of technology. In 1959, the BBC appointed its first science correspondent to BBC News.

What's more, the NHS had arrived. If before, doctors and broadcasters had encouraged self-reliance partly because there wasn't organised, accessible state medical care to meet any new demand, now the system was up and running, and the public had to be encouraged to think medical and use it. The introduction of the NHS helped generate and legitimate the medical approach.

There were other changes. Until the end of the 1940s, the language of wartime collectivity still prevailed in the public domain: the nation was talked of largely in aggregate, as sharing a social fate. But along with economic expansion came notions of consumer choice and product diversity: the population came to be addressed more as consumers and individuals. So the idea of complex, technological, and individual medical treatment found a fertile soil. The so-called pharmacological revolution played a part, too; the discovery of the sulphonamides convinced people that raging streptococcal infections, from pneumonia to puerpural fever, could be curbed. The use of pencillin in the war effort, the subsequent development of streptomycin, tetracycline, and other antibiotics, and later the anti-depressants – all were seen as heralding the control of disease.

By the second series of YLITH, broadcast in 1961 and based on London teaching hospitals, Duncalf has become quite transported by a belief in the potency of medicine and doctors: one draft of a pamphlet accompanying the series talked of 'a superior race of beings whose calling raises them from the ordinary level of human fellowship'.[65] The new series also had a new theme: the importance of medical research and the value of the scientific method, reflecting the late 1950s expansion of academic medical research and the prevailing belief in research as a panacea. And it marked the beginning of television's infatuation with the prestigious London teaching hospitals.

There was another difference in the second series. This time, the programmes came with the imprimatur of the medical profession. The BMA blessed them in advance, announcing that 'We are glad to see any attempt to extend people's knowledge of what really goes on in hospitals.'[66] Volteface indeed, but there was nothing serendipitous about it. The BBC had allocated a trusty senior executive to work on the programme, liaising with the medical profession and the Ministry of Health. The doctors had been co-opted.

Why had the BMA and the medical profession largely displaced the Ministry of Health as the pressurising body to be soothed and placated? The establishment of the NHS, far from diminishing the power of the medical profession as it had feared, had increased it: through skilful negotiation, doctors had retained their 'clinical freedom' (freedom from state interference into treatment). With the post-war development of welfare, the State's direct power was increasingly refracted and mediated by the professions in education, medicine, social services, and the law. And as it acquired esoteric techniques and medical skills, the medical profession had an increasingly secure knowledge base from which to claim professional autonomy and power.[67]

But there was another significant factor which shaped the second series of YLITH: television's technical and cultural development. The first series was a mixture of filmed operations shot on clumsy 35mm film cameras (the only technology then available) and live outside broadcasts. Filming in the confines of the operating-theatre was unwieldy and required special lighting. But the second series used videotape recording (demonstrated for the first time inside the BBC and in the United States in 1956), using a technique developed jointly by Smith, Kline & French Laboratories and the BBC, whereby the operation was viewed through a mirror suspended above the operating-table, the image being reversed and corrected electronically. A 'miniature' hand-held mobile TV camera augmented the operating-theatre coverage. Duncalf believed that mobile videotape recording revolutionalised the programme.

In other ways, too, YLITH reflected a certain coming of age of television. New communications technologies, it's been suggested, are initially largely parasitic on the existing media, and only later begin to develop their own, specific forms.[68] The birth of YLITH exemplifies the process. In the earliest TV medical programmes such as 'Matters of Life and Death', the radio lineage shows through: at best, they were illustrated lectures and discussions. But radio couldn't transmit the spectacle of operations; TV could and did.

I want to suggest, too, that by the second series of YLITH, the imperatives of television – for drama and excitement – had begun to play a major role in shaping programmes. The priorities of the medical profession were no longer automatically and over-ridingly the priorities of TV medical producers: it was equally if not more important to fashion a television programme which worked effectively as *television*. No longer was there a generalised view of the public and its needs, identical to the medical conception of the public: the BBC had a new constituency, the audience, and was trying to satisfy its wants. The job of mediating medical opinion to the public had become equal, or even secondary, to this new idea – giving the audience what it wants.[69]

There was some tension between these competing imperatives (medicine's and television's), as an interchange between Duncalf and Aubrey Singer, Assistant Head of Outside Broadcasts and overseer of YLITH, reveals. Wrote Duncalf,

> You ask for pace and attack and a 'journalistic and dramatic opening' to some or all of the programmes ... I must ask that you do not press me to ask these sensitive VIP medicos to approach their subject in a manner entirely foreign to them. The drama is there without advertising it and I would not like to risk damaging our good relations by trying to inject a 'Sunday Pictorial' approach.[70]

Singer replied,

> I am fully aware of the difficulties under which you work. However, you should be equally aware that the BBC and the viewer is your first responsibility in planning this series, and that naturally while we do not wish to offend the medical profession, our first duty must lie with our audience.[71]

Here already was a generation of broadcasters attending to the needs of the medium and constructing their own notion of the audience. By 1966 Singer, who had become Head of Science Features, was elaborating his belief that 'the televising of science is *a process of television*, subject to principles of programme structure and the demands of dramatic form. Therefore, in taking programme decisions, priority must be given to the medium rather than to scientific pedantry.'[72]

Those old YLITHs seem very dated today. The patient is scarcely seen, merely a slab of flesh under the gown.[73] Fletcher himself was subsequently critical of the series' naive and unbounded enthusiasm for all things surgical.

> We tended to overemphasise the significance of the operation .... YLITH did spend nearly all of its time in hospitals and operating theatres. It concentrated on the dramatic aspects of

medicine ... if we were to do a new YLITH series ... it would be less enthusiastic, more critical, and I should certainly want to quiz the doctors and surgeons about the evidence they had for claiming their treatments were successful.[74]

The series did return in 1980, and although it was still wide-eyed about high-tech medicine, there were changes. The new presenter claimed that they'd tried to get away from the mystique surrounding the medical profession: 'Doctors are no longer being shown as rather wonderful people doing mysterious things to patients from somewhere on high. And for that reason the accent is very much on the patients' reactions and questions.'[75]

3

The Birth of the Patient

Lay lobby: the rise of the medical consumer

It's hardly surprising if radical voices were muffled in health and medical debates in the 1950s and 1960s. The NHS was still in its infancy, the idealism of its early days not yet tarnished, with institutional practices and medical power uncritically accepted. It was heretical to criticise the NHS except in quantitative terms: not enough beds, not enough new building, etc. Critics of the ideology of state welfare spoke almost exclusively from the Right. But by the late 1970s, the consumer critique of medicine was commonplace, and nowhere more so than in the media. Representatives of patients' organisations or self-help groups were routinely included in media debates about medicine alongside the doctors, and one study in the 1980s found consumers appearing in 67 per cent of programmes about medicine.[1] What had happened?

Pre-eminent among a bundle of social changes was a shift, starting in the 1960s and prevalent both on the Left and in public discourse generally, from production as the site of struggle to consumption as the contested sphere. The old 'workerist' notions – that the only valid struggles took place in the factory or down the mine – were edged out by the new interest in the community and the home: you could be just as oppressed in the privacy of your own bedroom, school, or GP's surgery. The language of social class and centralised, industrial struggle gave way to local and community organisation. And in public debate, consumerism was the new ideology: in the 1960s we were all reconstituted as consumers. The traditional indicators of class had apparently evaporated: peers dallied with proles, upwardly mobile plebs made bucks, and all wore jeans. Consumer preference and style seemed the only distinguishing features. Class seemed old hat.

The new divide, as expressed in public debates, was between the producers and the users of goods and services. Industry was suspect, no longer the post-war klondike, but a source of often shoddy goods about which a multitude of new consumer groups began to complain. The State, which hitherto (post-war) had seemed a benign provider of welfare, a cushion against the blows of the market and the ravages of war, appeared repressive. After a period in which the need for more services had been the critical issue, interest now moved to the *nature* of the services provided. And, some time after housing, education, and welfare had been scrutinised and found wanting, we became sensitive to the ideologies which the state delivered along with health care.

Anti-professionalism became rife, with growing public awareness of the ways in which medicine, the law, and architecture were, in Ivan Illich's phrase, 'disabling'.[2] Medical and state definitions of mental illness were challenged in the 1960s and 1970s by the anti-psychiatrists, maverick doctors such as Laing and Cooper (Thomas Szasz even arguing that madness was 'manufactured' by the state[3]) and by feminists. The very vocabulary of illness was being contested: where once physiology ruled supreme, critics were now seeing moral values in operation.

Disputes about medicine and professional control weren't confined to sedate academic outlets. In the United States, malpractice suits mushroomed: the doctor's authority and skill was contested in the courts, campaigns, and the streets. Politics was redefined. Once the sphere of politicians, politics was now seen to infuse everything, and there was a whole rush of books on the politics of anything from education and sport, to health and fertility. Anthropologists attributed the 1960s and 1970s American and European social concern movements in part to the post-war growth in higher education, producing more educated people than could be absorbed into industry. With economic growth and the development of the public sector, there were vast new cadres of employees in the arts, social science and services, humanities, as well as government, none of them involved in the industrial sector. A larger proportion of the population of working age was disengaged from the production process than ever before. The economic and educational boom together produced a cohort of articulate, critical people with no commitment to commerce and industry.

A major force in the emergence of the patient was the Women's Liberation Movement, which identified the personal as political. As it developed in the late 1960s and early 1970s, medicine became an early target, partly because, with the medicalisation of reproduction, the healthy woman (in contrast to the healthy man) could expect to come into intimate contact with the medical profession at regular periods in her life, over contraception, abortion, and childbirth.

The women's health movement refined and significantly developed the critique of professional power by analysing the gender aspects of medical ideology and the doctor–patient relationship: it wasn't simply doctors and patients, it was usually male doctors and female patients, and accompanying the prescriptions came prescriptive notions of how women were meant to be. Feminists identified the sexual politics of sickness, condemned the difference in status between expert and consumer, validated women's experience, and challenged the 'objectivity' of medical knowledge in a ferment of groups, meetings, conferences, events, and writings.

They also offered strategies for change. Information, controlled and propagated by women for the benefit of women was one, the sharing of experience was another; self-examination broke the barrier of individualism, and self-help was promoted as a way of countering remote, authoritarian professionals. A rash of self-help groups was formed for every conceivable condition, and a mass of literature demystified medical issues, the most important *'Our Bodies Ourselves: a health book by and for women'* by the Boston Women's Health Collective first published in 1971, and a bestseller around the world. As one feminist put it,

> Through all these efforts, we engendered a minor cultural revolution: detailed information on women's health issues is no longer a kind of contraband, spread through the underground press or word of mouth; in fact, you might even find it in *Family Circle* ... the women's health movement legitimized the notion that we have the right to know and decide about procedures – from sterilization to hormone treatments – that affect our bodies and our lives.[4]

And what of the media? It adopted the new approach with alacrity, and amplified it. Although a full-frontal feminist analysis of medical ideology was rarely to be seen or heard, consumer discontent about medical practices became in the 1970s a significant strand in medical and consumer programming, with whole series devoted to it.

By the mid-1970s, the medical approach to health and medicine was being visibly and extensively challenged in the media. For once, medicine's problems seemed more prominent than its achievements. And the problems were represented not just as those of individual patients and doctors, but as endemic to doctor–patient relations. Above all, the lay voice had become a legitimate commentator on medicine. But if the media weren't uncritically and unambiguously reproducing the dominant values of medicine (the past decade's medical broadcasting displaying contradictions and oppositional tendencies aplenty), the rise of the consumer approach also wasn't a triumph of the radicals as against the traditionalists, proof of the mass media's openness to dissent and intrinsically democratic nature.

Indeed, the growing importance accorded to the consumer critique mirrored trends within medicine itself: medicine had anticipated it and made it possible. Over the past twenty-five years, the medical profession had increasingly focussed its attention on the doctor–patient relationship, coming to see it as problematic. The medical literature was itself preoccupied with the issue of communication between doctors and patients: a standard teaching manual which, in 1916 and 1949 treated the doctor's cross-questioning of the patient perfunctorily, by its 1975 edition was stressing the importance of the patient's social circumstances, suggesting ways of improving the doctor–patient relationship, and seeing history-taking as above all 'a two-way process'.[5]

The consumer approach as seen on TV, though it was frankly critical of medical practice, didn't fundamentally unsettle medical dominance or technology, since it was a criticism increasingly being endorsed both by the medical profession and the state. It was a way in which a critique of medicine could be both made and contained, proving attractive to mass media who've historically been cautious about legitimating radical groups. Indeed, the consumer approach integrated easily into the existing media framework. The notion of self-help appealed deeply to broadcasters and journalists, since it hymned the individual, triumphing over anonymous bureaucracy – the frontier mentality played out in your own living-room. The media applauded romantic little-person-against-the-state stories as proof of the resilience of human nature. (The American media particularly loved it, as it seemed to endorse free market philosophy and the American dream.)

What it left out was the social structure. Individuals in consumer approach programmes, though their gender may have been acknowledged, were generally scooped from their social class, culture, and race, and all endowed with equally robust selves to do the helping. (And bad luck to the working-class woman without the energy, time or confidence to challenge her doctor or join a self-help group.) The consumer approach in the media was generally myopic over the differences in power which different patients brought to the medical encounter, and their origin outside the surgery door. Consumer programmes also rarely acknowledged that many of the problems – which we were being exhorted to overcome individually – resulted from the social structure, needing intervention at the social and political and not just the personal or professional level to eradicate. In its obsession with illness as experienced, and medical responses to it, the consumer approach ignored the production of illness.

Its targets above all were medical relationships, and it frequently reduced the problems of the doctor–patient relationship to one of communication. The changes it sought were often cosmetic: doctors should tell patients more (what they tell is unproblematic), should listen to them more, should give them more choices (who could disagree?). In certain situations, they should agree to doctor them less (let them self-help it away). At its softest edge, the consumer movement was doing no more than adding courses in bedside manner to the medical curriculum. As such, it was quite compatible with the medical approach.

Certainly the crescendo of lay voices in the media did raise some important questions about medical dominance, change the representation of doctor–patient relations, and put the patients' experience squarely onto the media agenda. But how far did the consumer approach in the media reflect, or contribute to, actual changes in doctor–patient relationships? It's hard to say, but one can't help but suspect that while our TV screens were crowded with reporters, presenters, and patients' representatives sounding off about the authoritarian, unresponsive style of GPs and consultants, most patients were sitting obligingly in their doctors' surgeries, as mute as ever.[6]

Is there a philosopher in the house?

The consumer approach hatched into a rather different creature in the 1980s, with the proliferation of programmes and articles on medical ethics. Ethical issues were seen as those where doctors' skills and authority didn't necessarily endow them with the moral ability to make the best judgments. Enter parents, legislators, the judiciary, campaigners, etc. Many argued that moral crises resulted from the development of new technologies which then posed new ethical questions, although others said that it was the expansion of medical power and authority over birth and death which provoked the controversies,[7] still others believing that the boundary between medicine and the law was being renegotiated.[8]

Certainly abortion, heart transplants, euthanasia, the switching off of life-support systems and in vitro fertilisation (test-tube babies) – all these and more provided material for press, broadcasting, and public debate. Following the publication of the Warnock Report in 1984, surrogate motherhood became the hot issue, with much elbowing by media organisations to scoop pictures of and interviews with the first commercially arranged British surrogate mother. And in America, the cases of Baby Fae,[9] two Baby Does,[10] and Baby M[11] attracted massive media interest. From 1982 to 1985, there was even a BBC TV programme, 'Doctors' Dilemmas', entirely devoted to medical ethical questions, discussed by doctors, lawyers, patients' representatives and philosophers – demonstrating the growing tendency to appeal to philosophy as the new, objective arbiter.

Media discussions about medicine and morals represented a response to the consumer critique of medicine and public anxiety about medical power. After the 1970s, the medical profession could no longer appear on TV making soothing 'leave it to us' noises, or outlaw all contact with the media as in the days of William Osler (see Chapter 1). It had now to defend itself before persistent critics. Medical ethics programmes and articles testified to the success of the consumer critique. Yet the ethical approach had its limitations. It certainly opened out medical issues for debate, and acknowledged the moral dimensions of medicine, but its very selection of subjects was revealing. Only certain issues – generally to do with the consequences of technological advance, and the redefining of the points at which life begins and ends –

were certified as ethical, as if other medical issues were ethically transparent. And yet *all* medical decisions are in some sense based on ethical and social considerations, though their moral and social code is hidden and taken for granted. Programmes on ethical subjects to some extent legitimate a 'keep out' sign above other medical issues, by implication the 'non-ethical' ones, and thus unwittingly endorse dominant medical beliefs about them. If surrogate motherhood is a problematic, medico-ethical matter then we must assume 'normal' motherhood isn't. And the treatment of breast cancer is rarely depicted as an ethical issue, even though the contribution of radiotherapy and chemotherapy to prolonging life is unproven, and some argue that mastectomy of any kind is unnecessary and not life-extending, and doubt the value of early diagnosis which itself raises ethical issues.

Medical journalists obviously have to choose stories – they can't discuss all the subjects all the time, but there's nothing intrinsic about which issues get selected (by the media, the medical profession, and the public) as morally problematic. They're often the site of moral, social, and political crises (see Chapter 8). What's more, an issue may get media coverage as a moral controversy because of factors unconnected with its importance. 'Doctors' Dilemmas' executive producer only chooses subjects which fit into the programme format, with a dramatised case treated by a real doctor in a situation they'd normally confront, and at least two ethical principles in collision.[12] The doctors were frankly chosen to generate the maximum drama and conflict to engage the audience.[13] Television has its own imperatives.

Programmes about medical ethics also – almost by definition – frame issues in moral or religious terms, matters of individual conscience or competing beliefs, largely outside the political domain. Like the consumer approach proper they tend to gloss over the social origin of doctors' and patients' unequal power beyond the surgery door. One 'Doctors' Dilemmas' programme debated whether doctors should be allowed to make life-and-death decisions about new-born babies. When the patients' representative interjected that perinatal mortality caused by class and regional inequalities already did that, there was a stunned silence. The presenter briskly moved the discussion on, and the issue was never raised again. The speaker had challenged and subverted the notion of ethics as an individual moral dilemma.

Body matters: anatomy of a health obsession

While ethical issues were being hotly debated, the media's agenda was altering once again: looking-after-yourself arrived. Almost no corner of broadcasting was safe. People could materialise on any programme sporting sweat-bands, running-suits, or leg-warmers – the uniform of the good life. Breakfast TV presenters (no respecters of antemeridian torpor) goaded sluggish muscles through punishing keep-fit routines, and talked cheerfully of a socially-acceptable form of masochism known as 'the burn'. Athletes described how they ate their way to success. Nutritionists were filmed simulating the average family's weekly supermarket trawl, ringing up on cash registers the hidden sugar, fats, and additives, and calculating the total health toll. Natural became a meaningless word of approval and fitness became a metaphor also applied to the mind, with books on 'cerebral calisthenics' offering mental workouts and fitness programmes. What had induced the new health obsession?

Some dismissed it as just another craze. Others saw it as a belated media and public response to changes in lifestyle, with the populace realising at last that their sedentary, fat-filled lives were making them sick. And there were those who thought the new approach resulted from greater medical knowledge about the causes of illness. Of course there'd been quite enough medical knowledge in the 1930s for nutritionists to enthuse over lentils and vigorously recommend wholemeal bread and physical jerks. And though consumption of refined foods had greatly increased since the 1950s, some said that public alarm over health was at its peak just when the nation's health was better than ever, what's been called 'doing better and feeling worse'.

But the reasons for the health frenzy lie less in bodies than in politics. The hazards which societies focus on express moral and social values. There are real and constant dangers to health and reasons for feeling vulnerable, but widespread worries and panics generally depend less on which dangers are dominant at any time than on which are thought significant – a perception which is shaped by economic, political, and ideological concerns. And the health obsession is better understood as the result of an economic, political, and ideological crisis.[14] The belief in medicine as a panacea had already been rocked by the consumer critique.

Environmental scandals – thalidomide, occupationally-caused cancers, pollution – had put the idea that illness was socially-caused onto the public agenda. Added to that was a crisis of costs afflicting most Western industrialised countries from the late 1970s. In the United States, the average American worker was devoting the equivalent of one month's salary to pay for medical care, and General Motors claimed it spent more money on medical insurance for its employees in 1975 than it did on metal for its cars.[15]

At the same time, although medicine's curative powers had been questioned and found wanting, the belief in medical care as a right was now fundamental to Western society: even the most rabid conservatives, however much they promoted private medicine and bled the NHS of funds, couldn't talk openly of slaying it. In such a climate, slicing away services needed justifying ideologically. If responsibility for health lay in your hands, what need for the State to provide ever-increasing funds to make you healthier?

The emergence of a new ideology works in complex ways. Governments in Britain and elsewhere didn't conspiratorially dream up an ideology of self-reliance to allow them to dismantle state medical services on the quiet. But the body and the body politic are connected, and the body is often the site of social struggle. In today's economically stringent mood (as in Weimar), self-restraint is urged, social 'waste' abhorred. There are campaigns against the consumption of fat (which takes on an almost mythical significance); leanness both administratively and physically is prized, bodies are worked out, disciplined, controlled.

The middle-classes turn inwards, and the body becomes the terrain for action and for the improving impulse. The 'survival of the fittest' takes on a new meaning. Rigour is valued, and the indulgence and experiment of the past (such as the 1960s) rejected. Illness becomes a violation of the social order: there is a moral duty to be well and self-denial, whether by aerobics or diet, is now a social act. Michel Foucault argued that, in eighteenth-century Europe, soldiers, whose bodies had been rigorously disciplined and transformed, became docile, conforming to the social order.[16] The 1980s cult of the body forms a striking parallel. Though apparently liberating and life-extending, the preoccupation with the body by social institutions can be seen as an extension of social control onto the body itself.

In the medical approach, health and illness were abstracted from the social relations which helped to shape them. Sick? You need pills, an operation, medical intervention. In the look-after-yourself approach, health and illness are again torn from their social context. Sick? You need bran and aerobics, muesli and jogging. The interaction between individuals and environment remains invisible, consumption still the solution. The shift is only in the kinds of goods and services ingested: from medical services to exercise classes, health foods, vitamins, slimming products, food supplements – the new elixirs and nostrums, the panoply of consumption which makes up 'body maintenance'. Take a class, open a packet.

Fears are merchandised, the solutions profitable. Like the old hawkers of patent medicines, the new health businesses borrowed medical pronouncements to make bucks. Arguing that 'stress has been linked to virtually every illness that plagues man', American fitness experts recommended the $1,495 Get-A-Way Chair (a reclining massage chair – you recline, it massages). The heart is the most important muscle to exercise, they said, so buy a treadmill (for $2,695). British colour supplements were advising on how to install a gymnasium into your own home or gadget your way to fitness with a £200 exercise bike. As the American National Centre for Health Education put it, 'Health is certainly selling, but who is profiting?'

At the same time, the health frenzy clearly addresses real anxieties about the debilitating effects of many aspects of contemporary life. Most people do eat junk food, lead sedentary and stressful lives, smoke and drink too much; it isn't good for our health. The look-after-yourself approach mobilises genuine bodily needs and desires, addressing authentic fears and, to some people, offering a sense of individual hope. For many, moreover, taking up a sport or going to a fitness class makes them feel better and (especially rare for women) is time put aside for themselves. Those who can, seize the opportunity, and use the new philosophy for their own ends and benefits. But look-after-yourself programmes, articles, and policies have also been accused of 'blaming the victim', substituting for the known social causes of disease an unrealistic idea of how individuals behave, and pulling threads from the fabric of daily life.[17] They depict a Toytown world, where Noddy and Big Ears never pay rent or have to queue for a bus, replacing 'is' and 'are' with 'ought' and 'should'.

According to orthodox health educators, through a three-part sequence known as knowledge-attitude-behaviour, people gain knowledge, change their attitudes, and then their behaviour. Look-after-yourself programmes reproduce this idea, which is prescriptive rather than descriptive, seeing people as (all equally) free to choose a healthier way of life. But critics argue that it's a mirage of the market: what passes for real choice is preference – to decide between bacon and beef flavoured crisps, although time and advanced detective skills (or living in a middle-class area with a wholefood shop) are needed to buy a snack for children not spiked with fat, salt, and additives.[18] And the look-after-yourselfers both inside and outside the media rarely consider the role of poverty in shaping diet.[19]

The media, in preaching fibre and fitness, seldom address other realities of their audience's lives. To many unemployed people, getting up seems more of a challenge than keeping fit, and women who work both outside and inside the home have enough trouble finding time to shop let alone jog.[20]

The TV and radio programmes also usually ignore other cultural determinants of health, like the fact that women are rarely free to choose their family's diet since people generally eat and enjoy the kind of food they were reared on – he wants what his Mum used to make. Families' food preferences are remarkably resilient and shaped by class, cultural and historical traditions as well as by budget, availability, and nutritional value. And broadcasters' appeals to health are often unrealistic because they ignore real conflicts in their audience's lives. A Scottish study found that heavy male drinkers already suffering from liver disease found it almost impossible to restrict their drinking (in line with doctors' orders) without conflicting with the norms of masculine behaviour in the North-East of Scotland.[21] And when a group of pregnant women were asked why they smoked, the reasons were far more complex than those generally given by orthodox health educators – ignorance or irresponsibility. For many of them, smoking was an important way of relaxing and a social ritual, when they could temporarily escape the demands of full-time motherhood. When a mother is smoking, her children don't climb up onto her; they're expected to entertain themselves. Smoking ropes off a corner of her life for a woman herself, providing a space often valuable enough to outweigh any dangers it might present to the unborn child.[22]

Of course, individuals *can* make effective and valuable changes in their lives and health, but to focus almost exclusively on personal 'lifestyle' without recognising the social, economic, and class factors which help shape it leads to an unrealistic overestimation of how far we can individually alter our behaviour, and may generate guilt and anxiety which cause further ill-health or dis-ease. It also neglects the ways in which collective action can change the determinants of our health, and make healthier choices possible or easier.[23]

How far has the media's fitness and fibre frenzy really changed lives? There's undoubtedly great public interest in food and its role in causing ill-health: halfway through its Food and Health Campaign, the BBC had received 250,000 requests for information. Yet it's also likely that more people know what they *should* be eating than actually are. It may be that more people feel guilty than healthy. But perhaps, even if the look-after-yourself propaganda hasn't actually changed lives, it might help create a groundswell of informed, angry consumers. Certainly there are new, processed food products available with less sugar, fat, and salt, though there's already been some backlash advertising (ads for butter proclaiming 'Welcome back'), and a financial journalist claims that 'what the food industry has done is to adopt a high-profile posture of concern while making as few, largely cosmetic changes as it can.'[24] At the same time, while broadcasters preached the message of healthy eating, additives in British food were increasing by 5 per cent a year,[25] and while public anxiety about pollution and environmentally-caused disease mounted, the Government set up an inquiry into the difficulties which the health and safety at work laws caused employers.

For most working-class people, look-after-yourself programmes are part of an ideology that they may read, hear and see, but which scarcely brushes the reality of their lives. A market survey in Bath found that the four top health issues were: being free from the threat of nuclear war; having enough money to live comfortably on; having an environment free from pollution; and being free from the threat of violence.[26] But the media, on the rare occasions they contemplate it, are mystified by the mismatch between knowledge and behaviour. As the makers of the Channel 4 health series 'Well Being' recounted,

> The funny thing is that we often know that we are eating the wrong things, but carry on regardless. For instance, we asked some sixth formers in Barnsley to talk about their diet. They knew that they ought to be eating fresh fruit and veg, but when they got the chance to buy their own lunches, they usually went for chips and gravy. . . . [The same with addictions.] The main question . . . was why people consume things that can only cause them harm. None of the experts we asked had any terribly clear answers.[27]

His life in her hands

The appeal to health and fitness is rarely gender-blind. More usually it helps develop and perpetuate images of manly and womanly behaviour. Health promotion literature and look-after-yourself programmes are generally aimed at women, though they often address men's health. Women are meant to wrestle not only with their own flab, but his too. In the television Flora margarine ads, Terry Wogan, his honey voice familiar, cajoled women to get their man using Flora instead of butter to trim his waistband and, by implication, preserve his heart (though in 1986 Flora launched a massive advertising campaign aimed directly at women, especially the growing market of young professional women). A 1979 Health Education Council anti-smoking campaign used TV commercials in which children played mummies and daddies: 'Daddy' comes home from work and looks for his cigarettes, while 'Mummy' gives him a cup of tea and, gesticulating towards the dolls, warns him 'not in front of the children'.[28] Sexism, like smoking, is learned young.

The look-after-yourself approach also reproduces nineteenth-century ideas about maternal sacrifice for the sake of the family, scapegoating women who already carry the major burden for family health. A study of early motherhood found that, far from being the irresponsible creatures implied by much of the health promotion literature, women suffered from a surfeit and a conflict of responsibility, and were uncertain how to meet the competing demands made on them, like when one child's needs conficted with another's, or with their husband or partner's needs, or their own. The rhetoric of preventive health exacerbated their anxiety and feelings of inadequacy, and often conflicted with the economic constraints which shaped their lives.[29] And many women dread look-after-yourself programmes which advise them to use fewer convenience foods, inevitably requiring more time in the kitchen – especially when many of them are trying to move out of it.

Still doctoring the box

With the spread of consumer and look-after-yourself programmes, and recurring reports of ethical crises, can the medical approach still be dominant? It's a curious paradox that, while the practice of medicine is increasingly curtailed by cuts and criticised, the social authority of medicine remains intact. Certainly, doctors' communication skills have taken a battering, and some medical programmes include a patient's representative as a matter of course. There are also many programmes offering health routines which don't need a doctor's prescription. Yet the medical approach seems to survive resiliently and quite healthily alongside.[30] Medicine has simply redrawn the boundaries of what it can do. And, paradoxically, on the box or radio it's usually doctors who discourse on how the individual can look-after-themselves, and still the doctor who lends legitimacy to the new health regimes. Indeed, the new emphasis on health has created for the medically trained new jobs in health promotion. Health promotion has been medicalised.

The ideology of medicine seems powerful enough to survive challenge, modification, and changing social practice. The look-after-yourself approach, far from supplanting the medical or consumer approaches, co-exists with them, often within the same programme. TV and radio magazine programmes often veer from approach to approach within one edition, depicting doctors both as successful curers of disease, as insufficiently responsive to patients, and as arbiters of when the patients should help themselves. And in the United States the three approaches blend easily even within the same story.

The arrival of the consumer and health education approaches lent diversity to the range of health and medical programmes, but the diversity is sometimes more apparent than real. Fundamentally, all three approaches share similar premises, emphasising illness as individually experienced and caused, playing down its economic and environmental origins, and to a greater or lesser extent deferring to medical definitions of health and illness. The box is still being doctored.

4 It's a Natural:

Childbirth and the Media

Baby love

Public debate and media coverage of childbirth have shifted dramatically over the past sixty years. The early look-after-yourself approach (women's maternity problems are caused by their own ignorance and irresponsibility) gave way to a medical approach (doctors are the experts on pregnancy, and better medical technology produces safer childbirth). Then came an explosion of programmes adopting the consumer approach (women are impersonally processed through pregnancy; obstetricians should respond to their needs). But invisible all the while was the environmental approach (childbirth is influenced by social factors like housing, poverty, and class).

In the 1930s and 1940s, media coverage of childbirth was as much about death as life. In spite of improvements in maternal and infant mortality, surviving labour and ending up with a live baby were the pre-eminent issues of maternity in the 1920s, 1930s, and 1940s, and matters such as the emotional experience of labour would have seemed an irrelevance. The Government tried to allay the frequent adverse publicity about maternal mortality in the 1930s, and films like *Motherhood* (a fictional 'documentary' propaganda film produced by the National Baby Week Council in 1917 with the slogan 'the race marches forward on the feet of little children') used the dominant look-after-yourself approach to contrast the feckless, gin-drinking mother with the caring one. *The Fight for Life* (1940), by American documentary film-maker Pare Lorentz, warned against the dangers of home births and emphasised proper diet for expectant mothers, while George Stoney's American documentary *All*

My Babies (1952) contrasted a dirty home, unprepared for childbirth, with the physically and psychologically ready mother.

Although the proportion of hospital births grew dramatically in Britain and America between the 1920s and 1940s,[1] and antenatal care, induction, and caesarian section increased significantly in the late 1920s and 1930s, childbirth was still viewed primarily through look-after-yourself spectacles, and by doctors as a natural and unproblematic event, part of women's normal, biological fate. It was also a private experience, connected with sex, and subject to similar taboos. So a 1945 BBC radio series on 'The New Baby' offered Dr Winnicott on the state of the mother's mind during pregnancy, and a female gynaecologist (promoting relaxation and psychoprophylaxis) on antenatal and postnatal care, but was silent on the subject of labour. Similarly, Charles Hill the Radio Doctor, in his 1950 guide to child-rearing, leapfrogged straight from nutrition in pregnancy to breastfeeding, pausing only to acknowledge the newborn's first yells and omitting labour altogether.[2] But though most women were still being delivered by midwives,[3] in the media, at least, the obstetrician was the unquestioned authority on pregnancy and labour.

In the late 1950s and early 1960s, medical power and intervention into childbirth grew rapidly, and in the media, a medical approach to pregnancy and labour (as to most other issues) was replacing the look-after-yourself orthodoxy. In 1957 Granada TV transmitted a film of a caesarian birth (to the disgust of many doctors who argued – shades of 'Your Life in Their Hands' – that such a relatively rare procedure couldn't possibly be relevant to a mass audience[4]) and in 1961 'Your Life in Their Hands' itself featured an exchange transfusion for newborn babies. Pregnancy and childbirth were coming to be seen as an exclusively medical matter, and there were no media outlets open to lay critics of medicalised childbirth.

If a crisis is a moment when the unsayable is first said, it's clear why BBC TV's 'Horizon' programme on the induction of labour, 'A Time To Be Born', provoked a medical furore in January 1975, causing the BBC to publish a special report defending its medical programmes. The film, based on articles in the *Lancet* and *The Sunday Times*, challenged the routine induction of labour for 'social' reasons (like the convenience of doctors) rather than 'medical' ones, and suggested that many women found speeded-up labours more painful and less satisfying. The programme, which was condemned by a *British Medical Journal* (*BMJ*) editorial and prompted questions in the House of Commons, was in the vanguard of a vigorous new public and media debate about medicalised childbirth, in which at last the labouring woman's voice was heard.

Actually on television, not so much the labouring woman's voice as the critical male obstetrician's. The main critique in the 'Horizon' programme came from a maverick doctor, Peter Huntingford (then Professor of Obstetrics and Gynaecology at the London Hospital), at odds with his colleagues on almost every obstetric orthodoxy from the undesirability of home births to the desirability of induction.[5] A telling indication of the extent of change in media coverage of childbirth was that nine years later, in 1984, Peter Huntingford had his own five-part BBC TV series, 'Birth Right', made by the Continuing Education Department (not noted for its iconoclasm). His criticisms of the medicalisation of maternity care, his doubts about antenatal care, hospital births, and routine induction, and his support of women's right to choose their style of labour, were presented as a legitimate part of the mainstream childbirth debate, and not the idiosyncratic obsessions of a dissenter.

But by then, such a critique was no longer novel. Consumer programmes about childbirth were unexceptional – there were three major ones in 1982 in a single week alone, part of what the *BMJ* called 'television's impromptu festival of reproduction'. Pregnant women were frequently filmed in a consultation or undergoing an ultrasound scan, and the image of the contracting woman, plus supporting spouse and exhorting midwife, became something of a cliché. Whereas in 1972 newspapers exclaimed at the novelty of a radio programme broadcasting a recorded hospital delivery,[6] in the 1980s it became a television commonplace to see the moist head of a newborn slithering out into the world. Such programmes marked a major shift in the media's representation of pregnancy and labour: the pregnant woman was now a person with feelings.

When the BBC TV consumer programme 'That's Life' mounted a special programme in 1982 based on audience replies to a questionnaire about the experience of childbirth, the overwhelming message was that most women wanted more choice in pregnancy and labour, which weren't just mechanical processes, but intimately affected by the emotions. How a mother felt about antenatal care, stressed presenter Esther Rantzen, would influence her attendance at antenatal clinics and childbirth preparation classes, and her feelings – whether of fear or trust – would shape the experience of labour and mothering. 'The experts can give advice – but whether she can take their advice depends on how she feels.' Programmes on childbirth, like other consumer health programmes, also investigated 'iatrogenesis' (the negative results of too much doctoring), examining the effects on mothers and babies of episiotomy, induction, and other routine procedures. Some also questioned the dominance of the doctor in childbirth.[7]

The consumer approach, though common, didn't wholly eclipse the medical approach. Radio phone-ins still fielded (as guest experts) orthodox obstetricians opposing home deliveries and ignoring the possible adverse consequences of hospitalisation, while other programmes cheerfully defended obstetric technology without letting the critics have their say.[8] Yet the proliferation of consumer programmes about childbirth was striking. What had caused them?

One reason was the medicalisation of labour in the 1960s and 1970s. Home births fell from 42.4 per cent in 1946 to 12.4 per cent in 1970.[9] Along with the increase in hospital births came the growth of medical intervention – more forceps deliveries and caesarian sections, fetal heart monitoring and the routine induction of labour, and extensive use of ultrasonic scans and epidural anaesthesia. Many women felt unhappy with these trends and though women had been critical of the management of labour for decades, in the 1950s and 1960s they began to organise against it. The National Childbirth Trust (NCT) was founded in 1956, and the Association for Improvements in the Maternity Services (AIMS) in 1960.[10] Both groups, active in the 1960s, became more radical in the 1970s. But though childbirth activists had been writing and campaigning for years, broadcasters only became interested when they gained a framework in which to make sense of the criticisms. The consumer approach provided this, and with its arrival the media started to sit up and take notice of the critics of medicalised childbirth, and their views on pregnancy and labour began to shape the media agenda.

The Women's Liberation Movement, for its part, had been uninterested in the subject of childbirth for several years. Motherhood seemed part of women's traditional sex-roles which feminists rejected as oppressive; abortion and contraception were thought more relevant campaigning issues. But as feminists got older and began having children themselves, the potential of childbirth as a feminist issue became apparent. By the mid-1970s, women's health groups saw a control over reproduction as a right. They lobbied for more women-responsive facilities and wrote angry books decrying the 'immaculate deception' practised by the medical profession when it claimed that birth was naturally risky, and safe only in hospital.[11] They advocated instead 'natural childbirth', where possible without medical and technological intervention.

These various campaigns found a receptive audience in a cohort of media women who were having babies. Esther Rantzen, 'That's Life' presenter and producer, became something of a professional mother, her maternity and postnatal depression making front-page news. She fed back some of her own experience into her programmes. And to TV producers in general, birth was an attractive subject, highly telegenic. It was dramatic, emotional, and generally had a happy outcome. It wasn't an illness, but could still mobilise the glamour of doctors and hospitals. It was also a visible, infinitely filmable event happening in hours or days, rather than a slow, invisible process. And since all of us have been born and most women still give birth, it had wide audience appeal. It was a natural.

As it happened, the childbirth movement and the media's babymania also reflected the preoccupation with naturalness and 'returning to nature' which marked this particular historical moment. Proponents of natural childbirth cast back nostalgically to a pre-technological Golden Age, and approvingly cited contemporary examples of Third World women giving birth in fields unaided and untraumatised, as if 'nature' could exist outside culture or history, and Third World women were purely biological beings or natural breeders (the obstetric equivalent of natural rhythm). The natural childbirth movement helped idealise pregnancy and labour, portraying women's 'intuitive' knowledge of childbirth as a kind of essential femininity (as if to be female was to have babies). The critique which emerged in the media also often fetishised technology, seeing it as bad in itself, rather than because it reproduced certain social and gender relations which women found oppressive.

Indeed, media coverage of childbirth consistently ignored women as a group. It was extraordinary, given that the criticisms of the medicalisation of birth had originated in bodies like the NCT and AIMS, how rarely women's campaigning groups were referred to, let alone filmed or interviewed, in programmes on pregnancy and labour. Even Channel 4's radical flagship series 'Crucible', its aim to examine the place of science in society, ignored the childbirth and women's health movements when it reported on the growing use of technology in pregnancy.[12] The programme interviewed women about their individual experience, but when it came to extrapolating from it and making a general criticism of obstetric practice, they turned to – Peter Huntingford.

There's nothing new in male doctors criticising maternity care. Indeed, the history of obstetric theories in the twentieth century can be viewed as a succession of canonised male experts (and it helps to be French). After Frederick Truby King, childrearing adviser who, in the 1920s, also claimed that pregnancy – though a natural, normal event and not a disease – required medical control, came Grantley Dick-Read, whose 'Childbirth Without Fear' (1933) suggested that instruction in relaxation (psycho-prophylaxis) might help women endure labour without pain-killers. Dr Fernand Lamaze, who added childbirth without pain to childbirth without fear by proposing physical and mental exercises to alter the perception of pain, became all the rage in America in the 1950s and 1960s. Next came Frederic Leboyer, author of *Birth Without Violence*. Uninterested in mothers but concerned at the brutal experience of birth for babies, he advocated a new, gentle method of giving birth, with dimmed lights, no noise, leaving the umbilical cord uncut for some minutes after birth, and bathing the newborn in water. He also attracted considerable media interest.

And then there was Michel Odent, who became the hero of British natural childbirth supporters after three peak-time television appearances in the early 1980s. Odent saw himself as applying the ideas of Ivan Illich to birth. He gave women complete freedom to choose their style and position of labour (except the freedom to choose painkillers) and never induced, preferring instead, where it would be dangerous to continue unassisted, to perform a caesarian. Many women in his unit gave birth kneeling in a paddling-pool. The Odent way of birth first appeared on British television in July 1981 in the popular ITV series 'Where There's Life'. Presenter Dr Miriam Stoppard, like Rantzen expansive about her role as a mother, was obviously taken with Odent's methods, declaring that 'as a mother, I can't help feeling cheated that I couldn't have had my baby in such a natural way and so instinctively'.

But it was Ann Paul, with her moving film 'Birth Reborn',[13] who really beamed the spotlight on Odent. She, too, had a personal interest, after an alienated, mid-sixties labour when, her husband banished from the delivery room, she was made to lie down though she found it uncomfortable, given pethidine and told to be quiet, and left alone on a narrow bed in the cold room.

> Even now, a nightmare of drugged pain and an atmosphere of cold indifference haunts me. . . . So it was with joy that I listened to Michel Odent discussing his deeply-held beliefs that women should dictate how they give birth by responding to their own primitive instincts.[14]

Paul's film passionately supported Odent, declaring him 'a radical challenge to modern obstetrics', and her commentary implicitly criticised high-technology conventional hospital births. A week later, Esther Rantzen's 'That's Life – Having a Baby' too showed film of Odent's methods.

But, if the particulars of Odent's methods were original, his critique of medicalisation hardly differed from that of the female childbirth movement. So why were the media so infatuated with him? The dominance of the male obstetrician inside and outside the media was part of a long process in which women and female skills were displaced from obstetrics. The transition from control by untrained women to control by formally trained men has been well documented.[15] As obstetrics became a higher-status, higher-class, male occupation, female midwives were gradually driven from their central role. Surgical intervention and eventually hospitalisation became more frequent, and forceps and other devices to speed up labour were substituted for support, time, and patience. Men had come to manage reproducton.

It's ironic that male obstetricians (and 'men-midwives') first introduced the very technology which the media-lauded male obstetricians later decried. Ironically too, the childbirth movement (with its articulate, organised groups of women) furnished the media with very conservative notions of gender, reinforcing an image of women as preoccupied with reproduction, and women's health as largely an obstetric and gynaecological matter. The media's obsession with childbirth also helped define motherhood as above all a biological process: to be a mother came to mean to have given birth, not to care for and nurture a child. The social process of mothering was ignored: TV producers, lingering over technicolour pictures of pregnancy and labour, omitted the issues confronting mothers in their twenty subsequent years of parenting – problems of childcare, isolation, mothers' social status, maternal poverty, the emotional demands of mothering. Maternal labour came to mean something happening in a labour ward, not a housing estate.

The preoccupation with birth, and not parenting, wasn't exclusive to the mass media but mirrored the way most obstetricians viewed reproduction – as a medical event beginning when a woman became an antenatal patient, and ending when she was discharged from maternity care.[16] Most women, on the other hand, saw having a baby 'not as an isolated episode of medical treatment but as an event which is integrated into other aspects of [their] ... life' and having 'implications for most of [their] ... other social roles'.[17] Though radio and television programmes on childbirth articulated and amplified many feminist criticisms of medicalised labour, they also reproduced medicine's narrow emphasis. While they reported the experience of labour to an extent and in ways unimaginable to their predecessors, they neglected the wider dimensions of becoming a mother.

Saving babies and the production of antenatal guilt

The chorus of criticism about childbirth, and women's anger at being impersonally processed through the system, didn't silence pleas for more technology. When broadcasters and journalists reported on 'high risk' women and perinatal mortality, they almost invariably pressed for medical solutions. Antenatal care rapidly came to be seen as a panacea, with an unlimited ability to reduce death and handicap, and various equipment seemed also to hold the key to saving babies' lives.

Pressure groups exerted a major influence on this coverage. The campaigns of the Spastics Society and the Maternity Alliance were especially powerful – well-orchestrated, about a popular cause (sick babies), and making unproblematic television. Ironically, just at the point at which perinatal mortality was declining, the Spastics Society's campaigns ('Save a Baby' (1977) and 'Prevention' (1978)) created something of a panic on the issue and, with a touching faith in the effectiveness of antenatal care and medical technology, demanded a government commitment of increased resources to prevent handicap. The Labour Secretary of State for Health responded by saying that 'expectant mothers must book in early at the clinic. The fact is that, whatever the reasons, mothers who are late in making arrangements for care in pregnancy are five times more likely to lose their babies'.[18] The Health Education Council's (HEC) 'Mother and Baby' campaign to reduce perinatal mortality was launched in 1980 in a burst of press and television advertising. It was consequently targetted at so-called late attenders, and followed the Government in associating late booking with perinatal mortality, though it only required an O level in social science to recognise that the correlation between late attendance and perinatal mortality wasn't necessarily a causal one. As an epidemiologist connected with the campaign put it, 'the late bookers are often high-risk mothers for a number of reasons, and ... these other reasons, which cannot be ameliorated by early attendance, may be the ones responsible for much of the high mortality'.[19]

Yet by the time of the HEC's press release, late booking had been reduced to 'ignorance or indifference' on the part of women, even though leading perinatal epidemiologists, obstetricians, paediatricians, midwives, GPs, health education officers, and targetted women themselves questioned the campaign, and even some HEC council members thought it a gross simplification. It had become the new orthodoxy, strikingly similar to the women-blaming government line in the early 1900s and 1930s, and it spread rapidly in the media since, whenever broadcasters took up the subject of perinatal mortality, they found a ready-made official explanation.

But the Spastics Society and the Maternity Alliance also argued that a high proportion of sick babies died because of lack of hospital resources, so they lobbied for hospitals to get more money. They were supported by obstetricians, paediatricians, and doctors in the rapidly growing speciality of neonatology. One person played a major role in shaping and publicising the lobby. Catherine Boyd, one of 1960s' much-photographed 'Jay Twins' and daughter of a Labour politician, had been a BBC TV 'That's Life' researcher. After having a handicapped baby, she became personally interested in perinatal mortality and the prevention of handicap, and for four years ran the Spastics Society's 'Save a Baby' campaign calling for more obstetric and paediatric care. She later helped set up the Maternity Alliance, working to change obstetric routines like antenatal screening, and the excessive, inappropriate use of caesarians. With her family connections and television experience, Boyd was uniquely placed to influence journalists. She supplied material to *The Sunday Times* and 'Man Alive' about high-risk women, and proposed 'That's Life – Having a Baby', made in association with the Spastics Society campaign. And when, in 1980, the Short Report asserted that there were at least 3,000–5,000 avoidable baby deaths a year 'if modern knowledge and care are universally applied',[20] (widely reported in the media under arresting headlines such as '5,000 babies need not die',[21] 'MPs call for £25m spending to stop baby death toll',[22] and 'Babies dying in cots shortage'[23]), the Spastics Society had been there first, setting the agenda with a 1979 report claiming that perhaps 1,000 lives a year alone were lost because of a national shortage of intensive care cots.[24]

Critics judged this a gross overestimation of the potential contribution of medical intervention, since there's a strong correlation between perinatal mortality and parents' socio-economic background. Working-class women have a higher chance than middle-class ones of having a baby who doesn't survive.[25] The call for more medical facilities ignored the documented role of poverty, poor diet, reproductive hazards in the workplace, environmental pollutants, drugs, and stress in causing perinatal mortality and handicap.[26] Yet despite the counter-evidence, doctors, health educators, consumer groups, and hence radio and television programmes, repeatedly offered up these medical and look-after-yourself approaches to perinatal mortality. Technological solutions were particularly attractive to governments and broadcasters because, though they didn't touch the social origins of illness, they provided specific goods and services to campaign for, in contrast to the environmental approach, which required major social change – something far too leviathan for most broadcasters (let alone politicians) to contemplate. If broadcasters and campaigners lobbied for more intensive care units or machines, they stood a fair chance of short or mid-term success.

Missing throughout the whole media childbirth debate was the experience of working-class women. The childbirth movement was dominated by articulate, middle-class women, and the poverty lobby (groups like the Child Poverty Action Group and the National Council for One-Parent Families) lacked the clout and medical endorsement to get the class dimension of perinatal mortality onto the agenda.

But the influence of the natural childbirth movement over the media was short-lived. Since its zenith in the early 1980s, there's been something of a media backlash against demedicalised childbirth. Birth is anyway no longer a hot media topic. British and American articles and programmes on pregnancy and labour (what few there now are) increasingly take a 'we wuz conned' line, quoting women who think the swing to natural childbirth went too far and created a new orthodoxy, and defending technological interventions into births – painkillers, epidurals, and all.[27] After what turned out to have been a brief interlude, interest in midwives (who still deliver the majority of babies) has waned again. And though the natural childbirth issue flared once more in 1985/6, when the media rooted strongly for obstetrician Wendy Savage, suspended from her London Hospital job for her pro-choice obstetric policy, the reporting was mainly confined to news coverage, and ended when the case did.[28]

Did the media's romance with childbirth have any effect? The vexed question of media effects is examined in Chapter 13, but maternity services have certainly become a little more liberal over the past few years. In many hospitals it's now possible to have a 'Leboyer birth', husbands or partners are common in delivery rooms, and increasing numbers of women walk about in labour. At the same time (and despite the concern of pressure groups), the use of fetal monitoring remains routine, and it's increasingly hard to get medical support for a home birth or often even an 'active' hospital labour.

There's been no significant shift in power relations between obstetricians and women off-screen nor, any longer, on-screen – as evidenced by the media coverage of the Warnock Report on reproductive technologies (surrogate motherhood, in vitro fertilisation, and embryo research) two years after the peak of childbirth coverage in 1982. The media debate about Warnock, almost without exception, took its agenda from the Report itself. And just as the Committee had failed to take evidence (in person) from any women's organisations, so too were they missing from the broadcast discussions. Men and women argued about the subject as philosophers, Catholics, doctors, Jews, leaders of voluntary or family groups, but never as women representing women's organisations.

As a result, a whole batch of questions – such as, in whose interests was the research being conducted? would women stand to gain or lose from it? and how would it affect different groups of women? – were never raised or addressed. Instead, the debate was posed as an ethical problem: traditional moral values versus scientific advance. Images of Frankenstein were pitted against visions of perfect babies or babies for all. If, in the deluge of programmes on childbirth, broadcasters had really taken on board women's experience of childbirth and mothering, when they later became transfixed by the subject of reproductive technologies, wouldn't they have turned to women's organisations to solicit their views?

5

Crippling Images

Disabled by whom?

The images of disability on the big and small screens are mainly medical and seemingly natural, uncontroversial and unchangeable. In the medical approach, disability results either from a cruel accident of nature (a genetic gaffe) or from Fate (causing riding accidents, sporting mishaps or car crashes). People with disabilities are courageous or long-suffering; we're invited to praise or pity them. They're applauded in 'aren't they wonderful' stories for triumphing over their disability, and for performing tasks as proficiently as the able-bodied (or even better). A blind woman climbs Everest,[1] a deaf woman is an award-winning professional percussionist.[2] Medicine offers them the possibility of a cure, or helps them function more 'normally' by supplying increasingly sophisticated technological aids, and charity is its sidekick, raising money and hope. The medical approach also encourages the take-up of prenatal screening and rubella immunisation to prevent handicap.[3] Programmes using the medical approach are usually presented and produced by able-bodied people, for the medical approach speaks to the able-bodied (and shows disability as seen by them); 'the disabled' are its objects.

The consumer approach, by contrast, addresses people with disabilities themselves, or their carers. Consumer programmes, often aimed at people with a specific disability like visual handicap or deafness, offer information about goods, services, and welfare benefits, reviewing new aids and equipment, and tackling problems such as access. They're strong advocates of self-help, acting (on air and off) as a clearing-house for self-help groups and charitable organisations. They're often presented by people with disabilities, and are broadcast either in afternoon magazine programmes or the 'ghetto' weekend morning slots reserved for minorities and education programmes.

The look-after-yourself programme, when it looks at disability, speaks of its prevention. It proposes personal ways of maintaining health and avoiding disabling conditions, for instance through preconceptual care.[4] It offers advice, given or endorsed by doctors, aimed at the able-bodied.

In the environmental approach, disabled isn't a noun or adjective, it's a verb. People are disabled by the society they live in: social institutions and practices disable them more than their physical or mental handicap. The environmental approach explicitly challenges the medical approach, rejecting the notion of handicap as a 'natural' condition or a medical fact of life inevitably bringing other problems. 'If a person in a wheelchair is unable to take an office job because there are steps up to an office building, are we to assume that the fault lies with the wheelchair user for not being able to climb steps? I would say the fault lies in the architecture.'[5] Similarly, the absence of sign language interpreters at public meetings or events denies deaf people access to the hearing world. In the environmental approach, attention is shifted from people with disabilities to the wider culture: the problem is no longer the disability, but rather the failure of the able-bodied community to accommodate it. Social interaction, rather than an intrinsic physical condition, is to blame. In the environmental approach, people with disabilities aren't spoken for by others: they speak for themselves.

Braving the media

The past two decades' quiet revolution by people with disabilities has gone largely unrecorded by the media. Able-bodied broadcasters are still (and increasingly) enthralled by the dominant medical approach. 'Cure' stories are favourites, like 'the miracle of the man who got his sight back after 36 years',[6] or the sick child whose leg was amputated, and her heel reattached as a knee fixed to an artificial leg. The disability movement argues that:

we celebrate deaf people, but they celebrate people who aren't deaf any more. They love stories about children who have been given marvellous new hearing aids, deaf people who've learnt to play instruments. . . . The emphasis is always on becoming as much like hearing people as possible.[7]

Courage is their defining characteristic. Children with disabilities must always be smiling, since 'a happy child seems to be the only acceptable image of disability'.[8] They achieve Douglas Bader feats of fortitude, as if individual acts of heroism represented the solution to their daily problems and disability was only an individual and psychological challenge, not also a practical and collective one. Exceptional disabled people are particularly popular, notching up achievements impossible or irrelevant to most people with disabilities – hence the blind mountain-climber or runner – even though the average British blind person is elderly, female, and usually hard up.[9]

This kind of coverage was especially prevalent in the International Year of Disabled People (1981), when 'children received bravery awards for lying in bed and undergoing operations. A thalidomide "heroine" made headlines for passing her driving test. Television news showed a compulsive tendency to film us struggling to make a cup of tea with an able-bodied commentary overlaid.'[10] Television often uses these images for its leave-'em-happy final news story, usually occasioned by a visit from Royalty.

Telethons: child appeal

Telethons, fund-raising television marathons, are the annual opportunity for celebrities and audiences to have fun while doing good. Simultaneously glitzy and worthy, they're usually 12- or 24-hour affairs, with celebrities dropping into the studio to chat or perform, and filmed inserts of charities needing money or showing what past recipients did with their's. Viewers and listeners phone in to pledge donations and the presenters, regularly announcing the total to date, exhort the audience to the finishing-line – the target sum.

Telethons demand enormous organisation – one used 650

telephones staffed by British Telecom telephonists. The BBC telethon 'Children in Need' ropes in every BBC local and national radio station, as well as the BBC TV networks. And the 1985 Thames Telethon completely displaced the station's regular schedules for twenty-four hours. Telethons originated in the United States, where the best known is comedian Jerry Lewis' Labor Day telethon, which has raised large sums for muscular dystrophy charities for nineteen years. When the BBC borrowed the idea in 1980 they decided that the British public wouldn't stomach the full American revelry, with its unrestrainedly heart-tugging appeals in a 24-hour non-stop variety show. The BBC version is a more muted affair, aiming to reach the (smaller, local) charities the other appeals don't reach. Its recipients are children with mental or physical handicaps (who get some 40 per cent of the grants), or those with behaviour disorders, in care, hospital, or living in under-resourced or stressful places. The sums raised by telethons are sizeable. Between them in 1985, the BBC and Thames TV telethons raised over £5 million, and in 1985/6 British commercial radio stations raised over £2.6 million in cash for charity through events like a Walkathon (a 25-mile charity walk).

But although the receiving organisations are understandably pleased to have the money, telethons have been roundly indicted by American disability activists for perpetuating damaging stereotypes of disability which outweigh the financial gains. While acknowledging both organisers' and donors' good intentions, they argue that they arouse 'there, but for the grace of God' feelings in their audience which oppress people with disabilities.

> In order to get their money, they have to humiliate me ... to me, a wheelchair is a solution, not a sentence. Because I use a wheelchair, I am able to do many things I otherwise could not. I am not 'confined to a wheelchair'. I don't 'face a life without meaning', and I'm not a 'poor, unfortunate cripple who needs your help'.[11]

Although British telethons are more subtle, their images usually more positive and optimistic, the British disability movement too deplores:

> fund-raising at a distance ... the twentieth-century version of the
> beggar in the streets. Even the begging bowls are no longer in
> our own hands.... [It] gives people a sense of doing something
> for us without bringing them into contact with us.[12]

Most British telethons focus almost exclusively on children, since cute youngsters undoubtedly head the hierarchy of tele-appeal, with less cute oldsters at the bottom. There's a total mismatch between the age of those people with disabilities who appear on telethons (and TV in general), and the age of the majority of people with disabilities in the general population. Moreover, although the BBC's rules specifically forbid them giving grants to relieve a statutory body of its responsibilities, disadvantaged groups are especially disadvantaged at a time of cuts, and telethons (since they rarely collect for luxuries) can't help but contribute to the idea that it's the job of private organisations and not the state to provide or collect essential funds. They also reinforce an image of people with disabilities as dependent on charity. Even where telethons increase the visibility of people with disabilities, their one-off occurrence inevitably smacks of tokenism.

For whose benefit are telethons organised? It's not always clear. Parts of the 1985 Thames Telethon were commercially sponsored, causing one TV critic to observe that

> no shove ha-penny contest went unsponsored. This made for
> wall-to-wall advertising and a steady line of executives crossing
> the stage like ants, each carrying a large cardboard cheque. 'Give
> a big hand to the chairman of Burtons' ...' Sponsored by those
> lovely folk from Panasonic.'[13]

Commercial companies gain a whiff of worthiness and all are beyond reproach when the vulgarity's for charity. Since telethons make the able-bodied feel bountiful (and many would be affronted to hear that people with disabilities feel oppressed by their pity), telethons may really be for the able-bodied. As the Controller of BBC 1, who authorised the first British telethon, said, 'It makes me feel warm.'[14]

Medico-charitable broadcasting has a long history. President Roosevelt, paralysed from polio in 1921, enlisted popular entertainers such as Eddie Cantor to raise funds for polio treatment and research via network radio on his birthday each year. But at the same time, Roosevelt resolved never to appear helpless, dependent, or defeated by polio, and so wouldn't allow himself to be photographed in a wheelchair. The press and media generally co-operated. Roosevelt, while he tried to improve conditions for people with polio, couldn't allow himself to identify with them for fear of damaging his robust political image, and many Americans never knew, or forgot, that their President couldn't walk unaided.

Could telethons be different? In 1979 United Cerebral Palsy (UCP), an American organisation known for it's 'look, we're walking' telethons, decided to change them. They wrote up the speeches the celebrities were supposed to make, asked people with disabilities to monitor the telethon, and set out guidelines stressing that telethons should show both adults and children and should reflect the degrees of disability typical among people with cerebral palsy. Celebrities were to be thoroughly informed about the condition and use appropriate terminology, avoiding terms like victim, poor, crippled, unfortunate, tragedy and other words arousing pity rather than respect. They were also to avoid asking viewers to give out of thankfulness that their own children were born healthy, and UCP outlawed images which placed undue emphasis on people with cerebral palsy walking and talking, leading to unrealistic public expectations and damaging the self-image of people with cerebral palsy who would never be able to do either. They also wanted to draw attention to the organisation's advocacy role in helping people with disabilities realise their own desires and needs, like gaining access to public education, barrier-free buildings and transport, housing, and jobs.

When people with disabilities monitored the telethon, they found it a significant but limited improvement. Though the main issues emerged, 'the celebrities are tuned to seize on the theatrics of the moment. Given national television exposure, they are not going to be held to tight, pre-drafted scripts. So when they see a moment of possible drama, they seize it.'[15]

Screened out

Sins of omission are perhaps even more significant in media coverage of disability than sins of commission. People with disabilities and the issues affecting them are largely invisible on radio and television. A common format is to have a discussion between someone who works *with* people with disabilities, and the mother *of* a person with a disability, speaking on their behalf, but not disabled people themselves. And people with disabilities are rarely invited to participate in media discussions about abortion, prenatal screening, or the switching-off of life-support systems for people with severe handicaps.

The vast majority of people with disabilities are socially and economically disadvantaged, yet TV and radio news programmes rarely report on the implications for them of events like health cutbacks or inflation, and though motorists, drinkers, and smokers are routinely interviewed after the Budget for their reactions to price rises, people with disabilities are never asked for their reactions to benefit freezes. People with disabilities are the largest section of the unemployed, yet they're never referred to in media coverage of unemployment.[16] Indeed, they rarely figure in mainstream programmes at all, and when they do it's usually *because* of their disability. Broadcasters and news journalists seem to assume that their audience is able-bodied, even though a significant proportion of them must have a disability since about one in five people in Britain have a severe disability.

There's also a rich store of newsworthy items which never make the news, including the segregation practised by public transport (only one London Regional Transport bus is wheelchair-accessible), and the embargo on people with disabilities by more than one-third of theatres, cinemas and bars, though 'if one able-bodied person were banned from a bus or cinema, there would be news stories splashed throughout the media'.[17] Some major charities pay people with disabilities less than £5 for a 40-hour week, but journalists find this story uncompelling. The law says that every non-government employer with over twenty staff must employ 3 per cent of registered disabled people, and though virtually every local authority and the vast majority of the country's employers including all but one national daily newspaper (the *Morning Star*) breach the law, the story is never reported. When Lambeth Council launched a concerted campaign to obey it, they attracted a 'loony council of the week' award from a tabloid newspaper.[18]

Disabling drama

Fictional programmes distort disability just as consistently as non-fictional. A study of American prime-time TV shows found that none of the disabled characters were over sixty-five, and 40 per cent of them were children. They were mainly working class, excluded from important family roles, living generally in schools and institutions. Two-thirds were single, almost half were recipients of some kind of verbal or physical abuse, most were regarded as objects of pity and care, and experienced a miracle cure at the end of the programme.[19] Another study of American prime-time commercial television found handicapped characters seldom appearing in incidental roles: in 85 half-hour slots, not one was visible in groups of shoppers, spectators, jurors, customers or workers. When people with disabilities were positively characterised, their handicap was central to the plot (and, by implication, to their lives): they struggled valiantly with conditions like blindness, but were never an astute college professor who happened to be blind, or the capable lawyer in a wheelchair. They were also often stigmatised as baddies, evil characters representing a threat to society in the tradition of Long John Silver or *Peter Pan*'s Captain Hook.[20]

In 1986 the British group Fairplay, campaigning for accurate media representation of the number and nature of people with disabilities, wrote to the producers of the soap operas 'Brookside' and 'EastEnders' to encourage them to introduce a disabled character. 'EastEnders' didn't. 'Brookside' wrote in a deaf character, and was the first British soap to do so, though she seemed to have uncanny ability to hear without the other characters making any concessions to her deafness.

On the big screen, disabled characters are frequently misshapen monsters and baddies. From the disfigured murderer of *The Phantom of the Opera* (1925) to the dwarf killer of Nicholas Roeg's *Don't Look Now* (1973), people with disabilities have been depicted as grotesques; outlawed from able-bodied society (Dustin Hoffman's lame, pitiable low-life conman, Ratso, in John Schlesinger's 1969 *Midnight Cowboy*); fixated on beautiful but unattainable women (Charles Laughton as *The Hunchback of Notre Dame*, 1939), and impelled to destroy what they can't join or have. Gnarled bodies often signify gnarled minds (Shakespeare's Richard III has a lot to answer for). At the other end of the spectrum is *Reach for the Sky*, the most popular film in Britain in 1956 and one of the most emblematic films ever made about disability, in which Kenneth More played Douglas Bader, the legless wartime aviator with the tenacious spirit. *Reach for the Sky* 'hangs like an albatross round the neck of every person in this country who's been conditioned to believe that it would take unadulterated heroism to cope with their disability'.[21]

Another recurring figure in films about disability is 'the able-bodied miracle worker from whom the central character draws the strength to persevere and learn to live a normal life'.[22] Women are often disabled in films to allow men to cure them (such as Rock Hudson in Douglas Sirk's 1954 melodrama *Magnificent Obsession*, who becomes a doctor to cure Jane Wyman's blindness for which he feels responsible). Thrillers like the 1967 *Wait Until Dark* include blind women (the ultimate victim), or they heighten the tension by using deaf women ('the last word in "dumb blond" '[23]).

Well-intentioned movies are even worse. The praised 1980 film *The Elephant Man* was based on the true story of Joseph Merrick, a Victorian man with a misshapen head, displayed as a fairground freak until rescued by a philanthropic surgeon who takes him to the London Hospital, where he's accepted by some of the aristocracy who recognise his inner gentility. The film was moving and seemed progressive: Merrick advanced from being exhibited to being admired as a sensitive individual. Yet once again, a kindly, able-bodied person provided the key to his improved fortune, while Merrick himself, unfailingly dignified and strikingly free of anger and despair, seemed wholly unbrutalised by his experiences.[24] His attempt to sleep in a 'normal' position finally killed him.

Less equal than others

Employment is the nub of the problem. As long as media images of disability continue to be shaped by able-bodied people, and intended for an able-bodied audience, the stereotypes will flow. The employment of people with disabilities in broadcasting and their media image are inextricably linked. When in 1986 Fairplay organised a survey of British TV companies, it found that, although most had equal opportunity policies, very few had a programme to implement them. What's more, they often cast able-bodied actors as disabled characters, producing unconvincing portrayals which the disability movement likens to those of blacked-up white actors in the past.

The effects of this exclusion from broadcasting on and off-screen are hard to determine. Certainly, people with disabilities are excluded from many other cultural institutions, and their daily experiences and material circumstances are as oppressive as any images. Moreover, the media rarely originate ways of thinking, and stereotypes of disability are as current in the broader culture as on television and film. Yet if the media have the power to reinforce, and their systematic fixations and omissions help fortify or diminish groups' claims of legitimacy, then the media coverage of people with disability must surely play a part in disenfranchising them. They themselves argue that broadcasting and films have helped reinforce negative attitudes towards them, and have failed to challenge stereotypes, dissipate fear and discomfort, or provide images of interaction between people with and without disabilities. At the same time, handicapped people themselves and their families aren't being exposed to images of handicapped adults living productive, comfortable lives in the mainstream of society.[25]

Broad cast

There has always been a small batch of films and programmes challenging the dominant approach to disability. The cinema furnished the earliest examples with its dramas about maimed returning war heroes, like William Wyler's 1946 *The Best Years of Our Lives*. A hugely successful sensitive rehabilitation movie, it showed a sailor who lost both his hands in the war (played by Harold Russell who himself had lost his hands in war training) withdrawing from the community until he was slowly coaxed back. Though some saw the ending as a cop-out (he adjusts to his new situation through the love of a fine woman), and others complained of a prying camera, lingering on his steel claws picking up cigarettes, the film raised public consciousness about the consequences of war-created disability.

Fred Zinnemann's 1950 film *The Men*, in which Marlon Brando made his screen debut as a soldier paralysed by the war, went much further. Set almost entirely in a hospital (the cast including forty-five real disabled war veterans), it portrayed Brando's problems in adapting to his disability and his fellow paraplegics' attempts to staunch his self-pity. Wholly unsaccharine in approach, it showed 'vets' dying and depressed, the problems caused by trying to adhere to able-bodied norms (Brando's obsessive attempt to be married standing up ends in failure), and the easy, oppressive pity of the able-bodied ('we make other people feel uncomfortable . . . we remind them that their bodies can be broken just like that, and they don't like it').

The Men broke a taboo by talking about disability and sex, but *Coming Home*, Hal Ashby's 1978 film about the effect of the Vietnam War on three people, was a sexually explicit (some thought voyeuristic), powerful presentation of disability. It showed a Vietnam 'vet', paralysed from the waist down, falling in love with the wife of a hawkish Marine Captain brutalised by his experience in Vietnam, and implicitly questioned which of the two men was the real cripple. Once again, it portrayed people with disabilities as angry, rejecting pity and charity, and physically active,[26] with all of them (except for Jon Voight in the main role) played by real disabled Vietnam veterans. And this time the man in the wheelchair got the woman. The film ended with the hero rechannelling his anger from self-destructively inwards to constructively outwards, by becoming politically active.

But latterly, American prime-time television has been leading the way in new presentations of disability. 'Cagney and Lacey' has been innovative, and in the show's 1986 season Cagney had a relationship with a man in a wheelchair, which drew an enthusiastic audience response. 'Dallas', too, included a deaf child; 'Hill Street Blues' has had disabled characters and themes; and the Public Broadcasting System (PBS) has introduced people with disabilities into children's programmes such as 'Mister Rogers', 'Zoom', and 'Sesame Street'. American TV commercials are also changing: a man in a wheelchair is unremarkably included in a group sporting 501 Levi jeans, a schmaltzy romantic couple use sign language (plus subtitles) to decide to go and eat at McDonalds,[27] and the blind man in a wheelchair is an IBM systems analyst.

By contrast, Britain is poorly served. There isn't a single British TV commercial which includes people with disabilities, and aside from 'The Singing Detective' – Dennis Potter's outstandingly authentic series about a man immobilised by arthritis, the skin condition psoriasis, and the attitudes of hospital staff – only the soap opera 'Crossroads' has made significant attempts to introduce disabled characters. As well as a character involved in a disabling road accident who subsequently used a wheelchair, and an educationally subnormal young man, the show in 1983 included a running story about mental handicap using a real Down's Syndrome child.[28]

But there have also been some fine British single documentaries using the environmental approach, such as a report on American disability activists campaigning for access to buildings, transport, housing, education, and jobs;[29] a studio discussion by people with disabilities about the attitudes of the able-bodied;[30] a film about a group of disabled people attempting to persuade a local authority to provide suitable housing and resources for them,[31] and a challenging programme about sex and disability.[32] Deafness has inspired some of the most interesting programmes, showing the entrenched prejudice against sign language, the lengths to which the able-bodied have gone to force deaf people to speak, and the deaf community's attempts to get proper recognition and facilities for sign language.[33] All the really innovative programming about disability has either originated from, or centrally included, people with disabilities themselves, who are moving into television as both presenters and producers. Perhaps the most exciting has been the new Channel 4 series 'Listening Eye' about the problems and rights of deaf people, and co-presented by a woman whose first language is British Sign Language.

Sign of the times

People with disabilities are campaigning to end the apartheid of disability in the media (and beyond). They want disabled people integrated into all kinds of programmes, including news and current affairs, documentaries and sitcoms, games shows,[34] chat shows, children's programmes, and drama, and in all kinds of media jobs from secretary and clerk, to presenter and producer.[35] They're supported by the Working Party on Disability of the ACTT (the film union), and the National Union of Journalists' 'Campaign for Real People' which urges journalists to avoid 'helpless victim' reporting and sensitise themselves to disabling language. People with disabilities have also proposed forming themselves into consultative committees to whom broadcasters can turn for advice, and advocated disability awareness training for directors, producers, and casting directors. And backed up by Equity, groups such as Fairplay are calling for 'innovative casting' – the casting of disabled actors in roles not specifically written for a disabled character, similar to the casting of black actors in parts where colour isn't important or relevant. In Hollywood, the Media Office Regarding Disability acts as a clearing-house for performers with disabilities, and has succeeded in increasing the amount of innovative casting.

People with disabilities want to speak for themselves.

6

Inside the Box:
Media Factors Shaping Medical Programmes

Departmental styles

As viewers, we're rarely sensitive to the institutional or departmental origins of the programmes we watch: BBC or ITV, Continuing Education or Current Affairs, it makes no odds. And yet, according to one executive producer, 'Department and traditional format are the most important determining characteristics [of programmes]'.[1] Departments develop their own traditions and routines, and come to embody different ideologies and approaches to science and medicine. In the BBC, for instance, 'Horizon' looks chiefly at the scientific, technical aspects of an issue, and 'Brass Tacks' at its social dimensions, and scientific and social often appear unrelated. Producers in all departments swiftly learn the departmental style, and they don't last long if they push an approach out of keeping with their programme's tradition or implicit policy.

There's a key difference in the representation of medicine and science between Science Features departments, and Current Affairs. In Science Features, interviews are collaborative, with open-ended rather than probing or insistent questions. They aim to squeeze from scientists and doctors the best televisual account of their work and its implications. Interviews in Current Affairs programmes, on the other hand, are more confrontational, seeing their subject matter as contentious, and setting up opposing expert interpretations.[2] Hardly surprising, then, that programmes adopting an environmental or political approach to health and medicine come almost exclusively from Current Affairs or general documentary departments, and almost never from science departments.

Networks and slots: money-spinning and status-winning

Slots embody the cluster of material and ideological interests which determine programmes. A programme's placing in the schedules – the season, week, day, time and network in which it's broadcast – crucially shapes its form and content, providing the limits of what is possible. Yorkshire Television's 'Where There's Life', for example, occupies the prime network Wednesday evening slot of 7 p.m., sandwiched between (and influenced by) the domestic soap operas 'Crossroads' and 'Coronation Street'.[3] According to the programme's first producer,

> This programme in summer replaces 'This Is Your Life' and has got to get the same ratings or you lose the audience for the evening, even the 'Coronation Street' audience, and the rest of the network will feel it. We do feel that. You know you have to produce something that's popular.[4]

As the product of a commercial company which must deliver the audience to the advertisers in order to maximise its profits, the series needed to get into the Top Twenty, and attract around 12 million viewers in order to 'hold' them and bequeath them to the following programme.

What would happen if it didn't? According to the Editor,

> Great pressure, pressure mounts: the other IBA contractors would be sitting round in their session and would say, Gosh, Wednesday night's really gone to pieces, and it's all to do with that 7 o'clock show. And no more would be said, and Paul [Fox, YTV Programme Controller] would know he's got to do something about it, so then he calls in and says, How's it going and can I help? And then, if it continued, after another three weeks' ratings still falling, you'd be under greater and greater pressure, and threat that the series would be removed, and there would be panic in the office, and pressure to try something else.[5]

The production team had a keen sense of what you could do on television on 7 o'clock on a weekday evening, and what you couldn't. They ruled out anything which took a strong political line on health and medicine, or which might alienate some of the audience, dismissing it as boring or groaning at its very mention. By contrast the human interest approach, with its potentially wide appeal, they welcomed. One-third of the first series of 'Where There's Life' in 1981 (fifteen stories, roughly one per week) was about birth or death, subjects the researchers considered 'relevant to everyone'. Hardly surprising that a programme aiming for a mass audience returned again and again to two of the few genuinely universal experiences.

A different sense of what is appropriate governs BBC TV's 'Horizon', which doesn't have to aim for a 12 million audience. Broadcast on Monday nights (9.30 p.m.) on BBC 2, it gathers prestige for the BBC, exemplifying public service broadcasting's task of edifying the audience. It gives a sense of science and medicine as part of the national culture. And it gets good reviews.

Inscribed in slots is the structure of ownership and control of their particular networks, and their ideology. The British Channel 4 was designed to give space to minority or previously excluded views, and has run several radical health programmes. But such protected channels grow rarer with the development of media oligopolies, where control over different media outlets becomes concentrated into fewer hands, with profitability the driving force. It's not often that station owners directly intervene to gag broadcasters, or caution them against offending big advertisers (though commercial influences sometimes impinge directly on programmes). The influence is generally less direct. In the United States – and to an increasing extent elsewhere – the leading owners of TV and radio stations have been absorbed into huge conglomerates, often with global interests, who also produce weapons, atomic energy, uranium mining, medical equipment and textbooks, soft drink bottling plants, and property. All of these products have health implications, but it would be surprising if TV stations encouraged investigations which could threaten their own economic interests.

In the final resort, in commercial stations the economic imperatives become irresistible. Such was the case with the Cable Health Network, an American cable station launched in 1982 on lofty ideals and the rhetoric of self-improvement.

> We are dedicated to providing programmes that will make a difference in people's lives. Viewers want to know how to help themselves to health, and the Cable Health Network wants to arm them with the information they need to do just that, in the form of high quality, diverse, motivational programmes.[6]

They wouldn't accept ads, they announced, for products traditionally advertised on cable TV if they considered them harmful, citing hard alcohol and Coca-Cola, and contemplating vetoing even cereals with high sugar content. But they would accept ads from the manufacturers of birth control devices, which weren't allowed to be advertised on broadcast TV.

Three years later, when I asked an executive the station's aim, he mouthed the words 'to make money'.[7] The station's advertising policy was now 'the same as everyone else', and he suggested that 'people watch TV to be entertained, it's mindless – they're not really interested in learning'. In 1984, the station merged with the 'Daytime' network to form a new station, 'Lifetime'. The health material was demoted from prime time and replaced by chat shows. The only remaining health material for the general public are two-hour blockbuster 'Informathons', sponsored by pharmaceutical companies – 'a soft sell'.[8]

Sanctions and rewards

Networks don't enforce their norms by crushing staff who step out of line with the full weight of institutional wrath. It rarely comes to a shoot-out. Broadcasters and editorial teams are generally middle-class, recruited from universities. They share class and cultural values, and join a liberal, educated occupational milieu. They soon begin to identify more with a peer group of fellow professional programme-makers than with the subjects of their programmes. (One study found that the chief 'significant other' for medical journalists was their colleagues.[9]) And they quickly learn what their station or channel expects of them: they're taken off subjects like occupational health if they're too zealous in pursuing corporate wrongdoing,[10] for instance, and given dud or low-status stories to work on if they repeatedly transgress. Or they're professionally stalemated by being confined to local programmes (low on professional kudos). Those who proficiently 'read' the institution and show a real understanding of its values, norms, and priorities are rewarded with promotion. There's still, for example, thought to be a 'BBC type' and a 'BBC culture', 'a tacitly agreed amalgam of styles and deportment'.[11] As a BBC Controller put it, 'I've been given this job because . . . I'm a certain kind of chap.'[12]

It's also hardly surprising if, when working under pressure and to deadlines, journalists reach for safe, familiar ways of doing things. Programme research rarely proceeds in a logical, theoretically coherent way; it veers and detours in confusion, with panic playing its part. Programmes and stories are often salvaged from fragments of interviews or ideas which haven't come off as planned. The last thing on programme-makers' minds at times like this is finding a fresh or minority line.

Broadcasting institutions also patrol the limits of the possible by a procedure which the BBC calls 'referral upwards'. If a producer doubts the suitability of a programme or interview or anticipates complaints from people with power, s/he must refer it up to the executive producer or department head. In practice, as one ex-producer put it, 'there is seldom any doubt about what the man above you thinks on any important issue. You can therefore avoid referring upwards by deciding them in a way which you know he would approve of.'[13] Certain subjects in certain institutions become unthinkable. Self-censorship becomes the prudent path to a quiet life.

The ultimate sanction wielded by the BBC and IBA is the right to ban a programme. But this big stick is rarely used: unlike the more informal institutional controls, it's very visible, and recent attempts to ban programmes in Britain (for instance, the IBA's banning of 20/20 Vision's programme on phone-tapping, and the BBC's banning of 'Real Lives' on Northern Ireland – both responses to anticipated or expressed government displeasure) have backfired, generating major public rows about censorship, leading to the eventual broadcast of the programmes.

The individual voice

Though these structural and institutional constraints play a major role in shaping programmes, they don't double-glaze production staff from all other personal and cultural influences. Inter-personal relationships play their part in determining programmes, and a producer's own beliefs about a subject are also a potent initial resource. Personal experience, friends, and a producer's preconceptions of what kind of material is relevant to the subject – all help seed programmes. But personal factors aren't beyond the reach of culture. An American magazine decided to run a cover story on medical malpractice because an editor, who lived in a suburb full of doctors, said it was the central topic of conversation at the parties he attended.[14] Individual experiences are still part of the social world. One TV medical producer described how personal experience can be limiting:

> You've a pool of ideas, coming from your circle in life – reading the *Guardian,* your friends. If you don't read about it, and you don't know anyone involved in it – say, a political approach to health – you wouldn't dream of doing it.[15]

On the other hand, personal experiences can sensitise programme-makers to new subjects. Medical TV presenter Joan Shenton, when a young BBC reporter on holiday in Spain, bought some tablets for a stomach ache which, instead of curing her, inflamed her body and almost killed her. She later had to have a hip replacement. As a result, she's campaigned for greater public awareness on health issues through TV programmes made with her company, Meditel, and one of her programmes in her Channel 4 investigative series about the victims of drug injury, 'Kill or Cure?', examined the harmful health consequences of pills to combat 'holiday tummy'.

Occasionally, newspapers or regular TV programmes take an unequivocal stand, and make a subject their own. *The Sunday Times* did so with the thalidomide issue, going far beyond what's considered usual journalistic practice, deciding that 'the complex but normal journalistic objective of analysing the roots of a tragedy had to be accompanied by a simpler but unique objective – winning more money for the children than the lawyers were going to obtain'.[16] Editor Harold Evans won his chairman's support to campaign on the issue, beginning in 1972 with an article, an accompanying editorial and opening headline, 'Our Thalidomide Children: A Cause for National Shame', which made it clear that it wasn't a normal feature.[17] The paper reprinted the article and circulated it to every MP, newspaper editor and television producer in Britain, the start of what turned into a five-year campaign to publish a 12,000 word article on the origins of thalidomide.

'It's been done'

The spaces which individual producers or one-off campaigns carve out for themselves are limited, though, by what's happening in the rest of the media. There's a curious tension in broadcasting between the desire to do things first and the herd instinct; between me-first and me-too. Journalists and broadcasters are constantly dismissing issues with the *coup de grâce* 'it's been done'. Trail-blazing is an important part of journalistic ideology, with the fourth estate fearlessly trading where none has before: You Read It Here First. Programmes must stake out their territory and build a claim to uniqueness. They do this by reference to other programmes.

In the months of production for the first series of 'Where There's Life', the search for a style was studded with references to 'Panorama', 'Nationwide', and 'That's Life'. 'Panorama', almost always referred to pejoratively, became a byword for seriousness. 'Nationwide' was threatening, because it was also a magazine programme in a similar slot; 'How would it be different from 'Nationwide'?' was a common response to proposed items. And 'That's Life', with its human interest orientation, was respected: they had no objections to becoming a medical version.[18]

Other programmes present a sense of the possible, but also the problem of how to do things differently, or do different things. There's a gravitational pull in the media towards novelty, but at the same time, journalists are remarkably imitative. There's a similarity and continuity in the view of the world presented by television, and its range of material on most subjects is heavily weighted towards ideas already elaborated through the mass media: 'on many subjects which might be treated by television ... there seem to be standard perspectives available within the media culture which are likely to be reinforced and repeated in the process of gathering material for a new programme'.[19] So the medical and look-after-yourself approaches are unthinkingly reproduced, and consumer programmes come in clusters.

One reason for the tendency for various programmes and different parts of the media to parrot each other is that they use each other as sources. One study found that almost a quarter of the subject ideas dreamt up in the first week of research for a new TV series came from press cuttings.[20] Another found that peaks in *Time* magazine's coverage of heart disease were followed soon after by peaks in coverage by other popular media.[21] Certainly, journalists spend a lot of time scrutinising other media and lifting stories from them, partly because the prior appearance of a story elsewhere means that a peer has already judged it as suitable (journalists, whatever their self-image, are a craven bunch) and as having 'audience appeal', so eliminating the need for an independent decision.

The media set the agenda for each other, and ideas circulate between them. In 1981, for example, the production team of 'Where There's Life' read a newspaper story about surrogate motherhood. They decided to fly out a surrogate mother from the United States for their second programme. To stir up interest in the programme they held a press conference to which representatives of fifteen publications turned up. It generated major stories the next day in four national newspapers, including the *Daily Mail*, the *Daily Mirror*, and the *Daily Express*. The story had originated in the press, been taken up by television, and then fed back to the press. The symbiosis was complete.

Coherence, charisma, and cracking good TV

Till now, I've largely been discussing television and radio by sifting out content and ignoring form, as if a programme's arguments were all that concerned its maker. But television as a medium has its own imperatives, and the raising of national consciousness is rarely the chief one. As well as entertaining their audience, producers try to construct a convincing argument in their programmes. 'The disorder and contradictions of an observed reality have to be transformed into an ordered and coherent, plausible and persuasive, vision of reality.'[22] 'Have to be': no programme could be made without an organising principle, a central idea with which to winnow through the acres of potential material. And TV, or so producers believe, is a canvas for bold strokes. Nuances and qualifications are dropped in the drive to make a programme powerful and arresting; caution, caveats, and uncertainty aren't telegenic, don't buttonhole the semi-attentive, or win prizes for generating joy, tears, or outrage.

Producers bring to their programmes a strong sense, shared in the media community, of what makes a good programme. Individuals at the heart of a film, for instance, must be charismatic. Speakers must be articulate (concise, confident, and fluent).[23] They must crisply and vividly encapsulate their story in metaphor, hyperbole, and the lingering, telling, quotable quote, and without significant speech defects or unattractive blemishes. Researchers are meant to screen for such characteristics. (I once set up an interview without noticing that the interviewee had gently clicking false teeth; the producer subsequently judged the interview unusable.) Interviewees, too, are quick to latch on to what's required of them, and producers often 'prompt' programme participants when they 'forget their lines'.

Researchers and producers cast documentary programmes with stock characters which match their preconceptions (and sometimes jokingly refer to someone being 'straight from Central Casting'). Such typecasting helps them process the everyday world.[24] A good story can also contradict a stereotype. A 'Where There's Life' researcher got interested in a report about the high level of illness in rural areas. But she jettisoned it when she discovered that it was because 'life in the country is more stressful than life in the city because of fewer jobs, far from health care, not because quietness is too much, which I'd hoped it would be'.[25] The story she'd hoped for would have reversed the rural stereotype (getting away from it all); when it turned out to be unrelated, she had no meaningful way of typifying it – it was too unprecedented to fit any classification. In this way, a small number of iconic medical images circulates through television, strengthened each time they're reproduced.

The victim and the detective

One of the most interesting aspects of the many genres used in medical programmes is how they enshrine ideas about expertise and lay experience. Lay people are invited to spill their emotional experiences before the camera or microphone. Their role in medical, health education, and sometimes consumer and environmental programmes, is as victims of unfortunate circumstances: they're cast as people-with-problems or sufferers-from-disease. They may also be triumphers-over-disease, or fighters-back-in-adverse-circumstances. They offer up pain and grief, injustice and joy. They illustrate the human condition which professionals frame; they supply the raw material which experts process into cause and effect, problem and solution.

Patients reveal themselves before the camera as they reveal themselves in front of the doctor: images of patients' breasts or genitals being examined are now common on television, and patients don't seem any more embarrassed disrobing on camera than in the surgery. But if patients are literally embodied in medical programmes, cast as a subjective person-with-feelings and a body, experts are portrayed as rational people with sentiment-free knowledge. Doctors, for example, are filmed in mid-shot, conveying 'close social distance',[26] which evokes both personal involvement and a sense of formality and neutrality. They're never shot, as patients are in close-up or very close-up, which highlights the emotions and downplays neutrality. And while patients are never allowed to look directly at the camera, and address the audience unmediated, doctors occasionally are.[27]

Another narrative convention which hymns medical expertise is the detective story genre, especially prominent in programmes like 'Horizon'. A classic example was in October 1981, Horizon's 'The Hunt for the Legion Killer', which retrospectively pieced together the successful American attempt to locate the source of Legionnaires' Disease, the illness which killed dozens of military veterans in Philadelphia in 1976. The detective story generates suspense and hooks viewers into the story, but, although it does admit false trails, red herrings, and blind alleys, it also reconstructs the research process from the point of view of its outcome, giving it a sense of consistency, coherence, and inevitability quite alien to research as it really is, and confirming medical expertise as ultimately rational and progressive.

Other 'Horizon' conventions also suggest that medicine is neutral, above and beyond politics. The programme has no in-vision presenter: once again medical expertise is disembodied, and doesn't depend on the credibility of an individual figure. The programme's commentary is spoken by Paul Vaughan, who has a smooth, white, middle-class, male voice with cultural authority, but without individual idiosyncracy.[28]

'Horizon' also tends to present a series of medical experts responding to an unseen interviewer whose questions have been edited out. The experts might differ slightly in their approach but they're edited together into a linear narrative which unfolds the medical tale. In current affairs programmes like 'Panorama' or 'World in Action', on the other hand, where the issues are seen as controversial and open (at least to some extent) to public scrutiny, the interviewer is seen and heard, and the programme cuts back and forth between interviewer and expert. Professionals are challenged either by a reporter, or by the editing which splices together a sequence of contrasting views, or by a presenter and others in a studio discussion. These techniques are rare in medical programmes, which maintain science and medicine's special status.

Human interest and the fly-on-the-wall

Another genre beloved by medical producers is the human interest story, in people-fighting-for-life tales. The human interest story is a way of both universalising and personalising human experience, presenting it as beyond the reach of social, political, and economic factors. In programmes like 'Where There's Life', contributors are stripped of their occupational roles: their jobs are almost never mentioned unless they're experts (doctors, psychologists), as if the experience of illness and health is similar whether you're a male Rolls-Royce-owner, or a black female single parent: under the skin, we're all alike.

Human interest stories are often shot in the verité or fly-on-the-wall style, short on commentary and long on impressions. Lacking the traditional mediation of the reporter, verité documentaries purport to get closer to their subjects, to follow rather than dictate to them. Verité film-makers try not to stage events or set up interviews. With the minimum of interference in 'the natural flow of things', a disinclination to reshoot scenes or use lights, they argue that the effect of the camera is negligible, and that they therefore present as accurate a picture of an institution or event as possible.[29] But their claims have been mightily contested,[30] largely on the grounds that fly-on-the-wall documentaries present just as partial and individual a view of the world as ordinary documentaries, and even more so: to edit down to a reasonable length the vast quantities of film they shoot when they're following and not controlling an event, more manipulation is involved.

Nevertheless they're usually gripping stuff, like Frederick Wiseman's 'Hospital' (a 1969 documentary shot at New York's Metropolitan Hospital) and the BBC 2 series on the Bolton Royal Infirmary, 'Hospital' (1977). Both offered day-trips into the demi-monde: vagrants, addicts, accident victims, the acutely distressed – all-of-human-life streaming through their casualty departments, tended by salt-of-the-earth staff. Both invited the audience to engage fleetingly with other people's anguish. Yet compelling as they were, both generalised and mythologised medicine, with one hospital coming to stand for all hospitals and presenting a chronological composite.

Verité captures institutions in a 'continuous present'.[31] The hospital has no past; its patients have no history – they're viewed only when they've become patients. Verité is limited to capturing what's visible, and is predicated on the notion that all that's important is visible, so that the more you see, the more you understand (the classic empirical fallacy). But the chief influences on an institution or its behind-the-scenes determinants may not be visible: verité cannot show context. And fly-on-the-wall documentaries can't raise extraneous matters: a seven-part peak hour BBC TV series in Spring 1981 on 'Heart Transplants', following the cases of several patients, didn't question the cost of heart transplants or discuss other alternative methods of treatment or prevention. Instead it enlisted viewers emotionally onto the side of transplants and into the personal dramas of the patients.

Such series, of course, never set out to be agents of social reform, or crash courses in political economy. This genre, like most others, aims above all to involve and interest the viewer: any ideas about the world and about medicine it may emit *en route* is, producers say, incidental. And though genres and narrative conventions enshrine particular ideas about health and medicine, they reinforce existing ones rather than originate new ones. It's also dangerous to deconstruct genres down to their informational content, and neglect the mythic levels they work on – as stories, as fantasies, as entertainments.[32] We ignore the power of narrative conventions at our peril: it's all very well critically analysing the traditional techniques of mass audience documentaries, but innovative documentaries challenging the conventions often end up laboured and indigestible. Who wants to struggle with an ideologically correct, creatively non-narrative documentary, after a hard day in the kitchen, the factory or the office?

7

Outside the Box:
Medical Expertise and the Power to Define

Journalists are umbilically connected with the world outside. Over the years they develop sources, people who sustain them with information, ideas, and stories. But outside groups also lean on broadcasters, wielding sticks as well as carrots in their attempt to influence the media. Who gets to be source, and how much influence they're allowed to exert, is a key factor in shaping medical broadcasting and results from entrenched, pervasive ideas about expertise and knowledge.

Recipe for a good source

The medical profession occupies a peculiar position *vis-à-vis* the mass media, simultaneously a major source for journalists and a powerful arbiter of medical journalism. It shares this dual role to some extent with other prestigious professions and social groups, but no other profession, except politicians, is so frequently depicted, and itself so consistently provides access, interviews, and speakers.

The medical profession also easily arouses broadcasters' and journalists' interest. Cuts to the NHS weren't the stuff of news until, in May 1986, *The Times* published a letter by consultants from twelve London teaching hospitals complaining about them. A rash of cuts stories followed. It's unlikely that a letter by nurses or ancillary workers would have been so widely picked up – they may well have lacked the clout or status to get a letter published in *The Times* in the first place. And when, in December 1987, the medical establishment protested publicly about the cuts, the issue was put squarely on the media agenda. Medical interest in a subject certifies it as important.

The British Medical Association (BMA) keeps journalists supplied with contacts and information: as a TV researcher I'd often ring 'that wonderful woman at the BMA' who could instantly furnish us with the name and phone number of an articulate, telegenic doctor on almost any subject. And the BMA itself makes news: its pronouncements on a broad range of subjects, including alternative medicine and food, are widely reported, and fortified by their impeccable pedigree. As the commentary on a BBC news story about a BMA slimming guide put it, 'Unlike other quack slimming cures, this one carries the full authority of the BMA.'

Once made, medical contacts – like journalists' other sources – endure. The hapless interviewee or provider-of-information little realises, after a brush with the media, that the researcher has inscribed their name in his or her most valued possession, their contacts book, and that they or their colleagues will be back, and back again. For contacts are generously shared among the fraternity and sorority of researchers: requests for an articulate cancer specialist/a radical dentist/or a pro-induction obstetrician rarely go unheeded in an office of journalists. The circulation of contacts is no accident: a contact known to you or a colleague not only saves time but is of proven credibility.

Once a contact joins the media circuit, it can become difficult to get off. This creates a small pool of certified medical experts, and limits the range of ideas diffused through the media.

It's official

But if journalists are addicted to experts they still have to choose between them, and most of the evidence suggests that they rely heavily on official sources. A study of American media coverage of a threatened swine influenza epidemic found that, in spite of the many hundreds of experts who might have been contacted for comment, the same group of medical spokespeople from government authorities was quoted to the virtual exclusion of anyone else.[1] This isn't particular to medical coverage, and yet it's especially pervasive in medical broadcasting.

Indeed, most medical broadcasters pride themselves on their close association with the medical establishment – in Britain, the Royal Colleges and teaching hospitals. It seems as if being part of the scientifico-medical establishment is itself sufficient in the media's eyes to make you a medical expert, even on an issue on which you have no specialist knowledge. Leading doctors and medical researchers become 'Anything Authorities'. 'The Anything Authority is someone whose credentials in one field are taken as valid for others.'[2] When an American researcher examined media reporting of the controversy over marijuana, he found that most of the reports cited scientific authorities two-thirds of whom had published no work on marijuana, and most of whom had done no work on the subject at all. In addition, prominent scientists, such as Nobel Prize winners in medicine, chemistry, or biology, or famous psychologists or paediatricians were solicited for their views: as 'celebrity' authorities, their opinions were canvassed, and thought valid, on a wide range of subjects.[3]

Government or quasi government bodies occupy a special place in the medical reporter's world. The Centers for Disease Control in the United States and the DHSS and the BMA in Britain are the official reference points, with the DHSS accused of increasingly blatant attempts at news management.[4] It's often been observed that journalists are hostages to their sources. When an American psychologist, author of a new book on anger, did the promotional media circuit she noticed that she was rarely asked by reporters how she knew what she knew, what her evidence or vested interest was, or why her views so differed from popular wisdom. Most reporters couldn't evaluate her work, and simply relished the controversy.[5] Medical research is often similarly treated.

From journals to journalese

Another major source is medical journals. One study found that science and medical journals generated more stories in two BBC radio programmes than any other single source.[6] Top American TV physician-anchor Art Ulene says that he regularly reads fifty-five medical journals and that 'they're a rich source of ideas'.[7] Of the three to four items covered weekly in BBC Radio 4's 'Medicine Now', at least one will have been chosen because it has just been in the news or appeared in a science journal.[8] Most medical journalists and programmes receive early, hot-off-the-press copies of medical journals such as the *British Medical Journal* (*BMJ*) embargoed until publication day, so that they can prepare stories to coincide with publication.

But why should broadcasters' dependence on medical journals be unhealthy? A *BMJ* assistant editor himself identifies one problem.

> Science advances by argument and one reason for publishing scientific articles is to expose them to critical assessment. Something published one week may well be demolished in the correspondence columns of the journal a month later. One newspaper may pick up the original article and ignore the subsequent correspondence, while a television programme picks up only the counter reaction that emerges in the letters. Those unfortunate enough to read the newspaper and watch the television programme are baffled. All truth is provisional in science, but the mass media are rarely capable of such sophistication.[9]

Moreover, medical journals – like all publications – have their own preconceptions and attitudes. The *BMJ* believes that low levels of lead aren't damaging, and rejected a study which found that lead was harmful to children's health on the grounds that its statistics were faulty.[10] It was later published by another medical journal. Medical journals are also notoriously unfriendly to positive studies of alternative medicine.

While they could hardly avoid containing beliefs and values, and obviously need to evaluate methodologically the papers submitted to them, medical journals are often seen as somehow above the fray. Above all, editors of medical journals (although they may and often do publish articles critical of medical practice and report adverse reactions to drugs) believe in the essential validity and primacy of the scientific method: they hold a torch for science. So in drawing stories from medical journals journalists are also ingesting and reproducing a dominant approach to knowledge and expertise.

Medical dissidents

The media's adherence to official sources is accompanied by the exclusion of dissident experts and voices. Dissenting opinion was under-represented in both Britain and the United States in the coverage of the artificial heart and heart transplant pro-grammes (see Chapter 9). The reliance on official sources can also erase whole issues. The California press missed the exis-tence of a serious asbestos occupational health problem within the state, because reporters didn't use workers as sources for their stories but relied only on official experts and government sources, who denied that there were even any asbestos factories in the area. Had they checked with the local trades union branch, they'd have discovered five asbestos companies in the area.[11]

Indeed, researchers have observed that 'Just call the chairman' is a set routine in many local papers. A man who had worked for thirty-nine years at an iron foundry was judged by one editor to be not a competent source about his destroyed lungs. The jour-nalist had to balance the evidence through an interview with the foundry's director, who denied any relationship between mineral dust particles and silicosis. In this case, the journalist was sufficiently involved to bring in a third source, a doctor, who agreed with the worker. But this balancing ritual doesn't take place when an authoritative source pronounces.[12]

As a reporter, your choice of source determines the material you end up with, and similarly the line you take determines which source you deem valid and important. Broadcasting institutions, if they're to trawl wider than official sources, need an explicit commitment to seeking out alternative views and challenging dominant ones. They need the confidence to ques-tion what is a legitimate source. When the *Sunday Times*, for instance, launched its investigation into thalidomide, they found that almost all the scientific experts agreed that the drug's teratogenic effects (producing congenital malformations) hadn't been foreseeable. But the paper hired a postgraduate pharma-cology student for four months to study the whole literature of tranquillisers, drugs, and experimental work on reproductive effects, and he discovered that, although animal tests to prove that thalidomide was teratogenic weren't in general use before the tragedy, tests did exist which would have suggested the dangers to unborn children.[13]

Doctors at large

When doctors and medical researchers take part in radio or TV programmes, they're accorded privileges which would turn politicians green with envy. When an interview is recorded, science features producers and presenters are generally keen to ensure that a scientist or doctor has expressed themselves in the best way possible, and that both sides are satisfied with the result. By contrast, most other programme participants are rarely consulted over whether they're satisfied with the performances they've given.

> It would be considered an unpardonable transgression of the fundamental tenets of broadcasting journalism if an interviewer in a Current Affairs programme asked a political interviewee to go through the interview again, and suggested ways in which his performance might be improved.[14]

Though broadcasting organisations formally retain editorial control, doctors are often allowed to view programmes before transmission and suggest edits on the grounds of medical in-accuracy. When BBC TV made a programme about a 7-year-old boy undergoing a hole-in-the-heart operation, 'the intention was to follow what we hoped would be a successful operation'.[15] Unfortunately the boy died, but the parents wanted the film to be screened. Nevertheless, the National Heart Hospital was invited to check the final version of the film for 'medical accuracy', and a carefully worded announcement was arranged to precede the programme, explaining that the boy's death was due to a rare, unforeseeable complication.

After the editing of the 'Hospital' series on the Bolton Royal Infirmary, a panel of twelve people from the hospital (and later a panel from the DHSS) was invited to preview it, the composition of the panel changing for each programme to include staff from the relevant hospital department. They asked for and got an expletive cut because 'it struck us as unprofessional'. And because of doubts about the emphasis and presentation in the programme on obstetrics 'which we felt might leave a most unfortunate impression in the minds of viewers as to the risks of hospital confinement', the programme was revised.[16] Such accommodations aren't necessarily bad; on the contrary, many groups criticising the media have been pressing for just such practices, but less powerful occupations rarely secure them.

As well as appearing on radio and TV, doctors have an unrivalled advisory status. In Scotland the BBC Medical Advisory Group, numbering senior Scottish hospital doctors and GPs, has had regular meetings with department heads (including news and current affairs) since the mid-1970s. Though unofficial it's acted as an advisory panel, helping to run programmes and providing feedback to the BBC on medical programmes. The BBC has thus literally internalised medical thinking.

Even more securely entrenched is Professor Ian McColl, medical adviser to the BBC Science and Features Department, and on hand to give advice to any BBC radio or TV programme. His advice is usually followed and if it was consistently refused, he says, he'd resign. He goes to the BBC regularly 'and they say, got any ideas?'[17]

McColl is a liberal doctor keen, in the tradition of his predecessor Charles Fletcher, to promote media/medical cooperation. He tries to quell medical hostility to the media, and holds most producers in high regard, understanding the constraints within which they operate. Yet inevitably, his advice reflects his position within the medical establishment, and his experience (he's Professor of Surgery at Guy's Hospital) as a consultant in an acute speciality in a well-endowed London teaching hospital. For example, although personally (because of his teaching position) he's not allowed to be paid for private practice, he sees private patients who then make a contribution to his department's research fund.

> My private practice colleagues like it, because it means that I don't disapprove of it. Yes, I am asked my advice on private medicine by producers: so long as guys do their work in the NHS, I don't care what private work they do.[18]

He's also been consulted by BBC News over cuts to the NHS. 'My reply is that it doesn't matter what government is in power: the cuts were coming because there had been such an enormous rate of expansion.' In the 1987 General Election, he defended the Government's health cuts at a Conservative Central Office Press conference.

McColl exemplifies the double role played by doctors, since he also appears in many TV programmes (though never suggests himself). In November 1982 a whole 'Horizon' programme was devoted to a portrait of him at work, but it never revealed that he was also the BBC's medical adviser. Much of the commentary was McColl in voice-over, so effectively the film was a self-presentation. 'They said you can change anything you don't like.'[19]

On drugs

If the medical profession is increasingly media-aware, the pharmaceutical industry doesn't lag far behind, investing large amounts of money and energy in marketing products, and trying to ensure a good Press. The pay-off can be immense: many think the initial success of 'Opren' came from its coverage in the popular Press as a new wonder drug for arthritis, causing patients to demand it from their doctors.

Drug companies also finance medical radio tapes made by medical public relations companies, broadcast on both BBC and commercial local radio, into which brand names have been slipped. According to one PR man,

I might approach a local radio station or a newspaper and say, I have an item here which might interest you. We supply the material, and they might use it themselves or use ours. You have to do it in a way that's acceptable, because non-promotional.[20]

But the pharmaceutical industry generally uses more subtle ways of harnessing media power. TV journalists and narrators, for example, often front or narrate drug company promotional films and videos, bringing the company the benefit of the cultural authority and aura of objectivity they command as presenters of, say, BBC science programmes.[21] BBC TV science presenter James Burke presented the promotional video for Opren. The industry also fosters close relations with the Medical Journalists' Association, and funds medical journalism awards.[22]

In search of a plug

Increasingly there's a continuum between marketing of all kinds and journalism. Journalists are spoon-fed material pre-packaged by commercial firms or PR companies in the form of press releases, conferences, staged events, ready-to-use tapes. Journalists – print, radio and TV – estimate that almost two-fifths of their editorial material emanates from public relations firms and industry press departments, and consider most press releases as 'factual'.[23]

Commercial companies borrow the legitimacy of doctors and medicine to give their products an altruistic sheen, and acquire the aura of science rather than Mammon. A classic example was the body scanner, a piece of equipment producing colour pictures of internal organs which in the 1970s received intensive coverage in American newspapers and magazines such as the *New York Times* and the *Wall Street Journal*, as well as in the British media. Many of the articles were drawn from press releases by the manufacturers of the technology, and included human interest stories about people whose lives allegedly had been saved because of the existence of a scanner, or threatened because their hospital had been denied the device by the hospital planning authority. Issues about the high cost of the scanner, and its relative usefulness, were rarely raised.[24]

Indeed, new medical technologies are hardly ever subjected to media scrutiny, especially if they come with a medical seal of approval. A press release, if it's headed 'Home Monitoring for Babies At Risk', and promises the presence at a press conference of a 'Research Obstetrician' to demonstrate a new fetal monitor on a pregnant woman, is irresistible (even if it's issued by a public relations firm on behalf of a company making medical technology) and will quite unremarkably generate a story in a leading Sunday newspaper[25] and the BBC 9 o'clock News.[26]

Journalism increasingly involves the rewriting of press releases. A study of the coverage of the Three Mile Island (TMI) nuclear plant by the local media *before* the major 1979 accident shows that local reporters relied almost exclusively on the press releases of the utility company running the plant, releases which emphasised the positive and upbeat, and downplayed plant problems as not affecting 'the health and safety of the public'.

None of the reporters interviewed were aware that the plant had been shut down 71 per cent of the time it was supposed to be in its 'start-up' phase in 1978.[27] There was very little in-depth reporting or investigative pieces, and only one reporter went to independent sources to help him understand the press releases or what was going on at TMI. Radio and TV didn't do any better. Before the accident, the study concluded, the utility company itself had helped set the agenda for local coverage of TMI.

Food, cigarette, and commodities companies, attempting either to exploit or challenge the health craze, now 'sponsor' academics to make out a case for their product. An American cable TV station ran a programme in which nutritionists, who happen to be employed by food manufacturers, discussed the nutritional merits of their companies' products.[28] And the Sugar Bureau paid the air fare, expenses, and fee of a respectable American academic to come and expound her pro-sugar views in Britain. As one journalist put it, 'This tactic works best when the interviewing journalist fails to make the link between the exponent and the expense account.'[29]

In the United States the distinction between advertising and editorial is particularly blurred. Kelloggs/General Foods approached the National Cancer Institute (NCI) to suggest a joint advertising campaign on dietary fibre. Both were anxious to lower the age and broaden the range of their target groups, and after extensive discussion an agreement was reached. The new three million dollar advertising campaign for All Bran (in print, TV commercials, and on cartons) incorporates a message from the NCI saying that eating more fibre may prevent cancer. Kelloggs' share of the breakfast cereal market has rocketed.[30] Some say it doesn't matter if the distinction between advertising and editorial isn't made clear, or if commercial companies subsidise health promotional material, arguing that as long as it's health-enhancing rather than damaging, it's irrelevant who pays for it. On the contrary, they say, let All Bran proudly display its government agency all-clear: it means one less ad for saturated-fat hamburgers or wholly synthetic desserts. But the blurring of boundaries between advertising and journalism increasingly obscures the source of news, misleading viewers and listeners who assume that news or features have been independently sifted and evaluated by journalists.

The latest way of getting a product almost subliminally familiar to audiences occurs in the cinema: it's 'product placement' in films. There are now more than twenty-five product placement agencies in the United States working on behalf of manufacturers to ensure that, for a fee, their products get prominently strewn around a film-set, unmissably in shot. Coca Cola and Pepsi even employ in-house placement specialists. Pepsi Cola reportedly paid 2 million dollars to be the only soft drink featured in *Saturday Night Fever*,[31] and Sylvester Stallone presumably didn't describe Wheaties cereal as 'the breakfast of champions' in *Rocky III* out of the goodness of his producers' hearts. Cigarette companies are also joining in, with Marlboro advertisements conspicuously exhibited throughout *Superman II*, and in the film *White Nights* starring Mikhail Baryshnikov, the camera lingered lovingly on the distinctive red and white Marlboro pack, presumably relishing the chance to associate cigarettes with the aesthetic, physical image of dance.

Product placement seems to work. The cuddly alien munched 'Reeces Pieces' sweets in Steven Spielberg's film '*ET*', and within just two weeks of the film's release the candy's sales had trebled.[32]

Commercial clout

Many commercial companies, worried at the potential damage of all the interest in health, have mounted extensive, expensive public relations campaigns to discredit health activists' criticisms of their products. They've made their own videos and distributed their own leaflets defending food additives and the processing of food. More than that, they've used their influence to put pressure on broadcasting executives and top brass. The BBC Food and Health Campaign, which broadcast several health education series in 1985/6, incurred particular commercial wrath. The producer was subjected to more outside pressure than he'd ever experienced before.

> The National Farmers' Union, the Sugar Bureau, the Confectionary Alliance – not only have they written letters to me, but some have threatened court action, and have already written to the Director General. What worries me is the pressure that's

applied more subtly, that we may not even know about, at the highest level, to the old boy network: 'these left-wing hotheads, can't they lay off a bit and give it a rest' . . .. BBC top management . . . don't see the campaign as an important thing, they only see that they're getting constant complaints from high-up people, and barristers' and solicitors' letters. I just feel that these pressures might have some effect.[33]

His colleague confirms that:

it really does make the high-ups very jumpy. There's a squad – the Milk Marketing Board, the Sugar Bureau, the salt manufacturers, and the MPs they sponsor, making regular visits. The poor producer is having to spend his time doing drafts of comments for the Director General, while the manufacturers just throw money at the problem, backed by very skilled PR. We're amateurs in trying to rebut them.[34]

But food manufacturers are novices in influencing the media next to the tobacco companies. In 1976 Thames TV made a powerful programme called 'Death in the West – the Marlboro Story', in which Marlboro cinema ads were intercut with interviews with six real life American cowboys, prototype macho Marlboro Men and former heavy smokers all now dying from cancer or emphysema, which their doctors attributed to heavy smoking. When CBS expressed interest in showing the film on American television, the manufacturers Philip Morris took out a High Court injunction against Thames TV, preventing it from selling the film or showing it again, alleging that Philip Morris had been duped into allowing its commercials to be used in a film it thought would depict smoking more favourably. Thames and Philip Morris subsequently agreed an out of court settlement, and all copies of the film (except one locked in Thames TV's vault) were handed over to Philip Morris, though pirated versions of the film found their way onto many local American TV stations, and CBS and NBC transmitted parts of it with discussions.[35]

Laying it on

Time was when no self-respecting voluntary group thought of tangling with the media. The notion of slicking up your message to interest a journalist or attract a film camera brought a Keatsian pallor to charities' cheeks. Pressure groups would overcome through the intrinsic virtue of their message, and not through the tricks and artful props of the media. All that has changed. Now even trades unionists take themselves off to centres for media training, to be schooled in the art of disarming Robin Day or sidestepping Sue Lawley. And special organisations have been set up to help pressure groups and trades unions present themselves effectively in the media.

Pressure groups have become part of the medical journalist's life. Many groups have a full-time press office, often staffed by ex-journalists, staging events which fit in with media needs, or coming up with telegenic victims or spokespeople to summarise the cause. The press releases flow freely, and voluntary and pressure groups can succeed in getting whole issues onto the media agenda. Pressure groups like MIND, the National Association for Mental Health, often liaise closely with TV companies, and sometimes collaborate on programmes.

The doyen of British campaigners is Des Wilson, whose publicity skills can catapault any issue onto a news bulletin or the front page. His media strategy for CLEAR, the Campaign for Lead-free Air, was immaculate. In trying to eliminate lead from petrol because of its risk to health (especially children's), Wilson and his fellow lobbyists were taking on the multinational petrol manufacturers. Yet, though they held only four press conferences, they received almost unprecedented media coverage during 1982–3, oiled by the use of some judicious leaks, and unashamed bargaining with the media.[36] Fifteen months after CLEAR's launch, the Government announced the future elimination of lead from petrol.

Though CLEAR was a media success story, it's rare for pressure groups to get such intensive and carefully designed publicity, partly because many of them lack status in producers' and reporters' minds. Journalists try to evaluate how powerful groups are, and in so doing reinforce their power or powerlessness. The College of Health, founded by Lord Young, veteran initiator of new groups which catch the mood of the middle-classes, may carry a degree of authority, but the Women and Work Hazards Group, Friends of the Earth, or the Campaign for Nuclear Disarmament are more likely to be thought axe-grinding tub-thumpers. And if charities, voluntary groups, trades unions, and pressure groups win coverage for their argument but it's presented as the viewpoint of a named pressure group, then far from putting the issue on to the media agenda, they may have only reinforced the marginal status of their argument. There are very few pressure groups considered authoritative enough to define an issue, rather than simply to react to it, and many have found their entanglements with the media bruising.

Beyond reach

If interest groups help shape media coverage of health and medicine, they also contribute to its silences and taboos. Certain issues are almost never raised. There have only been two billed TV programmes on racism in the NHS over the past five years. Nurses are so rarely given a platform that BBC TV recently came up with a six-part series on what it's like being a nurse.[37] (A similar series on doctors would be considered old hat.) Ancillary workers in the health service are almost never given the opportunity to talk about their experience. (A six-part series on what it's like being an ancillary worker is unimaginable.) A study of five women's magazines over a year found practically no articles on the health of elderly women, even in a magazine one-quarter of whose readership is over sixty-five.[38]

Most of these silences reflect the contours of social power. Black people, working-class people, old people, can't apply significant pressure on the media, and a protest by a group of elderly women about their omission from a programme is unlikely to generate the impact and possible consequences of a complaint by a group of doctors. But it isn't only a question of social power, but also of legitimacy. Health workers' trades unions may have the clout to organise strikes, but the media coverage they receive has been consistently hostile, falling in with government definitions of the problem, if not the solution. The health unions have become increasingly alive to the importance of public relations and press officers, but it hasn't improved their media image. And just as important as access to the media is the power to silence the media and deflect or discourage certain lines of thought: this is also unequally distributed.

In an attempt to improve the media coverage of science and medicine in the United States, the Scientists' Institute for Public Information set up the Media Resource Service, which responds to nearly 2,500 calls annually from electronic and print journalists in search of sources on scientific and medical issues. While they give out the names of scientists and doctors with different, and often conflicting viewpoints, from academia, industry, the Government, and consumer groups, so far at least, according to its Director, the service hasn't made American medical reporting any less gee whiz or 'Eureka!' in tone.[39] A British Media Resource Centre was launched in 1985, with three years' funding from the CIBA Foundation, notching up dozens of calls on health and medicine from TV and radio in its first fortnight alone. Yet such initiatives are unlikely to substantially alter media coverage of health and medicine, which is shaped less by ignorance of particular sources than by the shared values of the media and certain social groups.

The conflicting values of the media and medical profession have been well aired. Yet what's more striking, but less acknowledged, is their ideological symmetry – both self-regulating professions, defending clinical or editorial freedom. One study found that though science journalists' and scientists' attitudes towards media coverage of science were similar, each group *perceived* a larger gap than actually existed.[40]

Playing safe

Journalists and broadcasters depend on official sources primarily because of science's special social status, examined below. As one American TV medical producer put it,

> It's very difficult for us to say that this scientific report is of scientific merit – we're reporters first. Generally our reaction is to call some other sources of information who have a lot of credibility.[41]

Since journalists themselves can't confer legitimacy (even though people gain a certain authority simply by having appeared on TV or in a newspaper), they try to protect themselves by using only certified experts and medical authorities carrying an institutional seal of approval.

Most journalists, even documentary-makers, are also plagued by lack of time and deadlines. If they had to check out the reliability of each source or piece of information, programmes would never get made and articles never get written, especially on understaffed local programmes or papers. They can't treat each source, each piece of information as equally provisional, all of it only allegedly true. They have to take some on trust. Going to centralised, official sources saves time and covers them. A 'Where There's Life' researcher complained that his fellow researchers' stories 'come from papers. Mine don't: they come from talking to people, it takes months.'[42] When he later researched a programme on asbestos-caused cancer, he traced over 300 Rochdale residents who'd died of asbestos-related disease, becoming such a familiar figure at the Register of Deaths that he was on first-name terms with officials.[43]

But fishing outside the mainstream doesn't guarantee a catch. As one medical journalist said, 'Always in an investigative project there is the question of whether it's worth it ... you can't always be sure you are going to turn up something. There's a tendency to wait for a state agency to turn up a report.'[44] A *Wall Street Journal* reporter covering occupation and health explained that

> You've got to get out and talk with elderly, sick, working-class Southerners who may not even be sure that it's important to talk to the Press. Too many reporters wind up being Establishment stooges, not because they're uncaring people but because they're middle class and don't want to struggle with speaking another language with different people.[45]

For medical reporters, as with any specialist journalist and broadcaster, there's also the particular occupational hazard of 'going native'. The longer and closer they associate with their official sources, the more they tend to see the world through the sources' eyes. The sources' worldview prevails merely by dint of prolonged contact. And you get to like the guys.

What's more, the risks to a journalist in crossing them may come to exceed the benefits. Medical reporters, like all specialist correspondents, depend on the goodwill of a professional community, the medical profession: access to medical contacts is crucial. If journalists were consistently to give space or airtime to dissident medical views, they'd find official doors shutting smartly in their faces. This helps discourage them from taking a critical line towards official medical opinion.

Media exposure: the pros

For many members of the medical profession, the decision to participate in a radio or television medical programme or press interview is a double-edged, finely-balanced one. Evaluating the rewards and drawbacks is a speculative, risky business. Broadly speaking, there are two camps: those who believe the rewards exceed the drawbacks, and those who don't.

One reason why some doctors and medical researchers take part in programmes or go public is through a strong commitment to sharing information and ideas. Another is personal gain. Some American physicians and dentists use the media to build up their practices, but it's a fiercely competitive field: one health and science editor of a major TV network news programme gets thirty letters a week promoting doctors.[46] To distinguish them from their rivals, American doctors are increasingly employing medical public relations firms to 'sell' them to the networks. Says one, addressing prospective clients in a dental journal,

> Many dentists realize there is a credibility in editorial comment that does not come with costly advertising. The media can provide ethical, dignified and effective promotional tools. . . . Few people consciously think of a personality feature or informative article as advertisement, yet that is just what it is.[47]

Mindful of their growing contact with the media, many doctors and medical organisations are trying to spruce up their image and become fluent interviewees and presenters. In America, where only the smooth and glossy win airtime, acquiring the right styles and skills has become a serious business. The American Medical Association (AMA) runs an annual conference, attracting over 100 doctors, to help teach physicians to become media-wise, with PR firms advising them on their on-air performance and dress.

While the British are less unabashedly entrepreneurial, some British doctors too have sought fame through the media, though on a rather more modest scale and in a more gentlemanly fashion. And in both Britain and the United States, at a time of growing cuts in medical research, media exposure is thought to benefit applications for medical grants. The science reporter of the *Washington Post* now as a matter of routine asks sources about their funding when she conducts interviews, so that she can make allowances for their motives if their grant is up for renewal.[48] An Oxbridge scientist warned the editor of BBC TV's 'Tomorrow's World' who'd taken him out to lunch, 'I am not a Snow man. I don't see the need to explain my work to the public.' Within a year he was explaining his work and its value in the most public way possible – on BBC TV's 'Panorama' – because his funds were being curtailed.[49]

But the popularisation of medicine, science, and medical research is regulated from within the medico–scientific community by a series of sanctions and rewards. Some say that popularising is a risky business because it takes medicine and science outside the closed scientific community, and exposes them to public scrutiny, and so it's entrusted to only the most copper-bottomed professionals who'll win respect for scientific values and institutions. A French study found that the higher up the scientific ladder you climbed, the more likely you were to take part in interviews and programmes, one of a whole constellation of activities in the political, economic, and administrative realms which prominent scientists undertake to mediate science to the wider culture.[50] But if the potential rewards from taking part in programmes are so large, why don't all scientists and doctors, when invited to participate, succumb?

Media exposure: the cons

Until recently, popularisation was highly stigmatised among doctors and scientists, and could backfire damagingly. As the French researchers note, it doesn't do a young scientist any good to be seen to be too interested in gaining media exposure: cultivating the media to hasten your professional ascent, and seeking public fame before you win the recognition of your peers, makes you suspect in your professional community and may even hamper your advance.

The same is true of doctors and researchers. A medical researcher working on a treatment for a debilitating inner-ear disorder agreed to talk to a local newspaper reporter about his work. The paper published a feature. Two years later, when the researcher applied for membership of a prestigious medical society connected with his research interests, he was told that, since the use of his name in the feature article constituted a breach of the society's ethics, he would be temporarily banned from being considered for membership.[51] And when a clinical researcher at the University of California Medical School was interviewed, he asked a science reporter not to mention his name, since the last time there had been a newspaper article about him, a couple of colleagues had remarked, 'Say, Doc, I saw your ad in the paper yesterday.'[52]

The medical profession's anxiety about publicity is part of its traditional antipathy to advertising, and its fear of being contaminated by association with 'quacks' and 'charlatans' peddling themselves and their nostrums. But once you've risen high enough in the profession, you're relatively immune from such accusations.

In this way, the professional needs of journalists and doctors converge. While journalists turn to official medical sources and prominent doctors and researchers to protect themselves and save time, it's only prominent doctors and researchers who are professionally secure enough to be able to risk media exposure. But why do journalists feel safe from criticism if they rely on information from a medical institution or big-name doctor, in a way that they wouldn't if they relied on a trades union, an association of social workers, or even a headteacher? The social status of science provides an explanation.

Scientifically speaking

Science is uniquely privileged compared with all other kinds of human knowledge. Mostly we think of science as bypassing the social, political, economic, and emotional conduits through which other human thought and ideas (literature; history;

economics; myth; dogma; religion; art; etc.) flow. Science has a hotline to nature, uncontaminated by individual point of view or self-interest. The objects of scientific study, the material world, are reckoned to have a stability independent of the person or people perceiving them. Science is thought with the thinkers removed, discoveries just waiting to be discovered.

This, crudely characterised, is the positivist or realist view of science. Positivists believe that science is objective knowledge, arrived at through the scientific method which, by trying to falsify theories through rigorous testing in experiment and observation, generates repeatable results and enables scientists to predict. Scientific and technical knowledge, in the form of universal statements or laws, is thus incontrovertible and uncontestable. But, increasingly over the past twenty-five years, this view of science has been contested. Anthropologists, sociologists, historians, feminists, philosophers, and others have argued that even the most technical aspects of science, technology, and medicine are forged by social practices shaped by beliefs, values, political and economic interests, which can be studied like those of other groups. Scientific facts are merely statements to which our culture allocates the status of 'beyond dispute'; the critics ask how they came to be regarded as 'scientific', 'medical', or factual in the first place. This approach has been used in many different analyses of science, technology, and medicine, and is sometimes called 'social constructionist'.

An influential study in 1962 drew attention to the way in which scientists often ignored or explained away results inconsistent with accepted theories.[53] Scientists, like everyone else, see what they expect to see. It's only when results persistently don't fit the dominant theory and anomalies and discrepancies can't be explained away that they're forced, reluctantly, to develop a new theory, which itself then becomes the new orthodoxy, and in turn inhibits the emergence of contradictory views. This study challenged the idea of scientific work as rational and objective, uninfluenced by scientists' beliefs and assumptions. Theory-neutral knowledge was impossible.

The idea of science as objective, said subsequent critics, also obscured the political interests of science and scientists. Scientific research is regulated to a great extent by research grants, whose allocation reflects the priorities and interests of the groups (particularly government agencies) who distribute them. So even scientists who personally attempt to distance themselves from political causes are involved in the social uses of science. And science has a powerful ideological role to play, since it can be mobilised to all sorts of causes and issues without its assertions appearing arbitrary or self-serving in the way that political or religious statements would.

The medical approach is fundamentally positivist, seeing medicine as the application of objective science, which develops incrementally through clinical trials and discoveries. Old treatments are discredited as outmoded, unscientific or quack remedies, while today's high-tech therapies are vaunted for their superior medical knowledge, and for increasingly vanquishing disease.

The realists and positivists retort that it's all very well criticising science as partisan and socially constructed, but so is social constructionism itself, along with all its criticisms of science and medicine. And without recourse to truth, how are we to choose between competing accounts of the world, or are all equally valid and interchangeable?[54] Is the medical approach any inferior to the environmental or consumer approaches, if truth can't be called on as arbiter?

It's curious that relativism is considered such a heinous intellectual crime, since it's tolerated well enough in most other fields of human life: although we can't unequivocally judge the worth of a relationship or job, we still make assessments and decisions based on probability, hopes, and values. All beliefs have authors, and reflect their authors' interests and values; science alone claims universal truth irrespective of who speaks or hears it. Social constructionism simply reinstates the social dimensions of medical and scientific knowledge, and restores them as political issues. It doesn't answer questions but poses new ones, so that debates about medical and health care, instead of pleading scientific objectivity, confront explicitly political questions, like whose interests policies serve, and where they originate.

The professionals

Medicine came to share science's privileged status, but it wasn't always so. In the eighteenth century, the (wealthy) patient was the dominant figure in the doctor–patient relationship, defining their own needs, and how those needs would be met. With the growth of the hospitals (which enabled the patient's body to be examined, using new equipment like the stethoscope), the doctor gained ascendancy, becoming the dominant partner in the relationship, not least because the new hospital patient tended to be poor. 'Thus doctors could now define the problems and the manner in which those problems were to be solved, according to criteria established by the profession, not by the patient.'[55] And when the State intervened to regulate the doctor–patient relationship, it did so to maintain the already considerable rights of doctors.

If the medical profession's status as authoritative expert is relatively novel, most doctors would insist that this reflects the relatively recent growth in medical knowledge and its curing capabilities. In other words, the virtual monopoly which the medical profession enjoys over treatment is in direct ratio to its skill. But while the growth of medical skills is clearly a factor in the increased public acceptance of medicine, the story of how the medical profession won its privileged status isn't simply a stirring tale of technical achievement. Medicine worked hard to become dominant and autonomous, to acquire the special privileges of a profession, which

> claims to be the most reliable authority on the nature of the reality it deals with. . . . In developing its own 'professional' approach, the profession changes the definition and shape of problems as experienced and interpreted by the layman . . . a new social reality is created by the profession.[56]

By excluding other occupations from sharing its claim to expertise and gaining a monopoly over treating illness, medicine won a right to define.

The doctor prescribes

Television and radio stations, as cultural institutions, naturally breathe in and exhale the prevailing ideas about medical authority and expertise. So while medical producers and reporters can be (and have been) critical of aspects of medical practice, they couldn't consistently challenge medical authority, or be fundamentally hostile to medical power.

But the media not only share dominant beliefs about medicine, they also help strengthen them. The expansion of medicine's power to define, known as medicalisation, has been fiercely debated in recent years. Critics claim that daily living has been medicalised by applying the labels healthy and ill to an increasing part of human existence.[57] More problems have become medical problems, and aging and pregnancy, drug addiction and alcoholism are no longer natural processes or human foibles and weaknesses, but medical subjects with their own medical specialities. Even if medicine has little in the way of cure or treatment to offer, its assessment is reported and taken seriously because 'today the prestige of *any* proposal is immensely enhanced, if not justified, when it is expressed in the idiom of medical science'[58] and 'the jurisdiction that medicine has established extends far wider than its demonstrable capacity to "cure" '.[59]

The critics of medicalisation argue that more and more conditions are redefined as medical problems in order to remove them from the political realm, and to control deviant behaviour (mental illness, obesity, suicide, crime, violence, child abuse, learning difficulties) when traditional forms of social control no longer work properly.[60] A problem is identified as an organic or physiological one, and a medical solution proposed. In this way, new diseases are regularly created, instead of examining the social and political causes of the problem. For example, children's learning disabilities or hyperactivity was almost unheard of before 1965, but by the beginning of the 1970s commanded an armada of paediatricians, neurologists, educational psychologists, and new drug treatments. Within a single week in 1974, hyperactivity was the subject of an interview on the NBC Today Show, a five-part series on CBS radio, and daytime radio talk shows.

Some say it's a huge exaggeration to claim that medicine is greedily colonising daily life, with patients addicted to professional treatment, when the medical profession – far from expanding – has actually been cut, and patients' visits to GPs haven't risen significantly either.[61] Others say that the critics of medicine not only over-estimate its ideological significance but also treat it as a monolithic institution, ignoring its differences and conflicts between doctors.[62] But whatever the arguments proving or disproving medicalisation, in public debate medical opinion on most matters undoubtedly has an unrivalled validity, as evidenced by the number of times that doctors are brought onto TV programmes to comment on an area of life which most of us would never in practice consult them about, even on ('life-style') issues they feel they can do nothing about. Their views on anything from school sports days to divorce carry the imprimatur of science. Medicine has provided the vocabulary and framework through which to think about problems, and subjects are increasingly recast in pathological and therapeutic terms: 'essentially, medicalization is the process through which people come to lose faith in their own knowledge and infor-mation. . . . The process is defined as medicalization because the tendency is for medical rather than commonsense views to pre-dominate.'[63] By using phrases such as 'research shows', 'doctors agree', and 'scientists say' – valuable shorthand when time is short – broadcasters also imply that research is uncontestable, and the medical profession unanimous.

Medicalisation operates perhaps more powerfully inside the mass media than anywhere else, since broadcasting has an unlimited need for the authoritative commentator who can sum up an event or practice and pronounce with certainty. Medicine's privileged social status makes it perfectly suited to the task. In recent years, there's been a growth in doctor-presenters who are used in this way. Like Charles Hill before them, they make producers feel safe: as one TV Editor put it,

> the reason we have doctors [as presenters] is that . . . it covers us . . . because the people we worry about are not Mrs Bloggs writ-ing a letter of protest, but an MP asking a question in the House, or the BMA raising the issue. Let's face it, it's realpolitik.[64]

But the social power of medicine, and the benefits to TV and radio producers of medicalisation, don't override the media's own priorities, and medical presenters must also satisfy the same criteria as other TV performers, and be personable and articu-late, adaptable and lively. Doctors whose primary allegiance is to medicine, who are too serious or crusading, who don't realise that TV and radio must entertain as well as inform, don't last long in the studio.

The trend toward medical presenters is an interesting media development because medical presenters aren't necessarily conservative, buttressing medical power and preaching patient compliance. On the contrary, in the doctor–patient debate, the medical presenter often roots for the other side. Indeed, the doctor-presenter as patients' advocate is a curious new media phenomenon. Miriam Stoppard often takes a 'power to the people' line. NBC's Art Ulene says 'I view myself as an advocate for the consumer,'[65] and, for their pilot programme, 'Where There's Life' brought in a well-known maverick Professor of Obstetrics as the presenter charged with defending patients' rights – so managing to simultaneously validate and invalidate the patient's point of view. The use of doctor-presenters as patients' advocate suggests that the medically expert are the only legitimate critics of medicine, and that even as medical practices are criticised, medicine's power as arbiter of truth is reinforced.

8

Moral Panics and Miracle Cures

Body politics

Broadcasters have always had a keen sense of the national interest. The sense of serving the nation generally only becomes explicit in wartime (embodied in figures such as the Radio Doctor), but peacetime reporting also invokes a national consensus and a common purpose overriding sectarian interests: these are the everyone-would-agree issues, the times when newsreaders use the national 'we' (as in the reporting of the Falklands crisis), or, their faces softening into a smile, announce 'And now for some good news.' The BBC has even put it in writing that it is 'within the consensus about basic moral values'.[1]

Moral panics and miracle cures are coloured by this sense of the national and the shared. As a pioneering study put it, 'Societies appear to be subject, every now and then, to periods of moral panic. A condition, episode, person or group of persons emerges to become defined as a threat to societal values and interests.'[2] Disease (or the risk of it) on a large scale lends itself particularly readily and symbolically to fears of a threat to the social and moral order, since even an individual's illness is considered a form of social deviance from the norm of health. (We're expected mostly to be healthy; being ill is an exceptional, disordered state.) Physical sickness can stand for the moral sickness of a particular social group, and a national preoccupation with illness often expresses anxiety about social disorder. If the moral panic represents a threat, then the miracle cure constitutes hope and expresses the belief that society can heal itself.

Moral panics often convey fears about sexual behaviour. The examples of herpes and AIDS are discussed below, and there have also been prominent recent scares about the contraceptive pill (the last occurred in the midst of the campaign against the prescription of the pill to under-age women, when the family and sexual monogamy lobbies were at their pinnacle); heroin addiction (partly a revival of the regular panics about youth culture); and cervical cancer (linking it with unregulated sexual activity by women). The conditions or illnesses worried over may well be risky – medico-moral panics are rarely whipped up from nothing. Women die from cervical cancer, and the heroin addict can lead a tormented life, yet these conditions have existed for some time. Why does a particular panic emerge at a particular time? When a subject suddenly materialises as an acute social problem, it generally enshrines and contains deeper worries. And why that problem, rather than this? There are many far riskier conditions than those panicked about. Some 2,000 people die each year from asthma attacks, yet who can recall a single news report about death from asthma? And colon-rectum cancer, which had the highest incidence rate of all cancers in America in 1977, and the second highest incidence in 1980, ranked seventh in frequency of daily American newspaper cancer stories in 1977 and sixth in 1980.[3]

Something other than their prevalence must swing reporters, doctors, and health activists away from one disease and towards another. A number of recent moral panics are at heart about gender. For a few months in late 1981, pre-menstrual tension (PMT) was rarely out of the headlines. The trigger was the court case of a woman who successfully defended herself against manslaughter on the grounds that she was suffering from PMT. In the same week another woman, already on probation for murder, pleaded PMT when she was tried at the Old Bailey for threatening to stab a policeman. The conjunction of these cases got the media's juices bubbling. It wasn't just a bespoke tabloid story ('The Tension That Made A Woman Kill',[4] 'Monthly Miseries Save The Killer Mistress'[5]). The reporting also quoted medical experts on how extensive the condition was, as if it followed almost inevitably from the fact of being female, and femininity was inherently pathological, if not psychotic. Women, once again, were nothing but their hormones, emotionally (even biologically) unstable.

But the fascination with PMT was as nothing next to the panic over surrogate mothers. Between 1983 and 1985, the media were saturated with surrogacy stories, passionately debating the morality of a woman carrying a baby she'd later give away. The PMT story may have had murder, but surrogacy had money and sex. A central theme of the reporting was 'moral distaste' for the fact that surrogate mothers were paid for their labours. After Kim Cotton, Britain's first commercial surrogate mother, candidly admitted on a BBC TV programme on surrogacy that the money would be useful, the *Daily Mirror* reported:

> 'I have this big house and only one carpet', she explained, waving across a field on the edge of which stood her bare-boarded mansion. And when the baby is born, and she is able to sink her heels into thick wall-to-wall Wilton pile, she can doubtless reflect on the success of her deal. Mrs Nearly-Well-Off did not allow her face to be shown during the interview, but her business-like voice and her self-confident manner suggested she was quite pleased with herself for discovering a profitable way to rent out her body.[6]

TV, radio and newspapers endlessly pondered the question of how a woman could bear to give her baby away (a generally uncontentious subject in the reporting of adoption). They sought out surrogate mothers who'd found it difficult, in spite of their pre-birth pronouncements, to part from their babies. And they speculated about potential emotional damage to the child. In their unremitting scrutiny of this unusual way of having a child, the media reinforced a discourse about normal child-bearing.

The normal mother doesn't part with her child. Surrogate mothers, by separating the biological from the social aspects of mothering, were throwing into question the whole idea of the natural mother. By emphasising surrogate mothers' emotional difficulties in handing over their babies, the media and others manning the moral barricades fortified the notion of the natural mother–child bond. The surrogacy debate was part of a succession of moral panics around maternal deprivation and bonding, all maintaining the need for intense mother–child intimacy to ensure the child's emotional well-being, and its ferocity this time was fuelled by fears over the disintegration of the family and women's increasing failure – through choice or circumstance – to conform to traditional gender roles in nuclear families. At the same time the 'right to a child' arguments of the defenders of surrogacy reasserted the naturalness of the mothering instinct, portraying childlessness as a desperate, unfulfilled, and abnormal state.

But why now? Surrogacy has been practised, unregulated and unfretted over, for a very long time, but it was only in the early 1980s that it produced a major moral panic, leading to the Warnock Report. The media coverage was revealing. The outrage over the commercial aspects of surrogacy – the moral crusaders were less aggrieved if it was conducted between sisters or unpaid – expressed anxiety about the changing boundaries between the public and private realms of life. Maternity had always been considered part of the private realm, and reproduction generally seen as the antithesis of production: pregnancy and mothering were meant to epitomise freely-given love, well beyond the exchange relations of capitalism. But now, even before birth, babies were caught up in profit–loss calculations. The phenomenon of 'rent-a-womb' presented an unsettling challenge to the notion of maternity as its own reward.

When a moral panic is in its prime, reporters and columnists are unstoppable. Each story that appears ignites further stories. The tabloids ruthlessly pursue their prey, appealing to 'public interest' and ethical importance as justification. And TV and radio must follow them, since the press helps structure broadcasting's agenda.

In 1978 there was the case of Lesley Brown, mother of the first test-tube baby. Reporters offered hospital staff £5,000 for ten names and addresses of test-tube baby patients, and used a local detective agency to try and prise information out of the staff. Journalists dressed up as boilermakers, plumbers, and window cleaners to gain entrance to the hospital. The time of labour was kept secret from all but one of the hospital staff, and when the news got out police had to be brought in to clear photographers away from corridor windows. These congregations of journalists become media events in themselves.

Yet moral panics are rarely media-originated, or purely journalistic confections. Certainly they illustrate some classic features of the media, such as news as olds, and present big, bold emotions – shock-horror and outrage, risk and danger – on which journalism thrives. But though reporters may fan or exploit existing fears to get a good story, they draw on demons not of their own making. Each moral panic has its own history, but fears of the threat of social disorder generally surface simultaneously in various social institutions and realms, with the media acting mainly as loudhailer, if sometimes amplifying beyond recognition.

The hope cure

Countervailing the threat to society as we know it is the re-establishment of an even better one. The reporting of breakthroughs and medical triumphs suggests that today's illnesses will be vanquished tomorrow. The most powerful guarantee of an Elysian future would be a cure for cancer, almost a victory over death itself. In 1980, interferon became the embodiment of hope and scientific prowess, commanding the headlines with talk of wonder cures for the Big C. Its aura as an elixir was heightened by its extreme cost – one pound of the stuff was once estimated to be worth $27 billion – restimulating the view that health could be purchased at a price.

The prospect of a restorative treatment for heart disease is similarly evocative, with stories about techniques like laser heart surgery or a new electronic pacemaker suggesting that the damaged can be made good. On Good Friday 1986, brimming with religious symbolism came 'the Easter gift of life: the baby who's been fitted with a pacemaker', a BBC report on the Nine o'clock News about a three-month-old baby fitted with the smallest type of pacemaker available, a story to reassure the nation – a good Friday indeed.

Both moral panics and miracle cures about children are particularly potent, the former suggesting a threat to the collective future, the latter its redemption. So there are regular stories about a whip-round to send a sick child to the United States (the epitome of scientific progress) for a medical treatment unavailable in Britain, with the recurring image of the hopeful child boarding the plane (though follow-up reports on the treatment's success or failure are rare). As one medical TV producer put it,

The words 'child', 'brain', 'laser', and 'America' all cause lights to flash in the average journalist's mind and score bonus points in his search for a good story. If the key words [in a potential story] had been 'old person', 'knee', 'physiotherapy' and 'Barnsley' the response would be underwhelming to put it mildly.[7]

The miracle cure is the chief vehicle for the medical approach, with medical research reduced to a few select, glorious results, their origin and process erased. It restimulates a belief that as the experts become more expert, they'll find technological solutions for even the most intractable medical problems. The miracle cure denies uncertainty and death; it hymns rational expertise, suggesting that everything is knowable and conquerable. While moral panics unite us in opposition to a dreaded group or condition, miracle cures bind us in optimism that the system is progressing, and each of us stands to gain.

But the moral panic and miracle cure are rarely neat halves of an equation. Indeed, a treatment like *in vitro* fertilisation is perceived simultaneously as panic and cure, threat and solution. So on the one hand, the test-tube baby programme has received hostile Brave New World media coverage ('Move to Threshold of Genetic Engineering', 'Test Tube Babies Raise Moral Issue', 'Babies Storm Growing', 'Ban The Test Tube Baby'[8]) with fearful talk of cloning, and of human tissue put to suspect uses. And later, the Press hounded the unmarried mother of Britain's first test-tube quads, and – shades of the 'normal mother' notion of the surrogacy debate – questioned her moral suitability for motherhood. On the other hand, the test-tube baby programme has received some of the most rhapsodic medical reporting ever seen.[9] It was the ultimate baby story. The media rejoiced as if the scourge of infertility as they saw it had been cured for once and all. The coverage at the same time affirmed the normality of the cases (again emphasising their desperate longing for a child, seen as natural maternal instinct) and their abnormality (the very term test-tube baby – coined by the media – suggesting life created by science, husbanded by doctors).

The reporting of the test-tube baby programme reflects contemporary ambivalence over technology, seen both as threat (images of Frankenstein) and panacea. Medical experts were also treated simultaneously as dangerous, liable to use their skills for their own, dark purposes, and as saviours, fertilising the infertile. The coverage of test-tube babies reflected a tension between the consumer and medical approaches, suggesting both that medical research should be controlled by lay opinion *and* allowed to advance unfettered.

The disease of sex

The media coverage of AIDS has been a textbook moral panic. For long periods, the disease itself was almost entirely buried beneath metaphorical meanings. In their characterisation of the virus as a gay plague, their differentiation of innocent and guilty victims, and their promotion of sexual abstinence, the media played a prominent role in freighting the subject with fear. Yet viewed historically, media coverage of AIDS is strikingly similar to previous moral panics about sexual disease.

During and immediately after the First World War, there was a rush of cinema films about venereal disease which implied that sexual promiscuity inexorably led to VD. They sang a song of chastity, equating extra-marital sexual activity, disease, and disgrace. The British *Damaged Goods* (1919) and the American *Fit to Fight* (1919) presented VD as virulently contagious and an ever-present threat to the social as well as the physical body, a danger to the integrity of the family in society, and contrasted dangerous and illicit sex with that which was clean and socially acceptable, within the family.[10]

In 1982/83 reporters were fixated by herpes, and a common, non-life-threatening, latent condition became the object of the full weight of moral crusaders' rage. TV programmes referred to 'the end of sexual freedom', and opined that it 'looks like a moral punishment for all the things we've been doing since the 1960s', that 'nature does fight back'.[11] Sufferers were shot in silhouette (a throwback to 1950s' interviews with stigmatised people), talking of terrible pain and no cure. And in early 1983, herpes and AIDS were being linked together in the same programme as if, as sexual diseases, they had common origins and, in sexual abstinence, common solutions.

Presaging the coverage of AIDS, there was free media speculation about herpes' contagiousness (could the virus be caught from toilet seats, sheets, towels, passed on to babies?) and sufferers testified to their misery as pariahs. Programmes and articles suggested that herpes had reached epidemic proportions, despite the lack of corroborative evidence, and stressed its incurability. As one observer noted,

> it is ... quite rare for a disease which is fairly harmless and which possesses no serious health threat to be presented or conceptualised in terms of its incurability. Herpes is no less controllable or manageable than complaints such as eczema, or athlete's foot ... the use of the label incurable must be examined for its symbolic value.[12]

The condition was consistently reported as a sexually-transmitted disease, though the virus was far more likely to be activated by emotional stress than sexual contact: indeed, sensational media coverage, by increasing stress, possibly itself exacerbated symptoms and increased herpes' incidence. For this and other reasons, it's been suggested that herpes is partly a media-induced disease. Moreover, by focussing on sexual contact as the cause, the media were inevitably setting up sexual abstinence, monogamy, and even celibacy, as the remedy, and suggesting that the sufferer was both agent and victim of their suffering.

The herpes scare, and the early days of the AIDS panic, coincided almost exactly with the health frenzy and the rash of look-after-yourself programmes. Both identified external pollutants (foods, sexual practices or partners) which we were to avoid taking in. Both invoked nature – a retributive nature which punishes those who transgress, whether by eating wrong foods or by sexual promiscuity. Both advocated rigid regimes of restraint. And both were presided over by the medical profession, even though there was little they could offer in the way of a cure. As one observer put it,

> In a sense, what the media treatment of herpes has done is to reset the boundary between legitimate and illegitimate sexual behaviour, by effectively demarcating an area of permissable sexual conduct over which medicine is powerful, and an area of prohibited sexual conduct over which it is impotent.[13]

The herpes scare, like the look-after-yourself obsession, reflected the prevailing economic and social retrenchment. In the media, herpes (like food) was as much about the Lean and Moral Eighties as about physical illness. And remarkably, media coverage of a minor, at worst troublesome, condition was almost identical to that of a debilitating, and almost invariably killing one – AIDS.

AIDS: an immoral panic

When AIDS came, herpes went – at least from the media. Apart from death, AIDS had something else that herpes hadn't: an already stigmatised social group to scapegoat. The reporting was typified by the *Sun* headline 'Gay Plague Kills Priest',[14] and the news story that

> Grim-faced ministers emerged from a Cabinet meeting, fearful that the killer plague AIDS will spark violence on the streets of Britain. The prospect of bloodshed as terrified citizens make 'reprisal' attacks on homosexuals and drug addicts is now seen as a real threat. Some gays are expected to retaliate by spreading the virus to the rest of the community through 'revenge sex' with bisexuals.[15]

Such coverage wasn't confined to the tabloids. A *Times* leader thundered, 'The infection's origins and means of propagation excites repugnance, moral and physical, at promiscuous male homosexuality . . . Many members of the public are tempted to see in AIDS some sort of retribution for a questionable style of life.'[16]

Although TV and radio were less explicitly inflammatory, they compensated with menacing music and the vocabulary of war (the disease would attack, was a foreign invader, people were under threat).[17] Programmes about AIDS came to sound almost like thrillers, and anthropomorphised the disease as if it were a dangerous individual which, with all the media coverage, it had almost become. And broadcasting amplified the panic by reporting so fully and uncritically the comments of the hang 'em and flog 'em (or at least, quarantine and criminalise 'em) brigade, by asking sufferers 'do you feel like a leper?',[18] by telling them that

'There is now a steadily growing fear that the nation's entire blood supply may be threatened by AIDS. . . . The safest thing to do is to store up your own blood', which led large numbers of people to refuse also to donate blood out of fear of contamination,[19] and by running a live electronic poll asking whether AIDS carriers should be compelled to carry identity cards because emergency workers could become contaminated (and failing to make clear that none ever had, so that 95 per cent of the audience answered yes).[20] Having done so, they then pitched in with stories about training to dispel health workers' fears – fears which had been fanned (in part) by the media.

Indeed, as fear circulated between the media and the public and back again, it gathered potency and simplicity. Journalists saw themselves as simply doing their job when they reported on police reluctance to bring AIDS sufferers into court ('Don't put them in spitting distance – magistrate'[21]), or firemen and ambulence crews' announcement that they'd no longer give mouth-to-mouth resuscitation of injured men, or theatre cleaners' threat not to clean up after a gay production,[22] or the banning of gay men from a working-men's club ('BANNED! AIDS fear club ousts gay couple'[23]), or quoted those saying that having a haircut could now be lethal.[24] Yet the diffusion of such examples contributed to the sense of panic surrounding the disease, and the image of patients as outcasts.

The clamour about a gay plague was an outcry about a plague of gays. No disease (and certainly not VD) had ever been characterised as a heterosexual disease. Since the disease isn't contagious, and the virus wasn't caused by homosexual intercourse, but (for a time, in North America and Europe) happened to be transmitted *through* that community, its description in these terms was highly symbolic. The presentation of AIDS as contagious was a metaphor for homosexuality as contagion, homosexuality as a virus,[25] reinforced by the imagery and fears of cancer. And the British media's depiction of AIDS as an American export fuelled its image as a gay disease, since the United States in the British media is often a symbol of decadence, and San Francisco reported almost exclusively in terms of its concentration of gay inhabitants (though the first recognised AIDS case in the United States was a heterosexual woman in San Francisco in 1976).

The death of Rock Hudson from AIDS catapulted the disease onto the American TV talk shows. It stimulated two contrasting trends in the media's coverage. On the one hand, homophobia became even more rampant: 'The Hunk Who Lived A Lie',[26] 'Hollywood made the legend, Rock Hudson lived the lie',[27] 'He died a living skeleton – and so ashamed'.[28] Hudson's death anchored the illness ever more firmly to homosexuality in the media's mind, and the coverage so closely linked his death with his dissimulation of his homosexuality that it almost seemed as if he'd died from deception rather than AIDS.[29] The media also stressed his weight loss, and the recurring image of the one-time hunk reduced to a gaunt seven stone became a powerful symbol of his reduction in status and loss of macho bulk – now, literally, a seven-stone weakling.

Hudson's death also generated many gossipy articles about Hollywood, where some actors and actresses were demanding blood tests from their leading men or women before they'd submit to a screen kiss. And there were made-for-media accounts of medical McCarthyism rippling through the film community, so that actors like Burt Reynolds had to issue statements denying that they'd ever, now or at any time, had AIDS.

But at the same time, the death of such a celebrated Known from the disease crystallised for many its deadliness, and gave media reporting an urgency and a reality lacking when the illness had been merely a medical curiosity. As a leading American doctor put it 'What has happened for America is that someone they know is being affected.'[30]

Had AIDS become a news story when it was originally identified, among heterosexual Africans in the mid-1970s, its media coverage would probably have been quite different. But since Africa (like other Third World countries) is only of limited interest to the western media, and its chief disease depicted as climate-induced starvation, African AIDS was invisible. It only seeped into the British media in 1985, when the Press picked up on a medical journal paper on AIDS and the international blood trade,[31] and another linking African AIDS with heterosexual activity.[32] After this, from late 1985 to mid-1986, articles and programmes on an African AIDS epidemic started appearing quite regularly.

Certainly, medical knowledge about the disease in its early

days was limited, but already in May 1983, while the British tabloids were cheerfully peddling their gay plaguisms, the *New England Journal of Medicine* was arguing that 'AIDS has to be considered a potent threat to the whole population.'[33] Yet it was only in 1985, after Hudson's death, that heterosexual AIDS first started to be reported seriously, with stories about haemophiliacs, women, and eventually babies. By 1986, TV presenters were routinely asserting 'AIDS is no longer a gay plague, anyone may be at risk.'[34] And the gay community, after three years as the objects of virulently hostile reporting, watched the heterosexual media wake up to the danger and start taking the disease seriously. The *Observer* proclaimed 1986 the first Year of AIDS.[35] Only if the deaths of homosexuals and Africans didn't count.

The acknowledgment of the heterosexual dimension of AIDS highlighted another trend in the coverage, the identification of people with AIDS as either 'innocent' or 'guilty'. Children were consistently reckoned to be 'the most blameless victims', 'the ultimate innocent casualties of the AIDS contagion'.[36] And heterosexual AIDS only girded the loins of the New Right, who believed that their time had come: seers pronounced AIDS the wrath of God or nature's revenge, journalists played decadism by declaring that the eighties had kissed goodbye to the sexual revolution of the sixties; advertising agencies were asked how they'd 'sell' monogamy; TV advertisers worried that their come-hither commercials would turn flaccid if placed next to government sex health warnings, and film and TV script-writers dreamt up new moral characters.

Was it all about AIDS? Other illnesses such as cervical cancer were reported in similar terms, featuring doctors saying 'What we've seen is a copulation explosion. What we most need now in the Western world is a massive epidemic of loyalty between sexual partners.'[37] And herpes had received the same media treatment. Perhaps the most graphic illustration of the social meaning of the coverage was the logo of one TV programme on AIDS, depicting a nuclear family, with Mum, Dad, and three children standing outside a detached house, and AIDS looming up in large letters at the bottom to threaten them.[38] With its emphasis on keeping sex wholesome and in the family, on keeping it heterosexual and regulated, and on branding carriers as Other, AIDS (like other moral panics before it) addressed fears about

the collapse of the family, and the separation of sex and pro-
creation, invoking medical sanction for traditional family values
(even though AIDS could be caught through only one
partner).

AIDS, like cancer, became a symbol of death and extinction,
enshrining a fear of being overwhelmed by the Other. Cultures
in crisis, such as Britain and the United States, shoring up
fragmenting and troubled societies, were hospitable environ-
ments. As one commentator put it, 'for the media it had been
chosen as a general signifier for the end of the world. Everything
nasty and threatening – urban violence, earthquakes, a failing
economy – was somehow ultimately symbolised in this
disease.'[39]

Scare stories about AIDS scared people, especially gay men. In
1983, doctors at St Mary's Hospital in London reported hundreds of patients suffering from AIDS-related anxiety, some of
them suicidal: they included a 35-year-old academic in good
health until he watched a 'Horizon' documentary on AIDS and
became convinced he was suffering from it, and a 40-year-old
gay man who developed 'an acute agitated depression' after
reading a newspaper article on AIDS. The gay community also
became angry about the American and British coverage, and
used the channels available to them to try and correct the mis-
information and prejudice which was rife.[40]

Not all the programmes and articles were bad. There was a
struggle over the meaning of AIDS, and the rare occasions that
gay men (more usually the objects rather than subjects of AIDS
programmes) presented their own views unmediated, they had
powerful and even encouraging things to say. The overworked
spokesmen of the Terrence Higgins Trust were much in demand
as media speakers along with sympathetic doctors, and some
programmes assembled useful information.

AIDS, as an infectious disease, appeared to conform to
disease-as-we-know-it, tapping resilient ideas about contagion,
epidemics, the plague, the Black Death. And, in keeping with the
medical approach, some of the reporting had a strong miracle
cure orientation, highlighting the search for a vaccine or a cure
and the hope of a technological or scientific solution. But doctors
couldn't cure AIDS, and the media were thrown into disarray by
divergent expert opinion. The British Medical Association's

warning, in early 1987, that anyone who'd had more than one partner in the past four years shouldn't give blood, retracted after the Government disagreed, prompted reporters to openly wonder about confusion among the experts. The media couldn't cope with the medical uncertainty and fell back on a victim-blaming approach: if you were promiscuous you deserved it.

No TV programmes adopted an environmental approach, or saw in the transmission of AIDS a map of international and national power relations. 'Panorama', although it acknowledged that even relatively rich African countries couldn't afford to screen all blood, drew the same old conclusions from its interviews with Black African prostitutes, who freely admitted that they continued sleeping with white businessmen to make money to send their children to school, so that they too shouldn't have to become prostitutes: Black women were a risk to White men, and not the other way round.[41]

AIDS told a gloomy tale about technology: there were predictions of whole continents being ravaged, while doctors stood helplessly by, and public figures insisted that a vaccine would take years, even a decade, to develop. Meanwhile, Challenger and Chernobyl were blighting technophoria even further. The disintegration of the American space shuttle, before millions of watching, dreaming Americans and their children, was replayed again and again in technicolour on television worldwide, becoming an icon of technological fallibility. The Chernobyl disaster also demonstrated that technology could kill. Amidst all this, images of technology the healer were highly prized. Few came more optimistic than heart transplants.

9

Take Heart:
Transplants and the Media

Heart transplants have always had a good press. The first (performed by Christiaan Barnard in 1967, when technology promised the moon, and soon after delivered) was widely reported as a triumphant surgical landmark though the patient survived barely three weeks, exemplifying the grim joke that the operation was a success, but the patient died. Since then, the coverage of transplants has become highly ritualised.

Heartwarming

Journalists regularly clone the heart transplant story, producing perfect replicas of previous reports. They stress the desperation of those waiting for a heart, and the fear that time will run out. The fatal alternative is made plain. The operation is depicted as offering the chance of a new life or future, an opportunity to vanquish death. Grief and joy are voiced, and the press conference following the operation is an aria of hope.

Cameras follow the patient's first post-operation cup of tea, the first meal, and their first faltering steps. Reporters talk of 'the emotive and poetic symbolism of the heart'.[1] Transplant patients are said to have 'joined a very exclusive club'.[2] And viewers are enlisted as partisans in their dramatic 'battle against rejection'. Human interest doesn't come in a larger size.

Transplant reporting is also almost invariably of the 'milestones in medicine' kind. It mobilises the drama of flight: the surgeon, racing against the clock, flies across countries to collect transplantable organs. Like the aviation pioneers, his flight path is illustrated by a map, the logo of a plane, or film of the actual flight.[3] Above all, medical skill is hymned. A small number of transplant surgeons have attained heroic stature in the media: almost any operation or pronouncement by Magdi Yacoub, Terence English, or Roy Calne are potential news stories. They're medical alchemists, offering the ultimate miracle cure.

So it's scarcely surprising that hospitals are lavish in providing media access to film transplants. Hospital administrators phone the Press Association to announce the results of their latest operation, sometimes alerting medical correspondents before it's taken place. In 1982, BBC TV gained six months complete access to Harefield Hospital to film a seven-part series on the subject. And since the first British operation at the National Heart Hospital in 1968, the post-operative press conference has become a tradition. As the BBC Science Correspondent puts it, 'Hospitals doing heart, and heart/lung transplants, quite like the publicity because it helps them raise funds.'[4]

The American Jarvik-7 artificial heart programme provided the most infamous example of medical orchestration of the media. In 1966, while awaiting a decision on funding for artificial heart research from the National Heart Institute, American surgeon Michael DeBakey sought and gained unprecedented publicity for the heart experiments – dubbed by some 'surgical spectaculars' – he was conducting in Houston, generating media hype about life-saving and superstardom for DeBakey. But even this was unremarkable compared with the saturation coverage achieved twenty years later by Humana, a profit-making corporation based in Louisville, Kentucky. Humana had attracted the surgeon William De Vries to their hospital with their offer to pay for 100 experimental operations. In November 1984, two days before De Vries operated on William Schroeder, Humana alerted the media. Some 300 news media representatives descended on Louisville, and were ushered into a well-equipped press centre and deluged with material. NBC's science correspondent said it was 'an atmosphere more appropriate to a major sports event than to a serious scientific or medical undertaking'.[5] Even the American Medical Association called it a 'Roman circus'.

The Humana press office had studied media coverage of previous transplants, and tried to learn from them. Doctors were available for two briefings every day, as well as for live appearances on the early morning network shows. Reporters were even provided with copies of the consent form Schroeder signed before the operation, and pathology slides of his old, diseased heart. The cost of servicing the media in the first weeks approached $300,000. As *Life* magazine put it, 'That's expensive news, but cheap advertising.'[6]

Schroeder's every post-operative belch was rapturously relayed to television audiences. He was filmed drinking his first beer, and receiving the disability allowance cheque which President Reagan had promised to expedite. One NBC reporter alone filed nineteen stories on him in just five weeks.[7] But the media euphoria about the operation obscured its experimental nature, and its expense. Nor, until much later, were journalists given details about his subsequent stroke and fever, leading to extreme neurological damage. Instead, Humana continued to issue press releases about his 'continuing progress', while dispatching doctors to Texas for a course on how to handle tough questions from reporters, and answer in the most optimistic way.[8] When the reporting finally turned sour, Humana declined to give out details about Schroeder or their next transplant patient because the media sought 'trivia like whether the patient had strawberries for breakfast'.[9] Yet it was Humana who had encouraged this reporting in the first place, with the media as willing collaborators.

Heart and artificial heart transplants fulfill almost every criterion of a good story. They're events, occurring within a day, featuring individuals with glamorous, dramatic illnesses, and abundant human interest. And they're olds. Almost every news report on a heart operation is identical, only the peg changes: the youngest patient, the first woman recipient, the first heart-lung patient, the youngest heart-lung patient, etc. They're also excellent 'good news' stories, plying hope.

Reports about artificial hearts and heart transplants recruit audiences to the case for transplants but, with rare exceptions, they almost invariably ignore the counter-arguments.[10] American coverage of the artificial heart consistently failed to examine the actual need for the device, alternative approaches to heart disease, the questionable use of uncontrolled clinical trials, or the difficulties or consequences of artificial heart development, including the later costs to society. Routine British coverage of heart transplants almost never raises the question of cost, or the consequences for the care of chronic patients and for other sectors of the NHS of diverting such substantial sums to surgery. Missing, too, is any sense of heart transplants' insignificant potential contribution to the treatment of major cardiovascular disease, killer of some 300,000 people annually in England and Wales. (Even fifty transplant centres working at full tilt couldn't make a significant impact, especially if patients' relatively short survival periods are taken into account.[11])

Above all, reporting of heart transplants, like most news reporting, stunningly fails to make connections. Reporters, following the medical profession itself, rarely engage with any of the contradictions created by insistent look-after-yourself reporting (preaching individual responsibility for avoiding heart disease) and the simultaneous panegyric over transplants (implying that doctors have the solution). The death of the longest surviving British heart transplant patient, Keith Castle, from narrowing of the arteries caused by his continued smoking, was generally reported in the obituaries as a triumph for surgery rather than for cigarettes.

The deaths of transplant patients are rarely accorded more than a few lines or seconds of airtime, compared with the time and space devoted to their operations. This is because transplants popularly connote the defeat of death: they couldn't possibly survive as miracle cures if equal attention was paid to recipients' deaths. And transplant stories almost never report medical disagreement over the value of the operation, though there are known and respected doctors who oppose it. When criticism is articulated, it leads to medico-media crises. Or it's incorporated into a pro-transplant piece, so that objections to transplants are raised only to be dismissed by its defendants.[12] A rare example of the critique of transplants gaining media prominence occurred in September 1980, when the *Evening Standard* ran an entire front-page article headlined, ' "Stop This Heartswap Epidemic": Transplants not the answer, says Guy's doctor.' The story's second paragraph supplied an explanation for this sudden attention to the other side: the critic had been speaking at the annual meeting of the British Association for the Advancement of Science, and so was easily accessible, had the flavour of an event, and was legitimated by science. It was also covered by the other London evening paper, picked up by BBC TV's 'Nationwide', BBC TV News, and ITV's 'News at Ten', and made it into all the national dailies the next day.

Although the medical profession regularly upbraids the media for its preoccupation with miracle cures, the reporting of transplants and artificial hearts closely follows the medical approach, taking its cue from official sources. In the United States, the artificial heart programme was significantly absent from the news in the intervals between clinical trials, when reporters would have had to seek out information individually rather than attend scientific meetings or surgical spectaculars en masse.[13] Just how closely the reporting of transplants follows the medical agenda can be seen in the coverage of one major story.

Treble chance

At 10.45 a.m., on 17 December 1986, I was with BBC Science Correspondent James Wilkinson in his office at Television Centre, when his phone rang. A BBC department servicing TV News called to let him know of a Press Association (PA) report on the world's first combined heart, lung, and liver transplant, just performed at Papworth Hospital. It was Front Page drama: Wilkinson had two-and-a-half hours to prepare a piece for the One O'Clock News.

He had no doubt that it was a good story.[14] Unlike Fleet Street, his first problem was that 'we haven't got any pictures', so he ordered up BBC library shots of Papworth. Then he began ringing the editors of the various news bulletins, to alert them. Given the shortage of time, they decided to bring someone in live to discuss the operation for the One O'Clock News. The editor of the lunchtime news guided him towards an ethics angle. Wilkinson had just the man, 'We had that ethical chap once before. Shall I try him? He's good at this kind of thing.' Dr Raanan Gillon, part-time at Imperial College and Editor of the *Journal of Medical Ethics*, was also a personal friend of Wilkinson's. Wilkinson talked to him briefly over the phone, and, since Imperial College wasn't too far from the BBC, he was booked.

By now, Wilkinson was busily writing a piece – largely reworked from the PA material – for the twelve o'clock bulletin. It was the lead item, accompanied by pictures of the surgeons. The story as written contained an implicit justification for the operation: 'The woman had been so ill that her heart would have failed had she had the liver transplant alone, so there was no alternative – she had to have all three organs replaced.'

The transplant again led the longer one o'clock bulletin, with a description over library pictures of another operation at Papworth ('the hospital is one of the centres of the world capable of carrying out such an operation'). But then the newscaster quizzed Gillon with a series of critical questions: how far is it all going to go? what about the high cost of the operation? and what of the controversy over whether the donors are actually dead? It was a commendable attempt to raise questions about transplants, but (perhaps surprisingly), Gillon was entirely positive, vigorously defending the transplant programme. No surprise, however, to Wilkinson, who said later,

> I had a pretty shrewd idea of his views – I've known him for years. He's not an extremist by any means. He sees both sides of the argument, and he puts both sides. I didn't look for someone who's critical of transplants. I could have done – there's a stage army. There's X [Wilkinson's second choice of interviewee, but unavailable] – he would have been more critical. It's very easy to look for reaction, to go to someone where you know there'll be critical feeling. I'm not in favour of that, because it implies a prejudgment: you think the thing is bad, so you go to someone who backs up your judgment.[15]

Precisely, of course, what he'd done: he thought the thing was good, so he went to someone who backed up his judgment.

By the Six O'Clock News, the coverage had changed significantly. It had become a much more unapologetic miracle cure story ('Our Science Correspondent James Wilkinson reports on another milestone in heart transplant surgery'). The logistics of the operation, and especially the various flights round Britain, some by helicopter, were illustrated graphically over a map of the country. Gillon had been reduced to one short answer defending the operation (partly chosen, said Wilkinson, 'because it was the right length, it was a clear point he was making, and it fitted in with the package'), giving no sense that there might be a compendium of possible criticisms. All references to cost had gone.

By the Nine O'Clock News, the story had changed again. Now it had dropped to fourth item, but had become even more firmly a breakthrough story, demonstrating the soaring trajectory of medical advance. Over graphics headed 'Transplant Progress', Wilkinson logged the 'milestones' of transplant surgery since 1979 (without identifying which of the patients were still alive), ending 'Today at Papworth, two teams of surgeons pooled their expertise and took transplant surgery a stage further.' But another new dimension had entered the story – human interest. A filmed interview with the patient's daughter and mother-in-law about their feelings concluded with the mother-in-law saying 'It just proves we've some wonderful people in this world.' Gillon was nowhere to be seen. The reason, according to Wilkinson, was

> mainly length of time, because we had two new ingredients, the mother-in-law and the daughter – two new interviewees who moved the argument on. And we rarely use someone on all three bulletins. The mother-in-law wasn't particularly good – a bit inarticulate – but the 9-year-old was very good, especially for her age . . . so we stuck her in first. But the mother-in-law was good saying aren't there a lot of good people in the world. I think it left people with a nice warm feeling.[16]

So how had the scope of the story been decided?

> Certainly there was a feeling in the office that it was a big breakthrough in transplant surgery. . . . You make a judgment where you think the truth lies, bearing in mind the scientific evidence and the arguments of the other side. Partly it's a feeling in the office – people who put the bulletins together are members of the public, they have feelings too.

While the story had been in its infancy, with little medical detail available, the vacuum had been used to raise critical questions about the enterprise, even if only to have them dispelled. But as the story ripened during the day, with the hospital supplying further details and the family press conference, the dominant medical view (with its abundance of technical and logistical information about the operation) had become irresistible. And with the human interest element, it would be sure to send viewers away with a glow.

Please give generously

What's the effect of this kind of celebratory reporting? With rare exceptions, the media operate as a recruitment office for organ donors. In a radio interview on the day of the triple transplant, a reporter interviewing the President of the Royal College of Physicians about transplants and brain-death entirely abdicated the journalist's role of challenger or devil's advocate, acting purely as prompter instead. Reporter: 'And the consequences of people then [as a result of one critical press article] refusing to donate organs . . . is that there is a desperate need for them, I would have thought.' President: 'There is a desperate need for organs to save lives that would not otherwise be saved.'[17]

Press and broadcasting also shake a collecting-tin in the Government's direction, invoking the image of patients' deaths through lack of money. And when the DHSS funded a cost-benefit analysis of heart transplants, the Press weighed in with, 'Ten patients could be given new hearts with the amount of money the Department of Health is spending on studying the costs and benefits of the transplant programmes at Harefield and Papworth hospitals, it was revealed yesterday'[18] – though of course that precisely begged the question. In the face of anything representing a potential threat to the transplant programme, the media have rallied round, effectively running a campaign for more money for transplants. In 1980 the *Daily Mail* even helped to establish the British Heart Transplant Fund.

Not surprisingly, with such vocal advocates, the money has been forthcoming. In March 1980, after a build-up of Press stories about the dire effects of the shortage of funds for transplants, and following a private donation of £300,000 to Papworth, the Secretary of State for Social Services announced a special allocation of expenditure for heart transplants. Further special allocations were made in October 1982, February 1984, and December 1984. This was in the thick of NHS cuts, at a time when NHS policy was apparently to divert funds from the acute sector to the chronic and preventive ones, yet the transplant programme – with its own special fund – was exempted. The normal decision-making route for allocation of NHS money had been circumvented, though almost any speciality (orthopaedics and geriatrics included) could have made a case for special funds and invoked images of patient hardship or death, except that for reporters they wouldn't have transplants' magic. Media coverage almost certainly helped the transplant programme achieve special status, and may have influenced charitable foundations into siphoning donations towards transplants centres. Later, the media intervened again more directly, this time soliciting organs, not money.

That's Ben's life

In 1983, 10-month-old Jamie Fiske was admitted to the University of Minnesota Hospital, to be considered for a liver transplant because of a blocked liver condition called biliary atresia. When no donor appeared, her parents decided to use the media. They sent a brief statement to the wire services and Boston newspapers, which produced stories about their daughter's need for a donated liver. Jamie's father then made an unprecedented appeal to the plenary session of the American Academy of Pediatrics' annual meeting in New York, urging the several hundred physicians present to look out for a donor. Finally the three major TV networks picked up the case, giving it nationwide publicity because, according to a University of Minnesota press officer, 'it contained all the elements of a great story – tragedy and despair, hope and determination, a father fighting the bureaucracy, fighting the medical establishment, doing everything he could to save his daughter's life'.[19]

A week later, as a result of the publicity, the parents of a 10-month-old boy who died of injuries after a Salt Lake City car crash asked their doctor to offer the baby's liver for transplanting. It went to Jamie. Throughout the day of the operation, the University of Minnesota fielded phone-calls from the Press at a rate of two per minute. There were letters, too – from Nancy Reagan during the search for a donor, and President Reagan after the operation. At the press conference (necessitated by continuing media interest) on the eve of Jamie's departure for home, Jamie's surgeon declared that the chance of finding a suitable liver for such a small child would have been very remote 'had he [Fiske] not made such a plea'.[20]

In 1984, it was Britain's turn. Doctors had given 2-year-old Ben

Hardwick, another sufferer from biliary atresia, a bleak prognosis. But after his mother Debbie read a *Reader's Digest* article about a successful American paediatric liver transplant, she discovered that a British transplant surgeon performed the same operation. The surgeon, Professor Roy Calne, told her of the dearth of small-enough livers, since the subject of transplanting a dead child's organs was hedged with taboo. She would need to swing public opinion behind her. 'I suppose the first step would be to find yourself a friendly television producer', said Calne,[21] who'd been enraged by the 'Panorama' report on brain-death four years earlier, but believed that if one programme could swing public opinion away from organ donation, perhaps another could swing it back.

So Debbie contacted the popular BBC TV consumer series, 'That's Life', to ask them to broadcast an appeal. The programme agreed. A film crew moved into the Hardwick's flat, filming a sequence of Ben blowing bubbles in the bath which was to become a regular part of news bulletins during the next few months. The programme-makers were clearly moved by Ben's plight, seeing it as open to a miracle cure: 'Here is this brilliant surgeon', wrote the programme's researcher, 'with the skill to save children's lives, denied the means to do so.'[22]

Ben's story, plus an interview with Debbie and quotes from Professor Calne, was broadcast in January 1984. The BBC was swamped with viewers' calls, and when the Press's interest was also aroused, the programme staff acted as protector and even family friend to the Hardwicks. In a sense Ben had been adopted by the programme, and when a donor was found, the Press reported 'Smooth Op For That's Life Boy', and 'Liver Op Bid To Save TV Toddler'.[23] The story began to take on the dimensions of a real-life soap, rocked by drama and emotion. The Press had tracked down the parents of the dead donor, whose subsequent press conference also made headlines. Meanwhile, 'That's Life' were giving weekly updates on Ben's condition, a cliffhanger to rival any TV drama, though the programme-makers got angry when the press confused it with a proper soap and started to write their own storylines.[24] Ben's progress continued to dominate the programme and the headlines for a few months. And then, in March 1985, he died. Given less than a year to live without the operation, he'd lived just over a year with it.

Many doctors saw it as a responsible use of the media, mobilising its power *pro bono publico*. As a newspaper leader said of Ben's case, 'Television is routinely blamed for every kind of social disorder. So it is warming to hear of an occasion when a TV programme has plainly done great and lasting good.'[25] There was also no doubt about the programme-makers' genuine affection for Ben and family, and their sincerity in attempting to help other children. And they succeeded to an unprecedented extent in raising public interest in the subject, and generating organs for transplant. The transplant co-ordinator at Addenbrooke's, the hospital where Ben had his transplant, said 'We've battled and battled away to bring the problem of finding child donors to the attention of doctors and patients for three years. The story of Ben managed to do more in just one week.'[26] Kidney transplants rose by 40 per cent after Ben's story, and the Parliamentary Under-Secretary for Health said 'I would like to say a very warm thank you to "That's Life" for the way it has brought home to so many people the unique life-saving value of transplantation.'[27] The programme led to a House of Commons debate in February 1984 (in which 'That's Life' was praised) on how to increase the number of donors.

Money poured into the 'That's Life' offices, and the programme hired a researcher to discover the most effective way of using it. She proposed a new, fully-equipped, fully-staffed intensive care room, the Ben Hardwick Room at Addenbrooke's and a new medical post, a paediatric fellowship to work at King's Hospital and Addenbrooke's, treating children with liver disease and those needing transplants.

Yet such media interventions into the NHS are seldom unproblematic. The local health authority – who apparently knew nothing of the proposal until two days before the programme announced it – estimated that the Ben Hardwick Room's annual running-costs would be £250,000 and not the £40,000 allowed for by the programme. They turned it down unless the programme could guarantee the full running-costs. A paediatrician complained, 'We are not going to be railroaded by politicians and the media because of a sob story.'[28] But as with the heart transplant examples above, so the liver transplant programme also managed to by-pass the NHS's decision-making procedures. In April the Minister of Health issued a press release expressing his concern over reports of health authority fears that the intensive care room would drain the district's funds, and suggesting that the liver transplant programme might become a 'supra regional service'. And so it did: in December, he announced a £198,000 grant to the paediatric liver transplant programme at Addenbrooke's,[29] and in January 1985 the DHSS declared liver transplants to be a national priority, allocating paediatric and adult transplants £2.3 million.

In all the stirring coverage of Ben and paediatric liver transplants, the rarity of Ben's condition was seldom recalled. According to Esther Rantzen's first report, only twenty-five babies born in Britain each year are suitable for this kind of operation,[30] compared with the tens of thousands of other conditions waiting for underfunded treatment, at a time of NHS cuts. Media campaigns such as 'That's Life's intervene to affect NHS priorities, orienting them almost invariably towards high-technology medicine. Their intervention isn't necessarily based on any measured consideration of competing needs, but more often determined by the cuteness of the patient. As he drove to see Ben for the first time, the 'That's Life' researcher realised that 'Until now I haven't really thought about what he'll look like. If he is so near death, perhaps he'll be very feeble, very sickly and – this is television – very unappealing.'[31] Rantzen warned the programme editor, 'obviously if the film is too painful, if he looks too ill, we may not be able to use it'.[32] But the assistant film editor, when asked 'How does Ben look?', replied 'Gorgeous', and the researcher concluded, 'That is the main hurdle crossed. If Ben looks appealing, the point of his story will come home with even more impact.'[33] But what if he'd looked unappealing?

Organ appeals worry many people both inside and outside the medical profession. An American director of organ procurement is disturbed that only the 'mediagenic' children may get the transplants. Another is unhappy 'if making use of the news media is the *only* way to get something you desperately need. That suggests that there's something wrong with the system.'[34] And a third argues that

> if it turns out that some families are able to benefit from publicity because they know how to manipulate the media, while others don't, then there is a whole new range of issues at the interface between journalism, medicine, and ethics. At the very least, it

raises the question of whether we should ever rely on what amounts to charity campaigns – that is, mass publicity to obtain contributions – to fund these procedures.[35]

The way in which organ appeals are framed also implies that transplants are inevitably life-saving. Jamie Fiske's surgeon, asked if he feared that news of the boy's successful transplant would raise false hopes, responded 'Jamie is an exception. If we were to do another half-dozen Jamies, we might end up with three [results] as good as Jamie and three that might not make it.'[36] Other British doctors and health administrators have deplored the heart-string plucking involved in cases like Ben's. Yet when in January 1988 'That's Life' ran a special seventy-five minute programme on transplant surgery promising to look at its controversies as well as miracles, they failed to include a single critic of transplants and cited objections to transplantations only to dismiss them. Generally the 'That's Life' team reacts bullishly to any criticism of paediatric liver transplants, dismissing it as wild and savage,[37] and never acknowledging that there may be legitimate counter-arguments unmotivated by malice.

Perhaps this is because, in portraying transplants as 'miracle cure', journalists feed the potent, hardy modern myth that personal tragedy and the uncertainties of human existence can be resolved by technology. What this obscures is that transplants *depend* on technology-aided tragedy, a life lost generally in a car crash. A most ghoulish example of this selective thinking was a TV ad on Channel 4 (broadcast when Ben's story was in its prime), featuring a car accident. Though viewers might have expected a public service warning about dangerous driving, it turned out to be an advertisement urging the carrying of donor cards.[38] When they do talk about transplant donors, newspapers and TV programmes almost invariably take the Biblical line that 'his or her tragic death enabled others to live',[39] and almost never simultaneously address the issue of death on the roads, although this may be a subject they feel keenly about and even campaign on, but as a separate issue. To link them would be to enter the murkier waters of comparative policy and relative choice, of ambiguity and conflict, of priorities and what influences them, muddying the purity of media appeals for the cutely needy and telegenically sick, and rusting the gleam of the miracle cure.

10

Crises and the Management of Controversy

Beyond dispute

Controversies aren't born, they're made. Similarly, subjects are cordoned off from controversy by a series of deliberate if invisible choices. When I asked the BBC Science Correspondent about his decision not to give airtime to transplant critics in the triple transplant story detailed in the last chapter, he replied,

> I don't think there's much controversy about transplants in general. I'm not anti-transplants myself by any means, and it's an established procedure now. . . . I certainly wouldn't want to stimulate an artificial controversy about transplants just by getting in a stage army. There's X who is always wheeled out – he'll always come over at the drop of a hat, and in the nuclear field there's Y: there's a well-known group of people willing to talk critically on the heart transplant issue, but it's got beyond that.[1]

So what's a genuine controversy?

> I think when something is not stimulated by the media; when an opinion is reflected in Parliament or a distinguished person has written a letter to the journals; or when you think something's new and dramatic and you're casting round and asking people's opinions about it.

Which people?

> I think you assess that by their degree of eminence in the field. I mean a humble houseman in the district hospital wouldn't carry

162

the same weight as an eminent surgeon at Barts or a President of a Royal College or an Opposition Front Benchman.

For this reporter, like his colleagues, the medical establishment is preeminent arbiter of the legitimate boundaries of an issue, with Parliament and politicians as secondary definers, though he'll break with both if news values (something dramatic) certify a subject controversial. But he almost always takes his cue on what's a controversy from official sources, and by seeking out the views of the powerful, medical broadcasters reinforce their power.

The BBC has a long history in deferring to official definitions of controversy. In trying to decide how much weight to give dissenting views, the Corporation has almost invariably adhered to official medical opinion, thus freeing the BBC from having to evaluate their validity itself. Over the years, challengers of medical orthodoxy got short shrift. The policy of the Talks Department in 1944 was that 'views which are regarded by the weight of medical authority as crank should not be allowed expression in broadcasts which profess to provide health education'.[2] Regularly but unsuccessfully between 1929 and 1952, the National Anti-Vaccination League lobbied the BBC for a chance to put across their views against diphtheria immunisation. As the Controversy Committee Minutes unabashedly recorded in 1929, 'When the subject had previously been referred to us we had employed evasive tactics and it was generally agreed to continue this policy as the subject is not deemed suitable for discussion.'[3] Even after the 1950 Beveridge Committee on British broadcasting, in response to demands from almost all sides for more controversy, had proposed broadcasts by important 'minorities with a message' (naming the League as one) in a 'Hyde Park of the Air', the League again got a polite BBC brush-off, prompted by the Medical Research Council and the Ministry of Health.[4]

Between 1936 and 1948 lobbyists for voluntary euthanasia also met the 'unsuitable for broadcasting' line and when, in 1948, the Abortion Law Reform Association wrote asking for a debate on abortion, they too were told that 'broadcasting is not a suitable medium for discussion of this subject'.[5]

Birth control didn't fare any better. The BBC saw itself as keeper of the nation's morals and refused all discussions 'touching upon debatable questions of sexual ethic', including birth control. In 1935, they permitted fleeting reference to the subject 'provided, however, that the speaker made it clear that the subject was a controversial one'.[6] Certainly, the taboos against public discussion of sex were strong and were not just the invention of a priggish BBC: when Mrs Pallis, in her 1934 talk on life as the wife of an unemployed man (see p. 39) obliquely referred to contraception, the BBC received sackfuls of letters complaining that the subject had been mentioned on radio.[7] The Corporation also feared that 'any reference to such a subject to the general public would produce a spate of immorality'.[8] When listeners wrote in asking why Marie Stopes wasn't being allowed to broadcast, the Corporation stressed that the contraception crusader hadn't been individually vetoed, but that BBC policy embargoed the whole topic: 'The subject of birth control . . . has never yet . . . been discussed at the microphone in this country. Broadcasting is not, in the Corporation's view, a suitable medium for discussion of this subject.'[9]

The Corporation's disinclination to discuss the subject wasn't just a matter of morals, but also reflected anxieties about discouraging the already 'under-fertile': in the 1920s and 1930s, the low birth rate generated an underpopulation scare, a fear that the middle classes would be swamped by the higher birthrate among the poor and unemployed, and that the resulting ageing population would have an adverse effect on consumption. When talks on contraception were proposed, the BBC offered instead discussions on population. Only in the mid-1950s did the Corporation finally broach the subject, and the reason wasn't any bold new frankness among broadcasters, but the endorsement of the State. In 1949, the population was growing again, and the Royal Commission on Population sanctioned women doing two jobs (inside and outside the home), therefore making it possible for birth control information to be freely given.[10] By the late 1940s, contraception was being recognised as part of the welfare state, and in 1949 new birth control clinics opened at the rate of one every five weeks. Finally in 1955, the Minister of Health visited the Kensington Family Planning Association (FPA), the FPA chairwoman appeared on television, and the work of the FPA was explained on BBC Radio's 'Woman's Hour'. There was even a *Times* leader welcoming contraception.[11] Birth control had only come onto the media agenda when the Government had recognised its value.

Yet it still remained problematic for broadcasters. In 1977, six days before transmission, a programme on public attitudes to contraception and different methods of birth control was banned, with the BBC insisting that the only acceptable programme on contraception would be one that wouldn't offend 'a sexually uncommunicative family watching together'.[12] And in 1983 a 30-second public information film encouraging boys to use contraceptives with the slogan 'If you're not man enough to use birth control, you're not old enough to make love' was banned by the Independent Broadcasting Authority (IBA) on the grounds that it would offend public sensitivity and condone promiscuity and pre-marital sex. It was later broadcast with the apparently more palatable catchline 'Any idiot can get a girl into trouble, don't let it be you'.

In the case of venereal disease, it was the New Deal in the United States which ruptured public silence. In 1934 CBS banned – moments before he was due to go on the air – a nationally-known physician, because he planned to refer to syphilis and gonorrhea by name instead of calling them a social disease. (Listeners heard piano melodies instead.) The banned physician Thomas Parran, from 1936 Surgeon-General, attempted to deliver a mortal blow to euphemism, aiming (as *Newsweek* reported) to 'put the words syphilis and gonorrhea into the language and people's mouths. Familiarity might breed respect.'[13] He used the Press to do it. His *Reader's Digest* article in July 1936 spoke freely about syphilis, and later that year *Time* pictured him on its cover, with an accompanying story on VD. 'The ice of journalistic reticence' had been shattered, the magazine declared, and the *New York Herald Tribune*, the *Chicago Tribune*, and 123 other papers followed suit, the *Ladies Home Journal* pitching in with a full-scale campaign to control VD.[14]

Britain lagged behind. In 1937 the BBC still believed that 'it would be a mistake to attempt to give broadcasts on social hygiene in any form'.[15] But the war's early days brought a rapid spread of VD: in 1941, there was a 113 per cent increase in the numbers of new cases of male civilians and servicemen with syphilis coming forward for treatment, and a 63 per cent increase among women. There was also a large increase in gonorrhea.

The Government was propelled into action, launching a vigorous propaganda campaign. Starting in 1942, there were question-and-answer posters about the disease, an intensive Ministry of Health press advertising campaign which continued for the rest of the war, and in November, for the first time in British broadcasting, the subject was raised on air in a talk by the Chief Medical Officer, Sir Wilson Jameson.

As in the United States, the campaign's emphasis was less on moralising than on encouraging sufferers to come forward for treatment. When, in October 1943, the Radio Doctor Charles Hill broadcast a discussion with the Radio Padre on prostitution and VD under the title 'A Blasphemy Called Lust' (causing a shock-horror headline in the next day's *News Chronicle*[16]), the Ministry of Information complained to the BBC of – among other things – their emphasis on morality. By 1944, Jameson was able to talk quite openly on the Home Service about venereal disease and syphilis, declaring that

> A great change . . . has come over the situation in the last two
> years. No longer are we shutting our eyes to this social plague,
> no longer do we refuse to discuss it, no longer are we
> withholding from young people information about its dangers.
> The old attitude of secrecy and hush-hush has not been entirely
> overcome, but it has suffered a resounding defeat.[17]

Once again, the liberalisation in broadcasting had followed, and indeed been initiated by, a change in government thinking.

A remarkably similar change occurred forty-five years later in the case of AIDS. At first, media coverage was almost wholly inflammatory and titillating, most programmes talking only in general terms of the disease's means of transmission and of prevention, while the Government's intended frank and full newspaper ads were vetoed by Prime Minister Margaret Thatcher, apparently on the grounds that they were 'only fit for lavatory walls'.[18] Ministers too outlawed explicit information, so that advertisements even as late as March 1986 contained only mild and 'inoffensive' terms. Parliament debated which was the best language to use, but the Government's first TV and cinema ads in January and February 1987 shunned detail of the disease altogether, preferring to use menacing music and mobilise mythic fears, with images of drilling rock and looming icebergs, as if the disease could be caught from hewing granite or cruising the North Pole. (These were apparently phallic images, and they baffled many while offending some: the *Radio Times* printed letters from parents irate at having to field 'Mummy, what's a condom?' questions from toddlers happening upon the ads at the tea-and-toast time of 5.35 p.m.)

The American media also came over all shy at the prospect of frank sex talk. The American TV networks, which had always prohibited contraceptive advertising, were still arguing in early 1987 that 'We believe birth control messages of any kind would be an intrusion on the moral and religious beliefs of our audiences.'[19] But by now the medical profession in both countries, and the British Government at least, were profoundly alarmed by AIDS. The British Secretary of State met with the broadcasters, and asked them to make an extensive, explicit intervention in support of the Government's public education AIDS campaign. They responded in February 1987 with an unprecedented, two-week, synchronised campaign by all four TV channels (and Radios 1 and 3), comprising thirty-three programmes in eight days alone, when taboos were swatted like flies. It became quite routine to see people demonstrating the use of the sheath by putting condoms on erect plastic penises, or onto a doctor's two fingers. Named callers-in to TV programmes unembarrassedly revealed that 'I can't keep it stiff' while the studio team candidly described almost every single sexual practice commonly known (or not) and estimated their risk.[20]

The American networks abruptly reversed their policy and decided that the nation could withstand condom ads after all, after their local affiliated stations had run one with a young woman saying 'I'll do a lot for love, but I'm not ready to die for it' and no one protested. Soon after the IBA too reversed its longstanding ban on branded condom ads on British TV. The disease that for over four years had brought the moralisers out of the woodwork was now, ironically as part of a repressive sexual climate, provoking a major liberalisation in the vocabulary, imagery, and admissibility of sex. It was a most extraordinary break with tradition.

In addition medical issues these days are more likely to be reported as controversies: a study comparing American newspaper coverage of science in 1951, 1961, and 1971, found that the controversies of science were reported much more frequently in the 1971 articles than in 1961 and 1951, especially in medicine.[21] Yet shifts are rarely absolute, unequivocally progressive, and part of a soaring graph of emancipation, as some historians would have us believe. Methods of control take on a new guise, dress up in different clothing. Perhaps the most powerful means of control over broadcasting still available to those with power is their ability to conduct and sustain a chorus of widely-publicised complaints – to effect a crisis.

On the critical list

The history of medical broadcasting is studded with regular crises. Anti-media broadsides and allegations of journalistic irresponsibility recur in the correspondence columns of the *British Medical Journal,* each time as if for the first time. The medical profession generally attributes crises to the media's inaccuracy, as if accuracy, objectivity and truth were unproblematic notions. Underlying the notion of accuracy is the idea of a single, correct clinical position, though as one teledoctor has pointed out, 'the "real issues" in clinical medicine can differ remarkably, depending on from which end of the stethoscope you try to observe them'.[22] At the heart of many crises in medico-journalist relations are medical disagreements, with the messenger as scapegoat. In this sense, medical crises are produced not by the media but by doctors' own differences.

The reporting of whooping-cough vaccine in the 1970s was an example. The medical profession angrily blamed the media for the dramatic fall in vaccine take-up after extensive publicity had been given to vaccine-damaged children; only three out of every ten children born in 1976 had been immunised two years later. But the media had picked up a study from a medical journal, describing 36 cases of children admitted to London's Hospital for Sick Children with severe neurological illnesses, 33 of them reportedly having received pertussis (whooping-cough) vaccine during the seven days before onset of the symptoms. So, though the medical profession has consistently rebuffed medical critics of the official policy of vaccination, believing it to be an essential public health measure, and though the critics of vaccination are a minority, the issue of vaccine safety did represent a genuine medical disagreement.

By reporting disagreement among doctors, journalists puncture the consensual membrane in which medicine and science has for so long been encased; when they (occasionally) depict medicine as a human and social practice beset by competing beliefs, rival theories, and acrimonious disputes (with a smattering of mistakes and uncertainties), they stray from its image as an unimpeachably rational, certain and objective science. The almost inevitable complaints of 'inaccuracy' are an attempt to restore certainty and unanimity.

Crises mostly occur when programme-makers break with official medical definitions. The outstanding 1981 ITV documentary 'Silent Hospital' about long-stay mental handicap hospitals, for example, rejected both the medical approach to mental handicap (handicap is 'natural', medicine serves the afflicted as best it can), and the consumer approach (shock-horror: wicked staff maltreat vulnerable patients) and instead adopted an environmental approach, suggesting that the patients' often difficult behaviour resulted less from their condition than their conditions. Instead of indicting the demoralised staff, it made it clear that nurses had to collude with the system in order to be able to work in such appalling, but socially-sanctioned, conditions. The film generated a major row, the Government accusing it of being unrepresentative and undermining efforts to improve the lives of mentally handicapped people, and the area health authority denying its allegations about the use of seclusion rooms. The Secretary of State for Social Services ordered an investigation and the row, a direct result of the film's departure from the medical approach, rumbled on for over five months.

Crises also occur when there's a shift in the representation of an issue: the 'Your Life in Their Hands' row was part of the change from the look-after-yourself approach to the medical approach, and the outcry following 'Horizon's 1975 anti-induction film 'A Time To Be Born' signalled the move to the consumer approach.

Medical anger is powerful, and it's often been directed at the media. The risk of medical uproar hovers over every critical programme: according to the BBC's former Head of Science and Features, 'Doctors are without doubt the most sensitive to criticism of any profession with which a television producer has to deal.'[23] But the real significance of crises in medical broadcasting lies less in the immediate outcry they engender than in their longer-term aftermath. They're almost invariably followed by medical demands for greater control over the media. That was the cry in 1958, and in March 1978 after yet another spat the *British Medical Journal* (*BMJ*) again suggested: 'Much more use needs to be made of medical advisers, whose brief should be extended to cover all medical television programmes. There is also a good case for establishing a small committee to monitor all programmes.' The call was even louder in October 1985, the *BMJ* suggesting 'We need a new framework where doctors can set the agenda.' These demands for control arise in part because doctors (astonishingly, in view of the kind of medical influence over broadcasting outlined in previous chapters) believe that their opinions and beliefs are routinely overruled or criticised by the media. Perhaps this is because the medical profession, used to being the dominant party in the doctor–patient relationship, feels that in their contact with the media the power balance is the other way round.

Certainly some medical grievances against the media are valid, though almost every single social group could (and does) complain about their misrepresentation, but the medical profession is rare in having the power to translate their complaints into a crisis. In this sense, crises function as a form of social control, representing attempts by complainants (generally the Government, industry, and the medical profession) to bring broadcasters into line. Crises are a way of policing broadcasters, reminding them of their precarious legitimacy and dependence on medical and political approval. And they seem to work, as evidenced by the consequences of a row, rivalling the 'Your Life In Their Hands' crisis, which erupted in 1980 after the broadcast of a BBC film. As a result of the programme, hospital facilities were withdrawn from BBC journalists making films on psycho-surgery and psychiatry, and only granted to other film-makers on evidence and promises of good behaviour. The medical outcry greeting the programme also scared off some producers contemplating critical medical programmes, and made journalists wary of crossing doctors for years afterwards. The film causing the uproar was the 'Panorama' programme on brain-death.

Your death in their hands

In October 1980, the *Radio Times* carried a frightening article called 'Dead or alive?' trailing the next edition of the BBC Current Affairs programme 'Panorama'. It gave three instances of people apparently dead and therefore potential organ donors but who actually survived. Alarm about the programme spread among doctors, and several sent telegrams to the BBC's Director-General who, on the morning of transmission, agreed to meet a deputation representing the Royal Colleges, the BMA, and the DHSS. The deputation asked for ten minutes of open discussion at the end of the programme, but this was refused (a refusal the BBC must have later come to regret). They were, however, granted a preview of the programme a few hours before transmission, after the Press had seen it. But the programme was duly transmitted, producing a medical uproar that raged for months and resonated for years.

The programme challenged the British Code of Practice's definition of 'brain death' by showing American patients diagnosed as 'brain dead' who narrowly escaped being used as organ donors and subsequently recovered. Under the British rules too, the programme implied, they would have been pronounced dead. The *BMJ* responded with a furious editorial, arguing that the patients featured wouldn't have satisfied or, they insisted, even come near to satisfying British criteria for certifying brain-death. A succession of stinging letters, reminiscent of those following the first 'Your Life in Their Hands' in 1958, filled the correspondence columns of the national newspapers and the *BMJ*. The programme-makers were accused of 'ghoulish titillation',[24] 'a wicked act',[25] using a 'devious tactic',[26] and making a 'biased and sensational investigation [which was] ... a disgrace'.[27] One doctor claimed that the issues were 'complicated and therefore unsuitable for treatment by peak-viewing television programmes devoted to entertainment and sensationalism'.[28] Another suggested it might be 'a calculated attempt to alarm the British public',[29] and many (including the Secretary of State for Social Services) worried that it would badly affect the transplant programme, deterring potential organ donors and their relatives because of the spectre of the removal of organs from the living. Reports of donor cards being torn up were common.

Meanwhile, a delegation of doctors representing the Royal Colleges, the BMA, and the Royal Society of Medicine met with the BBC Director-General to discuss new guidelines for medical television programmes. The following day the Director-General, 'because of the public interest in the issue', conceded a follow-up programme.

But the crisis wasn't over. Medical representatives, negotiating with the 'Panorama' team over the form of the second programme, insisted that up to half of it be devoted to their own explanations of the British Code of Practice. The 'Panorama' staff, on the other hand, were determined that, before the live discussion, *they* should explain the code, arguing that it was unacceptable for a Current Affairs programme to allow another professional body to assume editorial control over a large part of a live broadcast. As a compromise, the BBC offered the doctors five minutes to comment on Panorama's exposition of the code, but the doctors said it wasn't enough.

After two meetings and an exchange of letters without agreement, the medical representatives withdrew cooperation and advised doctors not to take part in the second programme since no lay person or TV reporter was qualified, they claimed, to explain the code. The BBC countered that the doctors' conditions

> would be unacceptable to any journalistic activity which lays
> great store by its editorial independence. There are no circum-
> stances in which the BBC believes that it would be proper to
> abrogate its full editorial responsibility for the content of
> 'Panorama'. We would be criticised if we did so and would lose
> the independence which the BBC has cherished over the years.[30]

The argument was in many respects a replay of the rows over medical broadcasting which had raged in the 1930s and 1940s between the BBC and the Ministry of Health. On one side the demand for the right of medical control (and the right of reply); on the other, the assertion of editorial independence.

The doctors won. In February 1981, the BBC transmitted a programme, chaired by television elder statesman Ludovic Kennedy, in which two groups of doctors, one supporting the

British code, the other critical of it, presented their own 20-minute films (without reporter), followed by a discussion chaired by Kennedy.[31] The crisis was apparently resolved, but not (as doctors had hoped) the issue: the object of the medical establishment's wrath shifted from the BBC to other doctors. (And this, some argued, was where it had belonged in the first place.)

So what had induced such a rabid row? Certainly, the doctors were genuinely alarmed at the programme's potential – and, it turned out, actual – effect on transplants. The following year was considered a 'disastrous' one for transplants. Said one surgeon, of requests to use organs for transplantation,

> In Cambridge we have had eight out of ten refusals since the programme appeared. Before the programme, it was virtually unknown for people to refuse permission. There's been a complete change of attitude by the public. It has caused, quite directly, in the region of about 100 deaths of patients.[32]

Yet the effects were short-lived. More kidney transplants were carried out in 1982 than in any previous year. The row had also resulted from many doctors' profound anger over inaccuracies and misrepresentations by some of their medical colleagues. One doctor who claimed in the follow-up programme that two people certified dead by the British criteria later recovered fully, subsequently withdrew his allegation. But, argued the defenders of the British Code, the programme had left the 'take-home' message that the living were being certified dead.

The brain-death crisis was another example of a medical disagreement, where the broadcasters were attacked for giving space to a minority medical view. Indeed, the origin of the first 'Panorama' lay in a debate in the columns of the *Lancet*, which struck the producer as potential material for a programme. As the BBC's Head of Television Current Affairs Programmes put it,

> 'Panorama' did not conjure the doubts about the definition of brain death out of thin air. . . . In the programme itself it was not a 'pipsqueak' reporter who voiced criticisms of the way we define brain death in this country, but eminent doctors from Britain and abroad. What 'Panorama' did was to bring the doubts into the open.[33]

Indeed, this may have been its most heinous crime. It removed medical conflicts from the sedate columns of the medical journals into the full glare of television. How often was a doctor seen on television accusing another of 'the height of irresponsibility'?[34]

Perhaps the medical profession was also irate that broadcasters represented brain-death as a controversial issue when, at least to the medical establishment, it wasn't one. Who had the right to define an issue as controversial? The power to determine the scope of an issue has been, as noted above, an integral part of official medical and state influence over broadcasters, and challenges are angrily contested. What's more, just as the row over the programme was hotting up, Ian Kennedy's polemical Reith Lectures on medicine were broadcast. In the BBC's most prestigious series of radio talks, Kennedy scrutinised the doctor–patient relationship and found the doctors wanting. It was a powerful boost to the consumer critique and, with the coincidence of the 'Panorama' programme and the Lectures, the medical profession must have started to wonder where it all would end. Not content with faulting their bedside manner, in 'Panorama' the doctor-bashers now seemed to be depicting them as body-snatchers – shades of Burke and Hare, and precisely the kind of callous, profiteering image they'd spent generations trying to dispel. The broadcasters were also alarming the public with the thought that death was no longer an unequivocal, biological state, but a medical decision as debatable as any other. And at stake was the transplant programme, high-tech medicine embodying some of medicine's greatest hopes and apparent achievements. In a sense, the dispute about 'Panorama' represented a medical backlash. After several years of consumer programming, the professionals were fighting back.

What the 'Panorama' crisis illustrated above all is how effectively they could do so. The very existence of the second programme attested medical power: by contrast in 1981, the combined might of 74 MPs, 23 trades union General-Secretaries, and a large group of academics, couldn't persuade either the BBC or the IBA to mount a series of programmes on TV bias. And however valid doctors' criticisms of the first 'Panorama' programme might have been, they were surely no more legitimate than the grievances of strikers, who have persistently complained about their misrepresentation by the media but have never managed to secure redress. In the second 'Panorama', moreover, the doctors were allowed to address the audience direct, without a reporter to mediate their case. This was the very pinnacle of media power, a privilege granted only to the incontestably authoritative – weather forecasters, newscasters, prime ministers, royalty, and in this case, doctors.

As Current Affairs programme-makers, relatively less dependent on the medical profession than their Science Features colleagues, the 'Panorama' team brought to their first film on brain-death an ideology different from that of science journalists. One can only speculate what would have happened if 'Horizon' had chanced across the subject of brain-death in 1980: how far would they have pursued it if discouraged by well-placed medical contacts? To most of the medical profession, however, the brain-death row merely confirmed that the BBC was continuing on its wayward path of doctor-bashing, diverging from sound medical sense and custom. Imminent changes in the reporting of alternative medicine were to show just how far the media could stray from medical orthodoxy.

A whole new way

Josef Issels ran a cancer clinic on holistic principles in Germany in the 1950s. It involved special diets excluding adulterated and harmful foods, and psychological work with the patient, and he claimed a 16 per cent 'cure' rate. The Bavarian Medical Association was implacably hostile, regarding him as a 'fraud therapist'. In 1960 he was arrested and charged with manslaughter (by preventing two of his patients from having surgery) and of fraud (by taking money from terminal cases). He was cleared of all charges and resumed his work.

In 1969 a BBC producer made a 50-minute documentary about him. But the producer's boss voiced doubts and reservations: Issels was still an object of suspicion, and on no account was the BBC to elevate him in public esteem, thereby spreading alarm and despondency among patients receiving orthodox treatment. There was also the question of the Cancer Act, which said that no claim to a cure for cancer could be made in the media. The producer was asked to destroy the negative and all the prints of his film. He didn't. Eventually in November 1970, after nearly a year of anguished heart-searching, a much shorter documentary than originally planned followed by a discussion programme were transmitted on BBC 1. Despite Issel's acquittal, the tone of the documentary was unmistakably hostile. The programme led to an inquiry into Issel's methods which received wide publicity and, according to tele-doctor Charles Fletcher, discouraged people from using alternative medicine.

In 1983, BBC TV broadcast (at peak time) a decidedly unhostile six-part series on the Bristol Cancer Help Centre, a holistic cancer advisory centre sharing many of Issels' views and practices, and working with people with cancer on meditation, breathing, relaxation, and diet.[35] In roughly a decade a major change had taken place, enabling alternative medicine to move from beyond the fringe: holistic treatment, once ostracised, was now being lionised. Yesterday's heresy had become today's unexceptionable philosophy. Even 'Horizon', BBC bastion of scientific orthodoxy, was touched by the change, and actually stimulated it with a positive report on holistic health in the United States.[36] And the favourable attitude percolated through to the news and the newspapers, so that when in 1986 the BMA issued a report damning alternative therapies, almost every bulletin and article covering it carried qualifying comments, from the BBC Science Correspondent's coda ('It's a BMA report, therefore to some it was bound to be biased'[37]) to the *Star*'s rather less inhibited verdict ('What a load of pompous poppycock').

What had brought about such a major change? One factor was royal endorsement of alternative medicine in general (the Royal Family are known users of homeopathy) and the Bristol Cancer Centre in particular (graced by a visit from Prince Charles): you could hardly hope for a greater helping of legitimacy. But even more influential was the changed social climate. As one programme-maker put it, 'alternative medicine is . . . riding high on the bad publicity given to orthodox drugs and surgery'.[38] The new enthusiasm for alternative therapies was part of a reappraisal in the wake of the consumer approach. Programmes, and alternative practitioners, stressed that the writing was on the wall for various orthodox treatments with their noxious side effects, while the alternatives used remedies derived from plants – nothing iatrogenic there – and holistic healers listened to patients and gave them time to talk.

There had also been something of a medical incorporation of alternative medicine. With the setting up of respectable medical groups like the British Holistic Medical Association, unorthodox therapies became almost another medical speciality, to be practised alongside the orthodox ones. By the 1980s, Issels himself had become a highly respected figure in Germany, and a valued contributor to the Government's anti-cancer programme. In its emphasis on the individual's responsibility and active participation in their own healing, alternative medicine also appeared to chime with the look-after-yourself approach: it was now uncontentious to suggest that patients should no longer be passive objects of medical intervention, but actively participate in healing themselves. And the burgeoning interest in alternative medicine expressed increasing scepticism about science and technology in general: alternative practitioners' perception of nature as a safe, gentle healer was wholly in keeping with the new green view.

But, though the shift between 1970 and 1983 was a substantial one, it's easily overstated. To some within the BBC the subject was still high risk. According to the executive producer of the Bristol Cancer Centre series, 'to long memories at the BBC it looked as if the Centre owed its existence and its philosophy to the "money-grabbing fraud therapist" '. The producers were rigorously cross-examined by the BBC hierarchy about their facts and motives.

> Six . . . documentary programmes devoted to a fringe treatment
> as yet unaccepted by the medical establishment, thereby
> investing it with an unjustifiable cachet, must under no circum-
> stances undermine the faith of cancer sufferers in orthodox
> treatment, and it must be stressed that what Bristol does in no
> sense constitutes a cure for cancer. Hovering over everything was
> the ghost of Josef Issels.[39]

BBC Publications declined to publish an accompanying book because the subject was 'too much on the fringe'.[40] And changes were insisted upon. As sharp-eyed *Radio Times* readers noticed, there was the significant addition of a question-mark to the original programme title so that it now read 'A Gentle Way with Cancer?'. A discussion programme was slotted into the schedules at the eleventh hour as a forum for the voice of orthodoxy. Scripts were torn up and rewritten. And as the producer explained:

> In each episode, the same points *must* be made: 'Bristol offers no cure' . . . 'there is no clinical proof that the Bristol philosophy works'. . . . 'Bristol is not a substitute for orthodox medicine, but a supplement and a complement.'[41]

The 'false hopes' argument weighed heavily on producers' minds when tackling holistic therapies. Yet, as Chapter 9 showed, the reporting of orthodox medicine (to the despair of the medical profession) also generates its fair share of 'false hopes', but broadcasters are rarely as edgy about the excessive expectations generated by miracle cure reporting (of, say, transplants) as by those which might be aroused by sympathetic coverage of alternative medicine.[42]

The reason is the special social status of science and the medical approach. So much so that almost invariably journalists covering alternatives turn to orthodox doctors to validate them. The entire first of two BBC TV programmes on the link between the emotions and cancer was devoted to scientific corroboration,[43] while a radio series on herbs noted typically that 'It is interesting that the ancient Chinese ideas about ginseng should be echoed in modern scientific findings.'[44] Producers' attempts to try to validate alternative medicine by appealing to the very belief-system it challenges are patently absurd: scientific proof is reached by double-blind trials, which aim at objectivity by eliminating factors such as the patient's beliefs, state of mind, and relationship with the doctor – precisely those at the heart of alternative treatments. And yet broadcasters have no way of legitimating alternative treatments *other* than by endorsement from the medical profession. In this sense, by using orthodox medicine as arbiter of holistic treatment's worth, media coverage of alternative medicine *reinforces* medical authority and power even while questioning it.

The new attitude to alternative medicine adopted by medical sympathisers, stressing its 'complementarity' with orthodox treatment, was reproduced by most TV and radio programmes, keen to minimise the areas of incompatibility. At its softest edge, alternative medicine could be depicted as offering psychological support, a benign help-mate or nurse aiding a patient's recovery while the doctors were out there doing the real hard curing. To a great extent, more favourable media attitudes to alternative medicine and the emotional components of healing merely mirrored the medical profession's own increased interest in the whole patient, body and mind, described in Chapter 3.

Holistic treatment was also unthreatening because it was reported in anything but a holistic way. The 'whole' patient was rarely depicted as extending beyond the patient's body, or immediate relationships. The environment and the social world were almost entirely absent. Indeed, media portrayals of alternative medicine 'psychologised' illness very much in the style of the look-after-yourself approach. Stressful 'life-events' were indicted as a major cause of illness, yet the fact that they didn't occur randomly in the population and their relation to social factors such as class, race and gender were rarely acknowledged. Programmes and practitioners emphasised that women who suppressed their anger increased their chances of cancer, without granting that women were socialised not to be angry or show it. To an extent, this wasn't the media's fault, since many alternative practitioners themselves took an equally limited view. But it meant that alternative medicine could join orthodox medicine on our TV screens without stoking the ire of the medical profession or politicians, and without provoking a crisis.

11

Curing by Caring:

The Doctor in Medical Drama

Medical dramas are what most critics hate to love. Tales of dashing young interns magicking away rare diseases while their impeccably white gowns stay pristine, of life-saving and problem-solving without doubt or demur, are readily derided for their soapy soft-centres. Television companies and audiences, undeterred, love them. So do I.

Doctors for all

It's hard to avoid the fictional doctor on television. An American study of prime-time (8 to 11 p.m.) network drama in the United States found health professionals outnumbering all other kinds, almost five times more of them than their real-life proportions.[1] And in 1977, 42 per cent of the characters in American daytime soap operas had health problems.[2] TV writers, producers, and networks are clearly addicted to fictional medicine: an actor suggested it was because medical shows offered 'blood without violence'. They certainly afford unrivalled opportunities for life-and-death drama and cliff-hangers ('Tony is on that operating-table right now fighting for his life. The least you can do is fight for the baby that both of you have created'), and though the hospital or health centre setting may be incidental – many medical dramas are simply soap operas about relationships – it allows a high turnover of characters, providing a place where different types of people can credibly meet.

But television companies have always been quite frank about medical shows' chief virtue. As the producer of 'Emergency

Ward 10', Britain's first medical soap which began on ITV in 1957, explained, 'TV at that time needed programmes with popular appeal, which would command and build a loyal audience, which would enable advertisers to know that at certain times of the day and week, there would be an audience. That was the prime need.'[3] And the medical drama is an almost certain audience-winner. 'Dr Finlay's Casebook' averaged 10 million, and 'Marcus Welby, MD' dominated the American ratings, one of the most popular American shows for years. The doctor shows easily leapfrog medical documentaries in the top ten, pulling in an audience sometimes more than five times larger. A cheap medical soap, like ABC's daily, daytime 'General Hospital', will earn back for its network in advertisements ten times what it cost to produce. And sometimes it doesn't even have to gain a huge audience to do so. MTM's 'St Elsewhere' had such low ratings that NBC decided not to renew it, until they realised that the show had very good 'comp' (audience composition): the audience may have been small but, aged between 18 and 49, from a high social class and with sizeable incomes, they constituted TV's prime advertising audience, with a better composition than series with significantly higher ratings. The show was reprieved.

The doctor as paragon

Television's saintly portrayal of the doctor owes much to the cinema.[4] In Britain in the 1930s, the state censor took care that the medical profession wasn't brought into disrepute: between 1934 and 1937, the British Board of Film Censors (to whom scripts had to be submitted for vetting in advance of production) banned nine proposals for films because they threatened the image of the medical profession. Shaw's *The Doctor's Dilemma* was among them. And a 1934 film about an agonising visit to the dentist was banned for a time for 'ridiculing the profession'.[5]

But such controls were largely unnecessary, for film-makers had discovered the value of the doctor as hero. Films like John Ford's major 1931 production *Arrowsmith* (based on Sinclair Lewis' novel) showed doctor–scientists risking their lives so that others could live. Idealistic young Martin Arrowsmith didn't want 'to just give pills to people, I want to find a cure for cancer'. He didn't succeed, but – next best – cured the plague in the West Indies. Other typical screen doctors were the abrasive, but caring country GP played by Robert Mitchum ('He wants to be a doctor – everything else is nothing next to that') in Stanley Kramer's 1955 film, *Not as a Stranger*, and Alec Harvey in Noel Coward's 1942 classic, *Brief Encounter*, a progressive advocate of preventive medicine who confided to the rapt Laura 'Perhaps . . . I'm a bit of an idealist . . . All good doctors . . . must have . . . a sense of vocation, a deep-rooted, unsentimental desire to do good.' Like Arrowsmith he ended – in that recurring emblem of altruism – by going to doctor in Africa.

Even screen psychiatrists were changing from – in the 1920s, 1930s, and early 1940s – baddies or fools with thick Viennese or 'Tcherman' accents, to goodies like Dr Jacquith (Claude Rains) in the 1942 *Now Voyager*, who transformed Betty Davis' maiden aunt Charlotte Vale (all heavy eyebrows, thick stockings, and sensible shoes) into a 'pale and interesting' sexual creature in stilettos and a picture hat. And even in Anatole Litvak's powerful 1948 drama of mental illness, *The Snake Pit*, so critical of mental asylums that British mental hospital nurses wrote to the British Board of Film Censors trying to get it banned (the Board cut several scenes instead), the main doctor was kindly and humane.

Why did the post-war cinema increasingly depict the doctor as paragon and medicine as panacea? Was it, as some have suggested, part of post-war liberal optimism, in which evil was nothing more than a disease, and thorny political issues recast in the smooth, value-free terms of science? Perhaps, but that was only part of it. Medical services in Britain and the United States were rapidly expanding in the 1940s and 1950s, yet in Britain at least there was a deep and longstanding lay suspicion of state medical care. While the birth of the NHS was welcomed in principle, in practice many feared bureaucratisation, and the loss of a personal relationship with their doctor. Films like the moving 1952 British-made *Mandy* can be read as a persuasive testimony that the state could care. In the tale of a deaf-mute 7-year-old, whose father was determined to keep her at home while her mother wanted to send her to a special school, the fear of state welfare was raised and dispelled. Father saw the school as a threat to paternal authority and a potential threat to the family unit. Mother was persuaded of its value, but once there Mandy couldn't settle in at night in the dormitory, with its looming workhouse shadows so different from her cosy home bedroom. Finally, with excellent results, she became a day pupil: the state, however benign the medical care it offered, couldn't replace the family altogether – the two must work together.

When television medical dramas started up in earnest soon after, this role of assuager of lay fears about state medical care was paramount. As the producer of 'Emergency Ward 10' put it, 'We wanted to overcome the pre-war attitude of the British public of hospitals as institutions, places to be avoided at all costs. We wanted people to respond to new research in medicine.'[6] Indeed 'Emergency Ward 10' (1957–67), which now appears as soapy as possible, was described at the time as 'documentary-drama' and was praised both by the Independent Television Authority and the British Medical Association for helping 'to relieve many members of the public of anxiety and fear about hospital treatment'.[7] The series used and was given ideas from the Ministry of Health: 'the programme was doing for them free the kind of job nowadays you'd have to employ Saatchi and Saatchi to do'.[8]

'Emergency Ward 10's soothing intentions today seem very blatant ('Alright Miss Palmer, you're going to be alright'), but it also displayed a number of other features which were to become standard in the medical soap: it was clogged with medical jargon ('Give him 15 ccs of hydrochloric acid in the contrapuntal muscle, nurse'), life-and-death crises and rare infectious diseases. There was a marked absence of porters, ancillaries, black nurses, and women doctors, while the doctors were boisterous young philanderers but with an unquestionable sense of vocation.

Their attempt to show doctors as benign, trusty curers was shared, quite explicitly, by the authors of other medical dramas. Richard Gordon, a doctor whose books formed the basis of seven British 'Doctor' film comedies between 1954 and 1970, described himself as medicine's chief public relations man.[9]

Certainly, TV's fictional doctors are decidedly different from their real-life counterparts. A doctor might be a cardiovascular surgeon (and many are – 'General Hospital' alone boasts two heart specialists), but the next week, with impressive versatility, he performs brain surgery.[10] A TV NHS psychiatrist gives extended one-to-one psychotherapy sessions, unperturbed by the fact that real NHS psychiatric treatment is almost entirely chemical, based on anti-depressants and drugs, with practically no individual therapy at all.[11]

Nine out of ten American television doctors are male, white, and young or middle-aged. Compared with other professions, they're relatively good, successful and peaceful. Less than 4 per cent of them are evil, half the number found in other professions on TV.[12] Only 20 per cent of them are general practitioners, while 23 per cent are neurologists.[13] They're also highly effective. In 'Marcus Welby, MD', incorrect diagnoses are made in only 12 per cent of cases, even though more than half the diseases are rare, and 20 per cent of the treatments experimental. In 'Dr Kildare', only baddie doctors make major blunders or significantly misdiagnose the patient. The young intern himself and most of the other physicians display consummate skill ('Tonight you were given the best medical care available to anyone, anywhere') and operate in the best interests of the patient.

Operate, literally, since surgery dominates the medical shows. Operations occurred in more than one-third of 'Marcus Welby' episodes, and in two-thirds of cases were dangerous, though only one death on the operating-table occurred in fifty episodes. In 'Dr Kildare', failed operations caused crises (suggesting that operations are normally successful), leading to punishment or increased self-knowledge on the doctor's part, so that victim didn't die in vain. Surgery, of course, occasions that icon of the medical drama, the operating-theatre scene: with its close-ups of masked, gowned and concerned doctors (the eyes have it); its cutaways to respirator and cardiograph showing the jagged tracing of the heartbeat flattening alarmingly; and the mounting drama of the doctor's clipped instructions as bleeps of danger accelerate and tragedy portends. It's the perfect metaphor for the medical approach: high-tech medical skills save lives while the patient, insensate, is acted upon. And how could the fictional doctors fail, with names so brimming with symbolism as Ben Casey, Kildare, Welby?

The organisation of medical care in TV dramas also has its conventions. Hospitals are rarely run by administrators, but by a single, powerful doctor who isn't status-conscious, authoritarian, self-interested, or inaccessible (all criticisms which have been levelled at medical top brass), but who shows flair and care. Meanwhile our doctor-hero works at the most languid pace, seeing one or at most two patients per episode, and sometimes keeping a 24-hour bedside vigil. In only 14 per cent of 'Marcus Welby' episodes were there signs that the doctor had other patients to see, and his visits were never interrupted by phone-calls not relevant to the matter in hand.[14] What's more, Welby never argued with his partner about money, the commonest problem in American medical partnerships.[15]

Patients are similarly extraordinary. One minute they're hale, the next they're doubling up, clutching their abdomen. Sudden acute attacks occurred in over half of 'Marcus Welby' episodes, generally when the physician happened to be in the patient's home because he was just dropping by. Only 8 per cent of patients in the show were working-class, and only 2 per cent over sixty years old. Ninety-four per cent were white.[16] In daytime soap operas (as opposed to evening doctor shows), patients' illnesses and cause of death are equally unusual: in 1977, there were only two cases of cancer (the second-ranking cause of death in the United States) on soap operas, neither of them fatal.[17] The reason, some say, is that soap characters aren't meant to die of diseases which the audience might be dying of.[18] Instead, they die by being hit by a truck, being pushed down a flight of stairs, being shot at, or tumbling out of aeroplanes. Homicide is the soap opera's number one killer, while heart disease comprises two-fifths of soap illnesses, though it's seen primarily as a male disease.[19] Women in soap operas, on the other hand, often attempt suicide and, though their pregnancy rate is eight times as high as that in the United States and exceeds that in the Third World, they also show an alarming tendency to miscarry. Miscarriages are a way of punishing soap opera women.[20]

Doctor in the mind

In this account, medical shows are simply escapist hokum, and their image of medicine-as-infallible appears to personify the medical approach. Yet this is to neglect a crucial dimension. One study found that, in almost half of American prime-time networked medical dramas, the doctor pursued a central problem into the personal life of the patient. And though the doctor solved the patient's medical problem in only under half the stories, in 100 per cent of the cases he resolved their personal crises.[21] In every 'Marcus Welby' episode, there was a psychological or family conflict, and in 74 per cent of the shows, the doctor became involved in the patient's personal life.[22] Like soap opera in general but in contrast to other TV genres like police[23] or adventure series, the focus of the doctor shows is the psychological. Like soap opera, the medical drama '*colonises* the public masculine sphere, representing it from the point of view of the personal'.[24]

Drs Kildare and Welby are psychological brokers, mediating the patient's emotions to their family and vice versa. They intercede in the patient's internal drama; like psychoanalysts, they tease out the emotional conflicts within. 'Give him a chance to face the man he was', counsels Kildare to the wife of an ailing, belligerent film-star. 'I'm telling you what you should do for your son', Welby advises the irreligious father of a sick boy who wants a barmitzvah. More like homeopaths or acupuncturists than surgeons or neurologists, they (in Marcus Welby's words) 'don't treat fingers or skin or bones or skulls or lungs, we treat people, entire human people'.[25]

Welby is always on the side of the patient, and sees things from the patient's point of view, trying to explain the meaning of their illness. These doctors aren't the doctors we know; they're the ones we want. Medical dramas' seeming lack of realism articulates needs unmet and covert longings. As one commentator has suggested, if popular culture appears escapist it's because it 'offers the image of "something better" to escape into, or something we want deeply that our day-to-day lives don't provide'.[26] David Victor, creator of 'Marcus Welby' and producer of 'Dr Kildare' put it crisply: 'Why not show what a good doctor *should* be?'[27]

Indeed, the TV medical encounter of the 1960s and 1970s was, strikingly, almost the exact reverse of most real-life encounters. The TV doctor's strongest suit is his communication skills while, as sheafs of sociological literature make plain, the real-life doctor is rarely so endowed. In one study of doctor–patient relations, though few patients seriously questioned their doctor's technical competence, more than half claimed he wasn't friendly, attentive to their feelings, or more than strictly businesslike.[28] Another study suggested patients feel that doctors are often unaware of their point of view.[29] On the other hand fictional physicians conform almost to the letter to an influential description of the good doctor, which suggested that the human skills a doctor possessed were paramount since many patients required not medical treatment but 'a dose of the doctor'.[30] In Drs Kildare and Welby, they get a year's supply.

But if medical dramas are idealisations which reverse real doctor–patient relations, they differ significantly from idealised medical documentaries such as 'Your Life in Their Hands', complementing them. In the standard medical documentary, the doctor is a scientific wizard with formidable technical skills, but the drama shows him with a superlative aptitude for handling emotions and reinstates the feelings surrounding illness (causing it, accompanying it, and resulting from it). The drama expresses the dimensions of doctoring missing from the documentary and the doctor as emphatic human being – and can be read as a commentary on, and a critique of, both the medical documentary and medicine as generally practised. On both American and British television, medical dramas first appeared at the same time as medical documentaries.

Medical dramas often came close to explicitly criticising the medical approach. Dr Kildare challenged a famous surgeon, 'In my opinion, Dr Becker, the patient's death was precipitated by the surgery', the intern clearly seeing the eminent physician as technically brilliant but emotionally stunted.[31] In another episode, Kildare warned a patient that 'I can't tell you that all you need is an hour under the surgeon's knife.' Before the spread of the consumer approach, the medical drama (along with the medical comedy and science fiction film) was the only media channel through which dissatisfaction with medicine found expression, albeit obliquely.

In another respect too, the medical drama embodied lay hopes and wishes. Many have pointed out that though house-calls were virtually obsolete in the United States and obsolescent in Britain, the television doctor was making home-visits with undiminished enthusiasm – for example in 82 per cent of 'Marcus Welby' shows.[32] But it was precisely *because* house-calls were becoming extinct that the fictional doctor so heartily maintained them. So with time: the more rushed real-life doctors became, the more leisurely the pace of their fictional counterparts. And the same went for money: as American medicine became increasingly profit-orientated, with tales of impecunious patients being turned away from casualty, American medical dramas depicted a medical practice where fees were almost never discussed, and patients never rejected because of their inability to pay. Messrs. Kildare, Casey, and Welby worked unstintingly in public hospitals or general practice, giving no thought to establishing a more lucrative private practice. In the 1970s American medicine was going corporate, increasingly part of the medical–industrial complex, but the doctor shows preserved the old-style gemütlich family doctor: avuncular Marcus Welby, in cardigan and with gladstone bag, reminded a patient and his wife, 'I've known both of you all your lives.' British TV in the 1960s also cast back to a time before medicine was high-tech and high science, depicting the doctor as socially familiar and personally concerned: 'Dr Finlay's Casebook' was set in a small Scottish town in the 1920s.

Patients, far from being confused between fictional doctors and real ones, seemed to be keenly appreciative of the differences and clear which they preferred. Actor Raymond Massey, who for years played Dr Gillespie in 'Dr Kildare', recalled a New York hotel doorman telling him

> I had a stretch in a hospital up in the Bronx last year. . . . It wasn't Blair General [the hospital in the TV series] but I saw you and Dr Kildare on TV twice while I was there. It was kinda nice to know you were both around.[33]

The medical profession is also highly sensitive to the difference between fiction and reality, which perhaps explains their ambivalent attitude to medical soaps. On the one hand, they work closely with the mass media. The American Medical Association (AMA) has its own Physicians Advisory Committee on Television, Radio and Motion Pictures (PAC), a panel of medical specialists formed in 1955 to give free advice to writers, producers, and networks and to scrutinise scripts. The AMA gave 'Marcus Welby, MD' its special achievement award in 1970, and in 1971 the actor playing Welby addressed the American Academy of Family Physicians convention, and was hailed as hero of the meeting: the GPs were thrilled that, after all the TV shows celebrating the hospital doctor, surgeon, and specialist, the lowly family practitioner was finally being fêted.

On the other hand, a doctor at a medical convention cited the Welby show as a factor contributing to the rise in malpractice suits against doctors. 'People see "Marcus Welby" and the other shows and then expect miracles of us', he said.[34] Others blamed Welby for inciting patients into demanding house-calls of their doctors, and David Victor has been accused of creating 'unrealistic' expectations on the part of patients,[35] an implicit acknowledgment that the doctor shows impugn the real-life medical encounter.

The father of medicine

Another recurring, and ridiculed, feature of medical dramas is the duet of doctors – the older mentor and the Young Turk who clash but together right the world's wrongs. In 'Dr Kildare' there was Jim Kildare, all burning idealism and fierce convictions until, tamed by the homilies of paternal Dr Gillespie, he learnt humility and respect for his elders. Then there was Ben Casey, a brooding, uncompromising loner who believed that 'this is a one-man business', and was gently checked by the sage Dr Zorba. In 'Dr Finlay's Casebook', Dr Cameron was the irascible but trusted GP, modifying Dr Finlay's zeal and energy. 'Marcus Welby, MD' reversed the formation: brash Steve Kiley was secondary to the star, experienced Marcus Welby. Often the neophyte doctor was a hearthrob, and the older male doctor explicitly a father figure.

But where were the women? They weren't, in the 1960s and 1970s, the doctors. Nor, it seems, the patients: 'Marcus Welby' had twice as many male as female patients.[36] Nor even wives or lovers. Welby was widowed, and young Kiley lived with him: neither had regular female companions. Gillespie had no visible wife, and Kildare only occasionally dated an attractive young nurse. The only major female roles in the medical soaps of the 1960s and 1970s were Consuelo, Welby's nurse who mothered the doctors and their patients, and Janet with the lilting voice in 'Dr Finlay's Casebook', a canny female mediator.

But if women were largely absent from TV medical dramas, they were there in abundance in the audience. The missing women were on the other side of the screen, and medical series were informed by the female gaze. Not only, as I suggested above, did the medical shows deal with personal relationships, but TV doctors also seemed to spend most of their time trying to make their (mainly) male patients more like women. Again and again the doctor attempted to persuade the patient to abandon his macho behaviour, to confront his underlying fears and weaknesses. Dr Kildare was forever telling a brawling, boozing film-star that if he continued to drink, fight, and flee his real problems he'd die, or cajoling the bragging son of a dying father to admit his painful feelings of love and hurt. The other doctors were equally energetic in attempting to prise open the human, specifically male, heart.

Moreover, by siting themselves in the domain traditionally considered female, medical dramas take on broader definitions of health and illness than those offered by the medical approach. Illness in medical dramas usually entails what psychiatrists call psycho-social transitions, in which 'old patterns of thought and activity must be given up and fresh ones developed'.[37] The doctor shows dramatise the resistance to and grief involved in changing our 'assumptive world', the constellation of feelings, beliefs, experiences, and plans. The patients are invariably at a crisis point in their lives. They can't face their life, or the old tactics are inappropriate. Most have communication problems. They withdraw and the doctor tries to persuade them to open up. Illness may induce dramatic reversals: strong people are felled, the weak find their power. And TV patients often can't accept that they're ill: the doctor has to help them confront illness, adjust their lives, come to terms with separation and death. TV patients end by being changed by their illness, beginning to let go of old hurts. So illness isn't depicted by the medical drama as just requiring a cure: it offers the possibility of resolution and reconciliation. And though this derives in part from the conventions of drama and the human interest story, it also redefines illness as more than just bodily hurts. The 1960s/1970s medical drama may have extolled the male physician, but it also endorsed the expression of feelings such as vulnerability and fear more commonly articulated by women.

In the 1960s and 1970s the United States and Europe were undergoing enormous social upheaval, especially in family relationships. There was widespread concern about the rising rates of divorce, and the effects of the growth in women's employment. The medical drama provided a wise man to mediate family relationships and restore harmony. And while dominant values were being contested, and chasms of difference opening up between the different generations, between black and white, between men and women, the doctor shows reasserted social hope and stability. One commentator suggested that their chief message was that

> times may have changed, but the things that count most, the basic values and ideals, have not. Eventually, one knows, James Kildare will become Leonard Gillespie. . . . When such a continuity is possible, the world, at its core, remains settled and steadfast.[38]

As the white male tele-doctor made good the damage and healed the hurt, the doctor shows offered reassurance that the system could succour and patriarchy provide.

From 'Dr Kildare' to 'St Elsewhere'

A striking difference between the medical drama of the 1960s and the 1980s is a broadening in the range of permissible subject matter. The trend had begun with 'Marcus Welby'. While an episode in the ABC series 'Ben Casey' (1961–6) had struggled for an hour to tackle male impotence without being allowed to use the word, 'Marcus Welby, MD' (1969–76) dealt openly with unmarried fathers and mothers, abortion, drug addiction, indecent exposure, and autism. CBS's 'Medical Center' (1969–76) also featured stories on abortion, homosexuality, drug addiction, venereal disease, impotence, artificial insemination, and rape – issues which would have been anathema in the Casey–Kildare era.

The new storylines reflected a general liberalisation in public discourse. Social problems were increasingly featured in documentaries and chat shows, and subjects like Down's Syndrome and vasectomy eventually became acceptable dramatic material for the doctor shows too. The American medical series 'St Elsewhere', which began its first season on NBC in 1982, eagerly grasped the new ethical issues which the documentaries had aired: euthanasia featured recurringly, AIDS and rape were sensitively covered. It seemed as if many more patients died. British medical soaps like ITV's 'The Practice' and BBC's 'Casualty' were based on actual published case histories. 'Casualty' – set in the night shift of the casualty department of a busy general hospital – was so crowded with topical issues such as rape, child abuse, alcoholism, overdose, and AIDS, that by the end of an episode the hapless viewer felt as if they'd done the night shift themself. Unlike Dr Kildare, the 'Casualty' staff rushed from patient to patient: they were overworked and stretched by cuts in the NHS. In winter 1986, the series even attracted Conservative Party wrath: 'If you listen to "Casualty" ', their spokesman claimed, 'it is like a Labour Party meeting. The general patois used throughout is so-called health service cuts.'[39] The BBC countered that the series was 'meticulously researched', and that it had 'taken hospital drama out of the cosy world of the 1960s'.[40] (Presumably the BBC hadn't watched its own previous series 'Angels', which had routinely covered issues like private medicine and NHS cuts.)

There were still subjects which medical drama and soaps shrank from. Only in the mid-1980s was an American soap character allowed to die of cancer. And NBC refused to allow 'St Elsewhere' to demonstrate breast self-examination, or mention the word 'testicle', and only reluctantly passed a VD storyline after having insisted 'We don't do VD. Can't you give them herpes?'[41]

'St Elsewhere' differed from 'Dr Kildare' in style as much as content: gone were the brightly lit, glossy interiors, the single hero (plus mentor), single story, dramatic music, and overacting. In came the ensemble piece, with a regular cast of twelve, low-key acting, humour, several simultaneous stories ('St Elsewhere' was a medical 'Hill Street Blues', from the same stable, MTM), and sets with peeling wallpaper and dark corridors. Indeed, if the operating-theatre scene was the icon of the 1960s medical drama, the corridor became the recurring motif of the

1980s drama, permitting long-tracking shots, busy scenes, and a whiff of institutional life.[42]

But even more striking than the change in subject-matter was the new image of doctors themselves, influenced largely by the spread of the consumer approach. When the consumer critics first found their voice, the doctor shows were dumbstruck: they all but disappeared in the mid 1970s and those which remained declined alarmingly. How could you fill dramas with flawless, unfailingly empathetic doctors while the documentaries and news programmes were busy featuring malpractice suits, allegations of medical greed, and examples of the peremptory treatment of patients?[43] The open articulation of consumer criticisms silenced the doctor shows, but only temporarily. By the early 1980s, a new generation of medical drama was emerging, incorporating aspects of the consumer critique, and the chief way in which it differed from its predecessors was by introducing a new character: the doctor as human being. While Dr Kildare was a waxwork physician, unblemished except for excessive idealism and hubris, the new cohort of TV doctors possessed emotional and physical problems in abundance. In 'St Elsewhere' alone, the chief of staff had cancer, the vice head of medicine had an autistic son, and the chief nurse underwent a mastectomy. These doctors had the same kinds of illnesses as their patients. One can't imagine 'Dr Kildare's' Dr Gillespie even having piles.

In its treatment of rape, 'St Elsewhere' was particularly innovative. A rapist at large within the hospital turned out to be a doctor (suggesting that rapists weren't necessarily mad strangers but ordinary men, and that physicians weren't all translucently virtuous). Among his victims were two women doctors. One worked through her distress and decided to transfer from forensic medicine to psychiatry. The other, plagued by her family's standards of achievement and perfection, couldn't come to terms with the experience, became a bulimia sufferer, and finally committed suicide. The rapist–doctor was eventually shot dead by an enraged nurse. High drama, but also portraying medical staff in a wide variety of roles, and with differing individual resources to handle crises. Similarly, in other episodes, staff members lost wives, suffered marital breakdown, got depressed, made a mistake, were trapped beneath a collapsed hospital ceiling, and had problems with their children.

Indeed staff and not patients are at the heart of 'St Elsewhere'. As in 'Dr Kildare' and 'Marcus Welby, MD' personal relationships and family crises remain the focus, but now they're rife in the doctors' own lives. Yet even in their new incarnation, the doctor shows still complemented medical documentaries. The general tenor of all programmes about medicine, fiction and non-fiction, may have become more questioning and less idealised. But while the medical approach continued to dwell on the doctor's technical prowess, and consumer programmes criticised the doctor–patient relationship, the medical drama showed the doctor as a flawed but breathing human being, with problems of his or her own. The consumer programme accused them of personal frailties and inadequacies which the medical drama explored sympathetically and compassionately. It supplied a rich new seam of stories.

The political is personal

In one respect, however, 'St Elsewhere' profoundly resembled 'Dr Kildare'. Its crumbling hospital St Eligius, like Blair General before it, is an emotional community into which the material or political features of life rarely impinge. Though, as we've seen, the show has tackled issues like medical malpractice, nurses' strikes, and fees, with which 'Dr Kildare' would never have sullied itself, they're transformed or redefined as personal events. The nurses' strike was shown almost entirely in its effects on personal relationships: the breakdown in relations between the Chief of Staff and the Head Nurse, the beginning of a sexual relationship between the Head Nurse and the union negotiator. The actions of a heart surgeon who unnecessarily inserted pacemakers into his patients – discovered by a young female doctor – were put down to individual greed, not situated in the financial context of American medicine. As in 'Dr Kildare' and 'Marcus Welby, MD', everything is played out on the emotional plane, depicted as an autonomous sphere, unconnected with material conditions and structural features.

What's more, and in keeping with the traditions of medical drama, almost every character who passes before the camera becomes known intimately by the viewer – their driving force, their flaws, their emotional problems. Here are no faceless bureaucrats or fleeting, impersonal encounters: the medical world is reconstituted into a world of personal intimacy and emotional proximity, the hospital reassuringly transmuted from alien institution into a familiar, domestic domain.

Diagnosing the system

Moreover, while the new medical drama showed doctors as only human, they almost always still shone with integrity. And whatever individual peccadillos the new TV doctor was allowed, the system of medical care s/he worked in was portrayed as ultimately sound and caring. But apart from the updated doctor shows there was another kind of emergent medical drama with a sharper edge. Its doctors weren't merely flawed, they were often corrupt. And their transgressions weren't those of the odd baddy, an unaccountably evil individual, but were depicted as endemic to the system, one which by its nature created self-interested profiteers. Fired by the consumer approach, these dramas didn't just entreat doctors to polish up their bedside manner: they questioned in whose interests medicine was really being practised. This was the radical critique.

The prototype was the 1938 film of *The Citadel*, A.J. Cronin's novel which caused a sensation when published in 1937, selling 25 million copies internationally and generating an entire, furious session at the British Medical Association's annual conference. Cronin's hero, Andrew Manson, was an idealistic young doctor who, seeing several cases of typhoid caused by bad drainage in the deprived Welsh valley where he worked, combined with a fellow doctor to blow up the sewer. When he noticed a similar cough among several of his miner patients and suspected that their work was to blame he started medical research in his home. But though Manson despised those of his colleagues preoccupied with etiquette and money, when he moved to London and established a successful West End practice, he too acquired wealthy hypochondriac patients and all the trimmings (moustache, bow-tie, Rolls-Royce) until a personal tragedy caused by an incompetent Society doctor sent him back to his ideals. The film's final speech blazed with commitment: 'if we go on trying to make out that everything's right inside the profession and everything's wrong outside, it'll be the death of scientific progress'.

Cronin's critique proved resistible to other writers of medical drama for almost forty years. Apart from Paddy Chayefsky's astringent Oscar-winning screenplay for the 1971 black comedy *The Hospital*, film and TV writers preferred, as we've seen, to make their criticisms of medicine obliquely, via the ideal doctor.[44] But in 1975, a remarkable American medical TV drama series which ran on NBC for four months crashed the conventions with abandon. 'Medical Story' was originated by Abby Mann, creator of 'Kojak', and inspired by personal experience. When his young actress wife was advised to have a hysterectomy, Mann sought a second opinion; a glandular disorder was diagnosed for which surgery wasn't needed, and Mann discovered millions of American hysterectomies performed unnecessarily, 'because it is a relatively easy operation but one in which the surgeons can make a lot of money, so they recommend it. It seemed evil and stung me into writing "Medical Story".'[45]

The medical team in 'Medical Story' (though the cast and setting changed each week) were overworked, understaffed, and generally indifferent to patient suffering. In one episode, a campaigning doctor organised a petition to protest against conditions, insisting that 'people are dying out there . . . because we do not have enough doctors and nurses'. 'Medical Story' showed the ideological and financial crisis in public health. It attacked 'institutional neglect', and depicted doctors either as preoccupied with their private work and simply practising on poor people or, along with nurses, unable to cope because of structural rather than individual failings.

> Our patients have no political clout. . . . The complexity and cost of modern medicine has grown beyond the ability of individual physicians to influence the system. . . . And since the Government refuses to get into the medicine business, someone else will. Business. And imagine the kind of physician who will function as an employee of that business ethic. Is that whom you want for your doctor?[46]

Talk that would have shocked the life out of Dr Kildare.

Yet what was still missing was the patient. In *The Citadel* they were all either discredited malingerers, bigots who smashed up Manson's experiments even though they were being conducted for their benefit, affluent neurotics, or grateful but mainly mute. 'Medical Story', although the opening of one episode was shot from the terrifying perspective of a patient brought into hospital with a heart attack, used them largely as evidence of medical incompetence or overwork. But in December 1975 a powerful BBC TV play placed the patient's experience centre stage. In Trevor Griffith's play *Through the Night*, a young working-class woman with a lump in her breast goes into hospital for a biopsy, and wakes up after the operation to find that she's had a breast removed. Griffiths wrote the play 'out of anger and fear', basing it closely on the experience of his wife, who kept a diary when she was admitted into hospital for a biopsy.

> It's really a demand for the audience to see the hospital as a site of so much more than romance between doctors and nurses. . . to ask questions about hospitalisation, the National Health Service, relationships between experts and non-experts.[47]

From the first, *Through the Night* invited us to identify with the patient. When Christine was wheeled to theatre, the camera followed her trolley-eye view of the journey. The doctors, who spoke in impersonal jargon, never engaged with her shock and sense of loss ('I don't know why they did it', she tells her husband, 'Nobody's said'), and their whispering group at the foot of her bed during the ward-round – which for consumer critics constituted a formidable symbol of medicine's objectification of the patient – was cleverly represented from her end, as inaudible. She later complained, 'The specialist, he never even looked at me, let alone spoke.'[48] The play concluded with an impassioned critique of medicine from a sympathetic young doctor who declared 'We have lost all idea of you as a whole, human being, with a past, a personality, dependents, needs, hopes, wishes. Our power is strongest when you are dependent upon us.'[49]

Through the Night made an enormous impact on its audience. More than 11 million people watched it and it was repeated in 1977. Almost 100 phone calls were logged by the BBC's duty-office on the night of broadcast; the producer and the *Radio Times* received a heavy postbag; and Griffiths himself got some 180 letters. The *Sunday People* opened its columns to readers inviting them to send in their own experiences of mastectomy. They received over 1,800 letters in ten days.[50] *Through the Night* was a timely drama, broadcast at the end of a year which had started with the transmission of 'Horizon's' programme (see Chapter 4) criticising the routine induction of labour, a year in which issues about the medical profession's treatment of women were clearly moving onto television's agenda.

Yet the play was careful not to question the medical aspects of Christine's treatment. Nice young Dr Pearce reassured her that 'you're better off now than you would have been if you hadn't come forward for screening', a debatable (and optimistic) assessment. Similarly, he argued that radiation treatment 'isn't very pleasant, but it might be worth it'.[51] 'Through the Night' was undoubtedly radical about doctor–patient relations but it was conservative about medical practices.

Yet writers and producers were becoming bolder in criticising medical treatment too. In 1978 a gripping thriller asked wide-ranging questions about the ethics of American medical care. In *Coma* (based on a book by ophthalmologist Robin Cook, screenplay and direction by doctor Michael Crichton), a female junior surgeon in a Boston hospital investigated the case of her friend left in an irreversible coma by a routine operation and, finding a disproportionate number of other similar cases, uncovered an illegal international medical organisation trafficking in human organs organised by medical top brass, who terrifyingly try to murder her.

Apart from its original treatment of gender, *Coma* mobilised all the paraphernalia for terror available in hospitals – packaged corpses, operating-theatres, anaesthetics. Crichton described it as 'a story that contains many elements of reality: the fear people have of surgery, the fear of dying at the hands of your doctor, phobias about hospitals'.[52] Its technophobic vision of the body subjected to an alien, totalitarian regime, in an institutionalised hospital where people are reduced to things, has been likened to that of sci-fi horror films. One of its chilling settings was the Jefferson Institute, a futuristic warehouse for comatose people where lifeless bodies dangled in mid-air, suspended by wires from the ceiling, fed by tubes providing vital fluids regulated by computer. The film also depicted American medical practitioners as a closed, conspiratorial group of back-scratchers, obsessed with money and power, and American medicine as corporate big business.

As the consumer criticisms of medicine gathered momentum, British television drama increasingly took up the issues in drama–documentary style. Peter Ransley's 1980 play 'Minor Complications', based on the true case of a woman undergoing a sterilisation which went seriously wrong, leaving her with gangrene, peritonitis, months of discomfort and pain, and impaired health,[53] dramatised patients' difficulties in trying to get compensation for medical negligence against the closed ranks of the medical profession. It helped launch a new organis-ation, Action for Medical Accident Victims.

But in October 1983 TV drama came up with its most un-equivocally critical offering about medical care yet. G.F. Newman's controversial four-parter, 'The Nation's Health', finally dispatched the beatific idealism of Drs Kildare and Finlay from the TV screen. Instead, young Dr Jessie Marvell moved through four 'problem' specialities – surgery; obstetrics and gynaecology; geriatrics; and psychiatry – increasingly dis-enchanted but acquiescing to orthodox medicine. The final image of the last film was of Marvell administering Largactyl in a padded cell. Based on three-and-a-half years' research, when he observed and participated in a variety of medical settings, Newman wrote it

> because the medical establishment is a closed, secret world. . . .
> I think the system is very corrupting: either you play by their
> ground-rules, or you don't advance, and most people want to
> advance. Junior doctors very quickly become corrupted by the
> system . . . yes, there are a lot of things that seem to go wrong
> with medicine in the films, but I don't think things often go
> right.[54]

Like Griffiths, Newman lambasted doctors for deflecting patients' questions with jargon, denying patients' distress, and favouring disembodied details of disease over a sense of the patient as a person; but his focus was much broader. He also challenged the efficacy of Western acute, high-tech interven-tionist medicine. In the first episode a cancer patient is railroaded by a consultant into 'heroic' surgery, which will remove part of his tongue, eye, and face. Despite suggestions of less drastic measures from junior staff, the consultant insists on carrying out the 'commando' operation, another kudos-winner to be inscribed in the medical textbooks. The patient dies on the way out of the operation.

Newman delivered an almost unqualified attack on the medical profession. Doctors, under his gaze, emerged as insensitive self-seekers, pondering their next sinecure over the first incision. They blithely offered their services privately in lieu of a lengthy NHS wait. They conspired with drug companies. And they were racist and sexist to a man. Medical talk on television was never thus. The series sometimes had a rent-an-issue flavour, with every conceivable criticism of medicine dramatised or alluded to, and in his unredeemingly bleak image of medical care Newman piled up the instances of corruption as if it were ubiquitous. Yet 'The Nation's Health' was outstandingly convincing in establishing the tenor and texture of modern hospital life. The power and aloofness of intimidating consultants and surgeons were depicted with devastating authenticity. The astonishingly good, low-key acting, the authentically grisly operations (real ones, which sympathetic surgeons allowed them to film), the harrowing scenes with no concessions to squeamishness, and the constant noise and briskness, combined to create a powerful drama in the verité style. Newman and director Les Blair also showed the hospital as a workplace with problems of industrial relations and steaming kitchens of a gross, Fawlty Towers kind. And the cuts to the NHS were ever-present, the pressure to find beds constant, the long waiting-lists routine, and the closure of a hospital wing depicted as an act of official vandalism.

The series attracted considerable critical attention, with one TV reviewer judging it 'the most appallingly authentic television programme about medicine I have ever seen'.[55] The British Medical Association complained, claiming it didn't reflect the high standards of care available in NHS hospitals. And Channel 4, preempting the criticisms, scheduled a monumentally dull studio discussion series 'Follow the Nation's Health' to follow each episode and draw its steam.

Official medical reaction to these highly critical programmes has remained constant, always fearful that viewers would be scared away from hospitals and doctors. In 1946 the British

Board of Film Censors temporarily banned *Green for Danger* on the grounds that any wounded soldier who saw it might be so overcome by the dread of being murdered by hospital staff that it would seriously jeopardise their recovery. And shortly after the airing of the first episode of 'Medical Story', the American College of Obstetricians and Gynaecologists issued a strongly-worded statement accusing it of being '*Jaws, Airport* and *The Towering Inferno* wrapped up in a hospital setting' and warning hospitals and physicians 'to be alert for patients who may be unduly frightened and doubtful of hysterectomy after viewing the program'.[56]

The fear of discouraging viewers from consulting their doctors (or the fear of medical accusations that patients have been frightened off) can operate as a constraint on dramatists and TV networks, who sometimes react nervously by anticipating or seeking out official medical reactions before transmission. In the course of making 'Through the Night', the BBC consulted the Director of the Department of Social Research at a Manchester Hospital, a Senior Consultant at the Middlesex Hospital, a member of the Department of Psychiatry at Manchester University, the Chief Medical Officer of the Health Education Council, the Mastectomy Association, and many other physicians and surgeons.[57] The text was revised considerably to accommodate medical advice, so that it didn't deter women with lumps in their breasts from consulting their doctors.

The good doctor

However much medical drama changed in the mid-1970s and 1980s, and no matter how bleakly it represented medical practice and bureaucracy, one character endured. The good doctor, repository of all the hopes we invest in medicine and the ideals we hold dear, remains an invariable component of even the most abrasive medical fiction.

Even such a critical play as 'Through the Night' had in young Pearce its good doctor rooting for the patient. He was instantly identifiable by the stage directions: 'Pearce speaks in an unsmoothed Leeds voice: undoctorlike'. In contrast to his colleagues, he greeted the patient by her name, asked to be allowed to examine her, thanked her after the examination and, sensitive to her nakedness, handed her a gown to cover herself with, while he asked her for her opinion. He treated her and the other female patients as sexual adults not desexed children, and used humour and colloquialism in place of impersonal jargon.

But most revealing was his role in the final scene. Although Griffiths structured the play from the patient's point of view, in the last scene Pearce displaced Christine centre-stage. The authorial speech, with its indictment of doctors for their failure to engage emotionally with the patient, was made not by the female patient but by the male doctor – the good doctor. By putting this speech into the doctor's mouth, Griffiths left his patient, Christine, powerless. Her only role was to sit and listen passively, a touch admiringly. And gratefully: she ended by saying 'thank you', and Pearce responded 'Don't thank. Demand.' This doctor wasn't only good at his own job, he mobilised the patients too. Presumably, the critique would have carried less weight coming from a patient: the doctor legitimated the patient's dissatisfaction with the system, and in so doing, subtly reinforced his own power as certifier of reality. In some sense, he was even reassuring about the state of medicine: if there were doctors like him, could there be that much wrong with the medical profession?

Only the most rabid doctor-basher would want doctors invariably portrayed as uncaring careerists, indifferent to human suffering. But the existence of the good doctor in even naturalistic medical drama means that doctors still aren't shown with the normal mix of good and bad: by always endowing one of them with pellucid virtue or perpetual empathy, dramatists are still failing to characterise them as ordinary humans. Moreover, by ensuring that one doctor at least always escapes the corruption or malaise of the rest, medical dramas shift our focus from the organisation of medicine onto the personal characteristics of individual doctors, as if their integrity protects them from the system within which they work, and could transform it. Even 'The Nation's Health' had its really benign doctor, Laurence James, who practised healing and, in his sensitivity to the mind–body connection, clearly spoke for the author, though the series did have him discriminated against and finally edged out. More instructively, 'The Nation's Health' showed – as few others have – the well-intentioned young doctor getting sucked into the system against her own volition, while *Coma* also broke with the good doctor tradition by vindicating the female doctor–heroine's anger, and not her altruism.

But the good doctor is generally so resilient an element that it's irresistible to medical comedies, too, even the most mordant. The doctors in the British 'Doctor' films may have got into an endless succession of japes and scrapes, but they always saved a life or two on the way. The medics in 'M*A*S*H' (film and TV series), though irreverent pranksters, rushed into action as unstintingly dedicated curers when the need arose.

The survival of the good doctor also indicates how entrenched and durable is our belief in the ultimate triumph of medicine, and in its infinite capacity. Even the profession's most outspoken critics who, in their films and plays affirm the urgent need for medical reform and reorganisation, tend to portray medicine's power to do good or ill as unlimited. If only it's harnessed by the virtuous, they imply, medicine will cure and heal. Only, perhaps, in soaps like the BBC's 'EastEnders', is the medical displaced by the environmental approach, with illness woven into the social fabric of the characters' lives. EastEnders have a breakdown because they're unemployed, become an alcoholic to cope with a lousy marriage, are hospitalised when attacked by a violent man in the street, have an illegitimate baby when still a teenager, become a prostitute to support themself and child. All of human life, and none of it magicked away by the good doctor, a relatively impotent though supportive bystander.

Drunk on drama

After the consumer approach had been absorbed into medical drama it was only to be expected that the look-after-yourself lobby would make their influence felt. In the late 1970s and early 1980s, studies started to appear charting soap opera characters' intake of food and drink. Nutritionists, argued the critics, had been too hasty in blaming advertisements for promoting a bad diet; it was the soaps and popular drama that were culpable. While the documentaries were crowded with health educators spurning fat and extolling fibre, American prime-time drama, it seemed, was full of people doing the opposite.

Soap characters scoff puddings and sugary foods, snack between meals, eat on the go, and to reward or punish themselves. Yet in spite of all this, they rarely get fat.[58] But though the critics were right to emphasise that soap characters rarely suffer the consequences of their actions, they didn't acknowledge that, in following a diet thousands of calories away from what nutritionists advise, people in soaps are very similar to those watching them. Indeed, meals in popular drama match ordinary people's experiences far more closely than those so heartily promoted by documentaries and cookery programmes.

The same can't be said of television drinking, scrutinised in dozens of studies. TV drinking inverts the real-life norm: fictional characters drink more alcohol than any other beverage, while in daily life it's the other way round.[59]

And TV drama doesn't show the adverse consequences of all this boozing. The drinkers don't die or lose their jobs or spouses permanently, or suffer debilitating physical effects, they don't kill people or beat up their families, have car crashes or start fires, and downing a few swift drinks never seems to impair anyone's capacity to shoot straight. What's more, a drink offered on prime-time is rarely refused. And American and British prime-time television infrequently deal with alcohol abuse or treatment: intoxication is more often presented as a joking rather than a serious matter. As one researcher put it, 'America's roughly ten million alcoholics and over 50 million teetotallers are "symbolically annihilated" from the world of televised fiction'.[60]

The researchers rightly argue that TV endorses a male view in which the consumption of alcohol and women are the hallmarks of masculinity, and legitimises and glamorises the use of alcohol. But Swedish research has urged caution in reading too much from crude content analyses which log the number of times a drink occurs but don't acknowledge the viewers' interpretive work, and the different meanings they may impute to similar images. The most that can be argued is that television drinking lends alcohol a cultural stamp of approval.

But the lobbyists were energetic. To effect a process they call 'cooperative consultation', researchers in California – one of them also a member of the Screen Writers' Guild – formed a board of writers, producers, directors, and studio executives. Through this, they made contact with those working in prime-time drama, and started to feed them the results of their content analyses. The researchers and lobbyists also presented their findings to the TV networks and in a newsletter on alcohol topics which was widely distributed in the TV industry.[61] They listed possible new storylines around alcohol, and when media personnel began to consult them with requests for help on alcohol issues, they came up with suggestions which fitted into the plot and moved the story on but also sneaked in some alcohol education.

In 1983, the Caucus for Producers, Writers and Directors circulated a White Paper drawing attention to the excessive use of alcohol in its shows. The Hollywood community had been galvanised, not just by the campaigners, but also by a car crash caused by a drunk driver which seriously injured two stars, Mary Martin and Janet Gaynor. The Paper asked,

> Have any of us as members of the creative community in Hollywood unwittingly glorified the casual use of alcohol in any of our projects? Have we written it as macho? Directed it as cute? . . . are we subliminally putting a label of 'perfectly okay' on alcohol-related behaviour and selling it to the American people? . . . The answer we fear is yes.

In 1986, an informal Caucus survey found twenty-two hours of prime-time programming which had cut back on scenes involving alcohol. The lobbyists – along with the health and fitness movement, and other social changes – were making an impact.

Look-after-yourself ideas and health precepts were infiltrating other shows too. American soap operas like 'Dallas' have firm no-smoking policies ('Dallas's star Larry Hagman, baddie 'JR', is a known and active anti-smoking campaigner). American daytime soaps started to count the calories: in one, a character began cooking high fibre–low fat meals for friends and family, while a health food restaurant opened in another. 'General Hospital's' disco provided opportunities for frenzied exercise, and almost all the female characters in 'As the World Turns' enrolled in an aerobics class.

In Britain, there was even a whole new genre, the look-after-yourself drama. The characters in the BBC Scotland daily soap 'Kilbreck' (funded by the Scottish Health Education Group) suffered from the gamut of health problems, while commercial radio's twice-weekly 'Devon Lanes' (funded by the Exeter Health Authority) fictionalised diet and health issues. In Radio Clyde's series of eight one-hour plays (co-funded by the Health Education Council), the hapless heroes became alcoholics and heroin addicts, suffered heart attacks and contracted sexually-transmitted diseases.

Indeed, by the 1980s, drama had become just as much the focus of pressure group lobbying as current affairs and documentary programmes. A representative of the American Cancer Society travels to Los Angeles every year to foster contacts among writers and drama producers: 'We just keep them abreast of what's going on in cancer. . . . My business is to inform them of what is possible to put on their shows.'[62] 'Whenever a new show comes out, we send them a note to suggest how the Red Cross could be worked into it', says the Red Cross official in Hollywood. 'I'll give the set director some Red Cross posters to hang in the background of a scene, and then when the camera pans, millions of people see', generating increased contributions and blood donations.[63] While 'Dr Kildare' and 'Ben Casey' gingerly hovered around ethical and social issues, today's good TV doctor, in between solving his own physical and emotional crises, is likely to be treating patients with problems hot off the front page, or generously supplied by a special interest group. Drama and documentary – their agendas are increasingly indistinguishable.

12

Playing Doctors and Nurses

Women: bewitched, bothered, and bewildered

The range of roles available to women in medical drama in the early days was limited. In films such as *Arrowsmith*, *Not as a Stranger*, and *The Citadel*, they were supportive spouses, standing by their pioneering but doubting doctor husbands, safekeepers of the ideals and first principles to which the men returned in the end. Sometimes, for the men to come to their senses, they had to die.

If they weren't saintly, the women in the medical films of the 1940s were unstable. Their femininity was problematic, requiring the therapeutic influence of the male doctor to help them adapt more comfortably to their gender. If, unusually, they themselves were a doctor (like Ingrid Bergman's coldly competent psychiatrist in Hitchcock's 1945 *Spellbound*), they soon thawed out, substituting for professional power a lovesick fixation – a return to the devoted wife role.

The TV doctor shows of the 1960s occasionally featured women as physicians, but almost always disparagingly. 'Why did you become a doctor?' Ben Casey asked a female colleague in the series' first episode in October 1961, adding bluntly 'I don't much care for female MDs – they're too unstable.' Though the woman responded wittily ('I flunked shorthand and typing – what else could I do?'), she was clearly only the romantic interest.

When not dainty, women in 'Dr Kildare' were ruthless (a male medical student's wife in an early episode was a selfish, petulant social-climber), insecure, or nurturant family mediators and pacifiers – though never all at the same time. Indeed, the old sage/young disciple male duo left women few major roles, except as objects or spoilers of male power. The doctor shows of the 1960s and 1970s may have been informed by the female gaze, as I argued earlier, but a feminist gaze it wasn't.

By the 1980s, at least one woman doctor was *de rigueur* in medical drama, reflecting in part the great increase in the numbers of women entering medicine. 'St Elsewhere's several female physicians (for a few episodes, the show even had a lesbian doctor) lived lives as turbulent as their male colleagues', who nevertheless tended to dominate the show.

Yet it's still rare for medical dramas to treat the problems women experience in medicine as more than personal conflicts, to be individually resolved. It was *Coma* which dramatised most unequivocally the problems faced by women in medicine, a theme preoccupying both its writer and director. The men in *Coma* were dismissive, patronising, or murderous towards the feisty Dr Susan Wheeler who, after challenging a male doctor, pursued the case of her best friend left in an irreversible coma by a routine operation. She recognised male prejudice ('you think because I'm a woman I'm going to be upset') and identified with the female patient. Instead of the vulnerable female victim at the centre of so many thrillers, she was a plucky, fearless heroine, and her lover, who dismissed her theories as paranoid, came to realise – in the film's vindicating finale – that she was right after all.

Still angels after all these years

Women doctors may be problematic to medical drama, but nurses aren't. Drawing on cultural ideas of nursing as a kind of professionalised femaleness, nurses are depicted at best as perpetual geysers of nurturance and intuitive mothers to the world. More usually on screen, they busy themselves handing doctors test results, glancing at temperature charts, mopping brows, wheeling trolleys, tucking in beds, and listening to physicians' insights. Time is no object. They also spend episodes sitting behind desks or work-stations, or becoming infatuated with doctors – tasks for which the only qualifications are an O level in Make-Up.

An early example of the screen nurse was provided by the 1940 British film *Vigil in the Night,* based on A.J. Cronin's novel, about two sisters who were nurses, one of them the Good Nurse, the other the Bad Nurse. (Matron signalled the theme early on: 'There is nothing in the world so bad as a bad nurse, nor so good as a good one.') When the bad one left a sick child for a few moments to make herself a cup of tea, he died. The good one, covering for her and pretending that she had been on duty, was dispatched from the hospital in shame. Eventually in a smallpox epidemic the bad nurse, responsible for a sick child once again, nursed him successfully to health but in the process, herself caught smallpox and died, so finally exorcising her badness ('I'm beginning to think I was a pretty good nurse'). But her sister, in love with the good doctor, continued to nurse unfalteringly and (unusually) gave the film's rousing end-speech: 'It's not futile, doctor, it's glorious. . . . We're here to serve, and if we do it well, we find pleasure, freedom, perfect freedom. . . . Come now Dr Prescott, there's work for us to do.' Throughout the film, all the negative and critical comments about nursing were made by bad nurses. Coming soon after an attempt to enhance the conditions, training, and pay of nurses, and to increase their number, *Vigil in the Night* had the flavour of a recruitment drive.

The good nurse was to prove as resilient an image as the good doctor. She reappeared in the 1963 British film *Nurse on Wheels,* in which Juliet Mills played a new rural district nurse who had to overcome hostility and sexism from the village before winning their acceptance. Patient, gutsy, efficient, and kind, she was also a terrible driver (as if, to counteract her competence, she needed to be endowed with some seemingly female scattiness).

Matron, of course, was right. On the big screen when nurses were bad, they were horrid. The bad nurse, generally a disciplinarian, was also a recurring character. The cruel mental hospital nurses in the 1948 *The Snake Pit* maintained the hospital's inhumane regime and, anticipating the vindictive nurse in *One Flew Over The Cuckoo's Nest,* trapped the heroine and straitjacketed her. The monstrously bureaucratic sister or matron, indifferent to human suffering, was also to become a feature of later film comedies (see below), where nurses were often identified with rigid institutional routines.

The doctor shows of American prime-time in the 1960s had no such prominent nurse characters, establishing instead a third enduring image of nursing, the nurse as nonentity. The most regular in 'Dr Kildare', Zoe Lawton, was in love with the intern hero, even trying to resign once because of it. Her chief role was as a foil for him, asking the choice question to which he could respond with brilliance. According to an exhaustive study of the image of nursing on American television, the 1960s TV nurse was invariably the doctor's handmaiden, a silent factotum doing little identifiable work.[1]

Apart from being good, bad, or background, screen nurses are also frequently sexy. In comedies especially, waddling precariously, their uniforms revealing curvaceous figures, nurses exude sexual availability, and use their access to the body of the male patient for erotic purposes. Pornographic films in particular promote an image of the nurse as promiscuous.

The 1980s brought surprisingly few differences in the media image of the nurse: despite great changes in the profession itself, the researchers found American television drama's portrayals of nursing in the 1950s and 1980s remarkably consistent. Even the costumes stayed the same.[2] Only one show escaped their censure. The CBS TV series 'M*A*S*H', which ran from 1972 to 1986, started out (like the film it was based on) with an almost ritual humiliation of women, especially of a nurse called Margaret (nicknamed Hot Lips). But the American researchers argue that she progressed into a complex, sympathetic figure: influenced by the women's movement, by the 1979–80 season the show offered 'the most genuinely professional view of nurses to be seen on television', despite its comedy format.

Even 'St Elsewhere' has been faulted for its depiction of nursing. The show was critical of doctors who presume nurses to be infinitely patient and compliant, and also portrayed negotiations over nurses' pay breaking down and leading to a strike, but the series was criticised by Nurses' Media Watch (NMW), an American pressure group, for what they saw as its old-fashioned representation of nurses – still mainly fetchers and carriers for the doctors, doing nothing more strenuous than give the odd injection. NMW was particularly angered by the speech of a former nurse at the hospital, explaining why she'd returned as a medical student. 'Medicine is such a challenge. I should've done this earlier in my life. But there was no support for ambition growing up. Women became nurses, moms – I was steered wrong.' A stereotyped devaluation of nursing as a second-resort occupation for unambitious women, protested NMW, despite the Head Nurse's vigorous counter-attack: 'It's boring, you take a ton of grief, no one recognises your true value ... but it beats being a med student any day.'[3]

Nurses' Media Watch, 'nurses working together for a new age of the media nurse; one in which television, movies, books, newspapers, and popular periodicals portray the nurse accurately and positively as an educated, responsible professional', has been lobbying the American TV networks since 1983, and nurses' anger at the mass media's failure to recognise and value their work is understandable. They claim that it perpetuates nursing's low status in the minds of policymakers and the general public, a status little enhanced by the early days of the women's movement since nursing epitomised the kind of traditional female occupation which many women ('St Elsewhere's' ex-nurse among them) were then spurning. It's not surprising that many nurses and their organisations reacted to their low status by stressing the contemporary nurse's professionalism and advanced skills, and wanting this side of nursing displayed on television. But such campaigns to improve the media image of nurses aren't without their difficulties.

In urging the media to paint the nurse as a paramedical figure, carrying out complex medical procedures as sophisticated as the doctor's, nurses' campaigns risk reproducing the inferior value given to caring skills, and validating once more the superior status of the doctorly, technical tasks. It's also somewhat ironic, because the TV doctor spends most of his time doing emotional labour and dispensing large doses of care, the kind of work which in reality the nurse and not the doctor does. Nurses want their fictional counterparts to resemble real-life doctors, whereas TV doctors are in some respects more like real-life nurses. Nursing organisations, while they're right to want their work's variety and skills to be properly depicted, sometimes seem to be pitching for a TV image which is all gleaming professionalism and high-tech expertise. God forbid that their work should be seen as 'merely' supporting the patient.

But whether the TV nurse becomes a surrogate doctor,

administering complicated procedures and proudly labelled professional, or remains the nurturing lady with the lamp, a self-regenerating source of tender, loving care, what's usually missing are the frustrations and difficulties experienced by real contemporary nurses. The low pay, long hours, effects of the cuts, exploitation during training, racism (few British TV fictional nurses are black), sexism, rigid hierarchy, exclusion from decisions about patient care, emotional stress, and the inferior status in Western medicine of caring as against curing – rarely are these the stuff of film or television drama. Though groups of nurses are increasingly lobbying for nursing's value to be properly acknowledged and for changes in their work conditions, only occasionally has British television drama tangled with these hospital subjects. 'Casualty' had them picketing (though a little comically) a local cinema showing 'Confessions of a Night Nurse' with banners saying 'Stop Sexual Harassment of Nurses', and made them sometimes irritable, but the only British TV drama series ever really to engage with the reality of nurses' lives was the BBC TV twice-weekly medical soap 'Angels'.[4]

With nurses of all colours, classes and kinds, 'Angels' took on every imaginable issue. Nurses were shown giving each other emotional support, but were far less idealised than usual (the title seemed deliberately ironic): they often shouted at each other, led tortuous private lives, and criticised nursing. And the series didn't focus exclusively on the medical staff: besides the nurses themselves, you were as likely in 'Angels' to see the hospital's laundry staff as doctors.

'Angels', in fact, raised many of the same issues about medicine as 'The Nation's Health' but, partly because as a soap it occupied a less prestigious slot, was shot on cheap video rather than expensive film, and its acting and direction were decidedly less brilliant, it never attracted the critical interest or public debate of 'The Nation's Health'. Perhaps, too, this was because 'Angels' was mainly about women – and unusual among TV drama for showing women in a working environment more frequently than men. Along with 'Coronation Street', 'Angels' was found by one study to be highly popular among women and girls for its high proportion of female characters, and its strong and positive portrayals of women.[5]

In stitches

Though medical comedies sometimes seem juvenile – antics only tangentially connected to medicine, adults still playing doctors and nurses – like most popular culture, they have a deeper tale to tell. And though there's little so lugubrious as a joke earnestly deconstructed, medical humour's important role in saying the unsayable about health, illness, and medicine needs recognising.

Medical comedies of every kind generally share two key features. Firstly, almost all medical humour expresses patients' anxieties about medicine and about entrusting ourselves to the hands of others. Secondly, medical comedy vents those anxieties by a process of reversal, in which the dominant ideology of medical care has gone for a Burton, patients' worst fears come true, and in various ways they avenge medical staff for their powerlessness as patients. If the doctor shows deal with our anxiety and disappointment with medicine by giving us the doctors we want, medical comedy does it by giving us those we dread.

This can be seen in the British 'Carry On'[6] and 'Doctor' films[7] made by Rank between 1954 and 1972 – when the medical approach was in its prime in TV documentaries, and before the consumer approach became widespread. The two series were, in fact, broadly similar (especially when Leslie Phillips took over from Dirk Bogarde as star of the 'Doctor' films), though the 'Carry Ons' saw the world through the patient's eyes, and the 'Doctor' films focussed more on the doctors' lives. Both dealt with fears about medical competence by presenting doctors who were unequivocally incompetent.

The comic duologues of Elaine May and Mike Nichols, performed on American radio, records, TV, and stage in the 1960s, also squeezed hilarity from medical nightmares by taking hospital romance to its extremes, with love declared while passing the scalpel, and doctors and nurses so romantically obsessed that they forgot about the patient altogether: a physician threatened to leave mid-operation if a nurse didn't agree to marriage, while another completely ignored a patient's dying gasps as he quizzed her for evidence of affection from his beloved female colleague.

In explicitly and merrily trumpeting medicine's uncertainties and failures, medical comedies resemble comic get well cards which, according to one study, express patients' alienation and their lack of control over their medical treatment.[8] But the medical comedy goes further and reverses this, humorously enfranchising the patient and disenfranchising the doctor. It could happen in a joke: performing doctor Rob Buckman, in his BBC Radio 2 series 'Get The Most Out Of Your Body', told one about a patient, lying helpless with the dentist peering at his upper molars, who retaliated by examining the dentist's nose ('bogey in the upper right'). Most exhuberantly, it occurred in the finale of *Carry On Nurse*, where the patients united to carry out an operation – drunkenly appropriating the doctors' role, surgeons for an hour.

But probably the chief source of patients' anxiety when ill is their embarrassment and vulnerability over strangers' intimate access to their body, and the loss of privacy in bodily functions – all the more acute in a culture like Britain where physical contact in public is avoided and privacy so highly valued. Perhaps this is why the bedpan humour of the 'Carry On' films has so flourished in Britain. Certainly, British medical comedies are awash with jokes about embarrassment, particularly sharp when a nurse (invariably glamorous or saucy) touches or sees a male patient's body, generating fears of sexual humiliation and diminishment, or loss of control. In *Carry On Nurse*, after forcibly removing a patient's trousers, the nurse chided him 'What a fuss about such a little thing.' In the 1973 film *The National Health* a male auxiliary shaving a patient's pubic hair for an operation warned him 'don't flinch or you'll do yourself a mischief'. And Marlow, the thriller-writing hero of Dennis Potter's fine 1986 BBC TV series 'The Singing Detective' expressed it all when, immobilised with an acute skin disease, and despite trying to distract himself with boring thoughts as an attractive nurse rubbed his body with anointment, he inadvertently ejaculated.

Inscribed in the scene was both the embarrassment of the loss of sexual control, and a reminder of Marlow as a sexual being. The two are connected. The study of comic get well cards suggested that they depicted nurses as sex objects in order to boost the male patient's status as dominant (therefore potent) male at a time when his potency was questionable because he was ill and hospitalised, and so dependent on and under the control of a female nurse. The same is true of medical comedies, where the nurse becomes either a sex object, thus restoring the male patient to the dominant, courting position, or a battleaxe, often a disciplinary matron played by Hattie Jacques, wielding her power excessively and ridiculously, and sometimes humiliated or humanised at the end. Medical comedies, by portraying nurses as excessively sexy or strait-laced, available or ludicrously authoritarian, reverse female power and male dependence.

In the case of the male doctor and female patient (curiously infrequent in comic get well cards, but a staple of film and TV medical comedies where the doctors are frequently philanderers), the films also play with the sexual tensions in doctor–patient relations, strictly policed in real-life medicine. Medical comedies are crowded with dominant, flirtatious male doctors and dependent, pretty female patients. Comic doctors' access to women's bodies occasions sexual innuendo and lust, and sometimes romance. If real-life medical practice tries to manage anxiety about close bodily contact between the sexes in medicine by a rigid adherence to the roles of doctor and patient, medical comedies openly exploit the sexual and romantic potential of the encounter.[9] But the comic doctor is rarely depicted as rapacious or bad, just indulgently winked at as irredeemably male. The medical comedy raises the sexual dimensions of doctor–patient relations only to contain them safely: the comic doctor ends up either rebuffed by the female patient or marrying her.

Medical comedies also tackle hospitals as institutions. In contrast to the doctor shows, where the hospital is fantasised as a place administered by one elderly benign doctor, the comic hospital is fanatically bureaucratic. Rules are all, and medical comedies make much of the fact that the places where we're dispatched when diseased and disordered so fetishise order, trying to contain and control the body and its owners ('Sister, investigate that odour', commands Matron in *Carry On Nurse*, as if astonished by its gall in escaping). The hospital's drill is strict, its routines systematically applied. Jokes of the 'woke me up to give me a sleeping-pill' kind abound. There's also a rigid hierarchy, topped by an aloof consultant, seconded by Matron, and descending thereafter: *Carry On Nurse* wittily parodies this when Matron's order is peremptorily relayed down the pecking-order from sister, to staff-nurse, to nurse, to student nurse, to the poor orderly at the bottom.

But the bureaucracy of the comic screen hospital, unlike the real one, doesn't last, and medical comedies invariably end in medical mayhem. Trolleys career around uncontrollably, patients with legs in casts are hoisted up perilously, ambulances crash, and there is usually a final set-piece where all inhibitions are loosed, and even starchy Matron unbuttons. The institution is finally subverted and disrupted by its wayward patients or staff, who've refused to conform to its unbending routines. Anarchy triumphs over bureaucracy, and the enforced compliance of most real-life hospitalised patients inverted.

The hospital and the NHS also seem to offer writers and directors an irresistible metaphor for the nation, as titles like *Britannia Hospital* (Lindsay Anderson's 1982 film comedy) and *The National Health* make plain. Partly it's because class figures prominently in British medical comedy. Consultants draw up outside hospitals in Rolls-Royces. Bow-tied, adorned with a red carnation, they sweep through the ward with their retinue, sometimes to the accompaniment of ludicrously majestic music. Long before the documentaries and dramas took aim at the lordliness of the consultant, medical comedies were lampooning them as pompous part-times, all airs and no toil. And while doctors in documentaries are generally impelled by higher motives, comic medics are often unashamedly greedy.

But no one is safe in medical comedy. Patients, too, aren't the tormented sufferers from life-crises of the doctor shows, or the objects of our empathy as in medical documentaries, but generally working-class malingerers. Like the comic get well card patients, they feign illness to evade responsibilities. Complainers and whiners for whom the care is never adequate, they're rarely seriously ill, and often endlessly hospitalised with a broken leg. Ambulance drivers, porters, and auxiliaries, also, are bolshy trades unionists, wheeling patients around pell-mell like inanimate objects and, in *The National Health*, indifferently puffing cigarettes over them. In *Britannia Hospital* they closed down the hospital at the merest mention of an extra task unpaid. Public service is out to lunch.

Yet for all the scrapes and japes, the comic doctor is rarely irretrievably awful. Although the 'Carry Ons' finished in chaos, the 'Doctor' films and 'M*A*S*H' invariably concluded with the good doctor performing the statutory heroics. But there's another kind of medical comedy, less farcical and more trenchantly critical. Feature films such as the 1971 *The Hospital* and the 1973 *The National Health*, and TV films such as 'The Singing Detective' (1986) and 'The Houseman's Tale' (1987), are a kind of documentary–comedy introducing, alongside the stock characters of traditional medical comedy, some novel features and a new satiric tone. Their doctors were tired: Dr Bird, the female houseman in *The National Health* permanently yawned, abstractedly dropped crucial papers, and fell asleep over the patients.

'Docu-coms' also deglamourised screen medicine by the ubiquity of death. Not for them the wholly hale comic patient whose only wound was a sore thumb, freeing them to whine full-time. *The Hospital* began with a death and was punctuated with a series of other accidental deaths (of medical staff) until it began to seem as if the whole hospital population was in for it. In *The National Health* almost the entire male surgical ward ended up dead (four patients, and the least likeliest surviving), with death treated as inevitable. 'The Houseman's Tale' featured five deaths in part one alone, the victims again mostly doctors. The medical staff in docu-coms, when they aren't themselves ill, are at best impotent bystanders, more often instrumental in sending patients to their maker.

The feature film *The Hospital* was the first to venture into this territory, with a hospital not only uncompromisingly money-minded – the woman from the accounts department asked a corpse in casualty 'Do you carry Blue Cross/Blue Shield?' – but also incomparably accident-prone. As the Chief of Staff Dr Bock, played by George C. Scott, put it,

> A man comes into the hospital in perfect health, and in the space of a week, we chop up one kidney, damage another, reduce him to coma, and damn near kill him . . . the entire machinery of modern medicine has apparently conspired to destroy one lousy patient . . . Let him go, before we kill him.

The docu-com is often an implicit commentary on the doctor shows, bathetically contrasting the TV doctor with real hospital life, all overcooked meals, soiled sheets, catheters and carbolic. No one milked this better than Peter Nichols, whose play *The*

National Health Or Nurse Norton's Affair was directed for the cinema by Jack Gold. Nichols intercut parodied scenes from an American medical soap (with its torrid doctor–nurse romance; glossy machines; whiter-than-white uniforms; flaring nostrils; meaningful looks and soaring music) with a bleak British men's surgical ward (full of pasty-faced patients with bladder trouble, ulcers and false teeth, all senile or very ill and dressed in frayed old dressing-gowns in a decaying Victorian hospital with peeling wallpaper, grey colours, and muted lighting).

For the grisly reality, Nichols drew on 'Carry On' humour, even using 'Carry On' actors like Jim Dale, and broad 'Carry On' jokes, while his Matron was quite as briskly jolly as any Hattie Jacques character, breezily telling the patients 'Get well soon. We need the beds.' But Nichols used the 'Carry On' style much more mordantly than the original to portray the indignity and pathos of illness and dying. Jim Dale's orderly, Barnet, joked about sex and death, cheerfully describing the routine of preparing a dead patient's body, closing the apertures and tying 'the how's-your-father with a reef-knot': the depersonalisation feared from hospital was complete, our most vulnerable places trussed and stuffed like poultry. Nichols also used the juxtaposition of glossy American and bleak British to comment on the declining NHS, its life-saving machines missing essential parts, and its medics fumbling and failing. Medical care, more than medical carers, stood powerfully indicted.

The NHS men's ward created by Dennis Potter in 'The Singing Detective' was strikingly similar, down to the infantalising nurses, the ward evangelists, and bedpan embarrassment,[10] but the medical sections of Potter's multi-layered drama used a bitingly articulate main character (Marlow) and a variety of narrative techniques to savage the medical profession for its failure to engage with patients' feelings – a consumer critique similar to Trevor Griffiths and G.F. Newman's dramas, but with unsurpassed rage and wit. The doctors on the ward round defended themselves with jargon and medical clichés against Marlow's depression, anger, and sense of humiliation. Though he implored them to acknowledge the ghastliness of inhabiting a body with a chronic skin condition ('Listen. Please listen to me. . . . I've reached the end'), they responded only with smugness (cuttingly dismissed by Marlow with a 'Never mind the blather. I can get that from a doctor, doctor') and suggestions of anti-depressants. Under Marlow's hallucination they transmuted into a chorus line singing 'Dry Bones' – to him, behaviour hardly more outlandish and surreal than their actual response.

But a two-part 1987 BBC TV comic hospital drama called 'The Houseman's Tale' (its transmission blocked by the BBC for a year on account of its profusion of sex and blood) showed how far you could go in comic medical drama in the mid-1980s. By now, humour was unexceptional in medical fiction and even the doctor shows invariably had comic sub-plots (the staff of 'St Elsewhere' and 'Casualty' were far droller than Drs Kildare or Casey, strictly one-joke-per-episode men). 'The Houseman's Tale' combined the consumer critique of the documentaries with some of the conventions of the medical comedy. Sex and drink were its young doctors' main preoccupations (the women again stereo-typically portrayed as sexually available nurses). Though occasionally grotesque, the medical staff were less bad than indifferent, and more usually hungover, mildly incompetent (the hero bungled taking blood), insensitive (a consultant roughly fingering a tearful woman's breast baldly declared that it would have to come off), or dishonest (a GP, who misdiagnosed a patient that died, never owned up). They rarely managed to save a patient. In 'The Houseman's Tale', the philandering, bungling doctor of the comedies, and the emotionally unengaged doctor of the critical documentaries, came together.

13 Unsound Effects?

The Media's Impact on the Audience

It makes them sick

Again and again, researchers cite television as a major source of viewers' health information, second only to doctors and dentists, and sometimes overtaking them. TV and radio documentaries also rate fairly highly as trustworthy sources of health information. From such studies, researchers have adduced the media's power to influence viewers, an idea to which the medical profession, the tabloid press, and politicians, have consistently subscribed.

The idea of the mass media as omnipotent has a long history. Among its originators were leading members of the 'Frankfurt School', social scientists such as Adorno, Marcuse and Horkheimer, who witnessed Goebbels' manipulative techniques and mass propaganda in Germany and who emigrated to the United States in the 1930s, disseminating a view of mass culture as monolithic, conservative and persuasive. The audience was seen as a *tabula rasa*, passive and powerless in the face of the mass media's irresistible ideology. This has been called an 'effects' or 'hypodermic needle' view of the media: mass culture 'injects' its ideologies into the consciousness of viewers and listeners who, like animals in laboratory experiments or Pavlov's dogs, react directly to the stimulus and modify their behaviour.

Later this view was buttressed by analyses of the power of advertising, such as Vance Packard's *The Hidden Persuaders* (1957), which depicted Madison Avenue as skilled brainwashers using sophisticated psychological techniques and subliminal appeals to persuade a mesmerised audience to consume. It's a view still current in the ideas of Mary Whitehouse and other anti-pornography campaigners who believe in the corruptibility of the audience; and in exponents of modelling theory, who argue that we learn new ways of behaviour by observing them in others, even on television. Such vicarious learning, they say, can reduce or increase our inhibitions about a particular behaviour, and they suggest that persuasive communications and mass appeals, though rarely producing simple effects, can initiate lasting changes in people's beliefs and behaviour.[1]

Certainly, some studies in the 'effects' tradition, measuring attitudes or behaviour before and after exposure to a programme, seem to corroborate them. Eighteen per cent of those visiting a clinic for sexually transmitted diseases after a BBC TV programme on the subject did so as a direct result of watching the programme.[2] Studies have found a causal relationship between media coverage of the adverse effects of the contraceptive pill, and the numbers of women giving it up. After extensive American publicity on Toxic Shock Syndrome, 33.9 per cent of adolescents surveyed changed the tampons they used, and 27.5 per cent stopped using tampons altogether.[3] When Angie in the BBC soap opera 'EastEnders' washed down a bottle of sleeping pills with a bottle of gin, two British doctors – reproducing the conclusions of American researchers – insisted that she inspired a rash of copycat suicides, though a subsequent study comparing parasuicides (suicide attempts) before and after the episode found the increase insignificant.[4]

Alongside the belief in the media's power to do ill, is a conviction in its potential for good. After EastEnders' Angie and Den visited a marriage guidance counsellor, local marriage guidance offices were reported to have been inundated with calls.[5] And BBC TV's 'That's Life' was credited in Parliament with encouraging the Department of Transport to run a series of road safety advertisements about special car chairs and harnesses for children.

Look-after-yourself campaigns: the unheeded message

But the most unshakable belief in the mass media's capacity to influence the audience for good is demonstrated by mass media look-after-yourself campaigns. Again and again, with undimmed enthusiasm and optimism, health educators dream up media campaigns to persuade viewers to change their ways. And again and again, health educators shake their heads in disappointment and incomprehension as their messages prove infinitely resistible.[6]

Smokers seem particularly unpersuadable. Almost every screen attempt to talk them out of their habit has either failed, been short-lived in its impact, or hasn't reached heavy smokers.

Other campaigns designed to change individual behaviour have also met with meagre success. An American cable TV campaign to encourage the use of car seat-belts, shown over nine months and equivalent to the type of major advertising effort which companies use to promote a new product, had no measured effect whatsoever.[7] Not one single listener consulted their GP after a BBC Radio Scotland broadcast encouraging them to seek flu vaccinations.[8] And a review of forty-nine mass media health education campaigns carried out in various countries between 1964 and 1979 found only small, short-term behaviour changes and unpredictable shifts in attitude.[9]

What's more, it's long been known that health education campaigns can backfire or generate unintended results. After a 1976 BBC Radio Humberside series, 'Is it Cancer, Doctor?', listeners were more likely than non-listeners to mention as causes of cancer some items which the series had stated *weren't* caused by cancer. An American radio broadcast in the 1940s warning the public to avoid unqualified X-ray operators left some listeners afraid of all X-ray treatment. And the British anti-heroin campaign arising out of the moral panic in 1985/6 reportedly made the drug a challenge to some young people, particularly since it was depicted as dangerous and unrespectable, the province of pale young anti-heroes.

Even where health education campaigns do appear to provoke measurable and intended changes, these often can't be attributed with any certainty to television programmes; broadcasters may well be preaching to the converted.

This proliferation of health education failures has generated its own genre, the where-did-we-go-wrong post-mortem, often with a social–psychological orientation. The audience wasn't properly targeted, segmented, pre-tested, or motivated, they suggest, or was given too much information. The message was too long or short, too dull or infrequent, too impersonal or vague, too unpopular. Essentially, it's seen as a matter of communication – finding the right slogan, fostering the right image, not seeming too authoritarian – or a marketing problem.

Those devising health promotion programmes swop ideas about the best way to ensnare the audience, and fashions change. Shock tactics and fear-arousing messages used to be shunned but came back into favour. Health education campaigns started trying to mimic commercial ads for unhealthy products, bringing in TV actors and rock stars – why should the Devil have all the best pop videos? They tried to avoid moralising, and positive rather than negative messages became the rage. Some believed that the public could be surreptitiously lured into health, Packarded into fitness.

But all the while most continued to believe that 'if the mass media are effective in the promotion of numberless goods and services to the consumer, then the media should be equally effective in the dissemination of health information',[10] until researchers gently pointed out the differences between commercial advertising and health campaigns. Those selling 'new-improved' catfood, argued the researchers, rarely had as their primary aim the conversion of behaviour: most ads mobilised and channelled existing predispositions. They were also directed at things which people wanted to do, whereas most health campaigns try to stop them doing what they want. And while health educators hold out the prospect of intangible future benefits, commercial advertisers offer immediate gratification. What's more, to the advertiser success can mean gaining a 1 per cent increase in the market, yet health educators consider a 1 per cent change in behaviour derisory.[11]

In the face of all this discouragement, health educators turned enthusiastically to what seemed to be the only two major successful Western mass media health campaigns, in Finland and California. The North Karelia Project to reduce high heart disease rates began in 1972. In its first five years, 250 articles on smoking appeared in the local newspapers; there were local radio anti-smoking messages; and forty-five different versions of anti-smoking leaflets were distributed. In 1978 Finnish TV ran a nationwide anti-smoking series, backed up by some 100 self-help groups in the North Karelia county, and there were further national TV series in 1980 and 1982 encouraging viewers to stop smoking, take up exercise, reduce fat, salt, and sugar. Orthodox health educators found the results impressive, with fewer middle-aged men dying from heart disease, and with 10 per cent of smokers who followed the programme (about 1 per cent of the population) giving up for at least a year.

The North Karelia Project had a head start in that it originated with the lay population: in 1971 the North Karelians petitioned the Finnish Government to do something about the county's extremely high heart disease rate. What's more, North Karelia is a largely rural county of 180,000 inhabitants in Eastern Finland, and Finland itself is a small and socially cohesive country with only two TV channels: its experience can't be blithely extrapolated to other countries. But what health campaigners noted was that the media were only one component in a much broader campaign which drew on local authorities and voluntary organisations, the dairy industry (which produced more low-fat products), doctors and nurses, and included social support, self-help groups, environmental modifications, and community organisation courses and seminars.[12] In addition, the anti-smoking campaign was backed by national legislation: a 1977/78 law prohibited all sales promotion of tobacco, and restricted marketing and smoking in public places.

The Stanford Three Community Study set out to test the mass media's effectiveness in contributing to the reduction of heart disease. It compared two Northern California towns, Gilroy and Watsonville, with a third, Tracy, over three years. Gilroy got a mass media campaign, consisting of public service TV announcements in English and Spanish, radio announcements and dramatisations, weekly newspaper columns, and leaflets. In Watsonville it was supplemented by intensive personal instruction of high-risk individuals, while Tracy got nothing – it was just measured. The two media towns showed improvements – their estimated risk of coronary heart disease was down by 17 to 18 per cent – but Tracy didn't. The project organisers concluded that 'the mass media can increase knowledge and change dietary behaviour', especially when accompanied by social support, face-to-face instruction, and the use of existing networks.[13]

Health educators took from these projects (especially the Finnish) the idea that the media's role in health promotion was enhanced when it formed part of a broader campaign. And they awoke to the value of back-up. Indeed, back-up became the panacea of the 1980s. Britain's new Channel 4 was particularly severely affected: for a time, it seemed as if almost every single Channel 4 programme was followed by the announcement of an accompanying leaflet or book. A new back-up organisation, Broadcasting Support Services, did a valuable job in staffing phone-lines and then sending out programme-linked information, but in the absence of other criteria, broadcasters and health educators often seemed to judge the effectiveness of their programmes by the numbers of booklets requested or phone-calls received. Information became fetishised and advice ubiquitous: though leaflets and radio experts often just referred viewers and listeners straight back to their doctor or to voluntary and statutory agencies,[14] they emitted a virtuous whiff of public service.

Increasingly, health campaigners came to abandon the 'hypodermic needle' view of the media, with its direct effects, and to adopt instead an 'aerosol spray' line: you spray it on, some hits the target, most drifts away, and very little penetrates. The audience was no longer seen as a homogenous group, reacting uniformly as a mass, and the media were no longer considered uniquely powerful definers of reality, able to change beliefs. They were viewed rather as reinforcing existing beliefs, and only able to influence directly where opinions were unformed or uncrystallised, or on a subject of which viewers had little personal experience. But, though this led health campaigners to think more closely about targeting their message and segmenting their audience, it rarely encouraged orthodox health educators to question their right to preach to the audience in the first place. They may have decided that their aim was no longer to persuade, but to educate, inform, stimulate, or promote (the term health education went out – in came health promotion), but there was no mistaking the one-way direction of all the information, and many viewers and listeners were riled by the top-down, prescriptive approach.[15]

Nevertheless, official faith in the power of look-after-yourself media campaigns to provoke changes in behaviour remains undiminished. Since 1985 the British Government has put most of its energy and funds for fighting AIDS into media public education campaigns, and in February 1987, the BBC and ITV unprecedentedly cooperated for a special nine-day stint of public service information programming. Only the nimblest and deftest channel-switcher could avoid it. Yet, though both found that the audience's knowledge had increased as a result, sexual behaviour remained unchanged, with no increase in the percentage of viewers using a condom.[16]

So what are the real effects of look-after-yourself mass media health campaigns? The prescriptive style of health campaign, with its active, dominant expert, and passive, dependent client, may actually constitute a barrier to people acting individually and collectively to take control of their health. An American community organiser, discussing look-after-yourself media messages, has claimed that 'one can hardly imagine more effective methods for emphasising the impotence of the powerless than these overwhelming voices of the manipulative outsider'.[17] In other words, the very act of propagandising the audience about the need to change their habits reinforces their subordinate position as the objects of other people's expertise, while simultaneously increasing their guilt. Orthodox media look-after-yourself programmes, if they have any effect at all, may be making the audience sicker.

By the same token, the value of useful media health education may come less from its explicit content than from its subtext. In 1982 the BBC, in collaboration with the Health Education Council, broadcast announcements on network television and local radio in twelve languages including Bengali, Gujarati, Hindi, and Punjabi, to encourage viewers and listeners to write in or phone for booklets in their own language detailing the health care and benefits to which they were entitled. The project was evaluated and found effective, the researchers observing among ethnic listeners 'an element of surprise and pleasure on hearing an announcement in one's mother tongue at prime-time. It was interpreted by some as a sign of acceptance and concern for ethnic minorities'.[18] This may have been as health-enhancing as anything in the booklets, however valuable they were.

Health educators have also, on occasion, used the media not to prescribe audience behaviour but to discover the audience's needs.[19] This type of programming shares some of the assumptions of the community development approach to health, examining health issues from a lay perspective, and validating the health needs which local people themselves have identified as important rather than imposing professional definitions. As the American community health organiser put it,

> there is no effective treatment that can be *administered* to the powerless ... it is impossible to *produce* health among the powerless. It is only possible to allow health by transferring tools, authority, budgets and income to those with the malady of powerlessness.[20]

This is an explicit rejection of the bland look-after-yourself idiom. It also upsets people in power.

The broadcasters' audience

Broadcasting institutions have rarely shared health educators' or governments' belief in the power of the media, and programme-makers themselves – perhaps because they've seen their programmes float off barely noticed into the ether – tend to have a limited view of their influence.

Nevertheless, broadcasting organisations use before-and-after effects studies to measure changes in attitude after exposure to a programme. They often test how 'correct' the audience's opinions are after watching a medical programme: has their knowledge of coronary thrombosis increased, are viewers more likely than non-viewers to know the purpose of the EMI-scanner?[21] One problem with audience research is that it generally takes the programme's intended message as a benchmark; the audience's knowledge is judged by how far it accords with the programme's. Viewers' dissent is regarded as a 'reluctance to believe some of the more unpalatable facts'[22] or, if they consider pollution a greater risk to their health than diet, they're thought to suffer from 'confusion'.[23] Most audience research on medical programmes conducted by broadcasting organisations itself reproduces dominant scientific and medical attitudes, and invalidates lay beliefs where they differ from them. (Suggesting that the chief purpose of the EMI-scanner is to make money for EMI is therefore not a correct answer.) Audience research, like any other kind of investigation, is a social product, telling us as much about the institution which originated it as about the audience itself.

Programme-makers themselves know remarkably little about their viewers or listeners. Feedback with the real audience is limited: most programmes' viewers and listeners are rarely surveyed and generally only counted. Those who phone or write in are often dismissed as atypical – cranks or axe-grinders. Producers, in thinking about viewers, are therefore obliged to invent them, often in their own image. 'I sort of use myself as a gauge' says an American TV medical producer,[24] 'it's me with the corners knocked off, me without having read books on medical philosophy', suggests a British counterpart.[25] They also fall back on caricatured stereotypes: 'we do say, what's the Huddersfield housewife going to think about this, but it just makes us check our ideas and ask if we're being too intellectual', said the executive producer of a medical series, while his producer cautioned staff that 'we've obviously got to steer clear of fuzzy-haired trendiness, which Mrs Jones in Acacia Villas will be fazed by'.[26] Interestingly, it's invariably women viewers living in the North which documentary and current affairs producers dream up, presumably to counter their own male, Southern bias and ensure intelligibility: they see Northern women as the acme of down-to-earthness, perhaps believing that if these viewers can understand something, anyone can.

The media researchers' audience

A key development in the idea of the active audience occurred in the 1960s with the adoption of a new approach called 'uses and gratifications', which argued that researchers should get away from the habit of thinking in terms of what television did to people, and look instead at what people did with television:

> By emphasising the gratifications that people derive from consumption of media materials, and the uses to which they put them in the circumstances of their own lives, this approach draws attention to the significance of what the audience member contributes to the interaction between him and a mass medium.[27]

In 'uses and grats' research, the producer's intention all but disappeared: it was now the audience who 'created' the media message in response to their own needs and their predispositions which shaped their interpretations. It was the perfect research approach for the late 1960s and 1970s, with its obsession with the consumer, interaction, and doing-your-own thing. And when researchers, like health educators, sensibly began to home in on local networks (primary groups became the buzz phrase), seeing the media as only one influence next to family, friends, workmates, peer group, neighbourhood, church, school, it was all in keeping with the new attention being paid to community. But 'uses and grats' attracted criticism. Though it instated audience members as active participants in the communication process, 'uses and grats' researchers saw the ways in which viewers and listeners made meanings in thoroughly individual and psychological terms, and were faulted for their failure to acknowledge the social structure – the class, cultural, gender, age, and subcultural dimensions which shape our understanding of programmes.

Recent audience research has gone even further in seeing audiences as (now literally) active parties in the viewing process. Observing television watching through cameras placed in TV sets in families' homes, researchers were astounded to see the audience, not quietly sitting in regimented rows hanging on broadcasters' every word (as they'd presumably anticipated), but eating, sleeping, making love, hoovering, fighting, and even leaving the room while the set was on – proof, they maintained, of how active and discriminating the viewer actually was. Broadcasting organisations loved the new evidence – conclusive proof that the media couldn't be blamed for every social ill. And again the new research paradigm fitted in with the *Zeitgeist*: it was free-market viewing, with family sovereignty.

Another strand of media research has examined both programmes and audiences, seeing programme-makers *and* viewers as creating messages, and trying to analyse the relationship between the two. Producers shape their programmes to 'encode' certain meanings; though the programme can be understood in many different ways, it has a 'preferred reading' which the majority of viewers and listeners will decode and absorb, though others will modify or challenge it according to their social class, gender, ethnic group, age, etc.[28] A programme's ideology, therefore, may be powerful but not irresistible, with particular audiences using programmes for their own particular ends.

Even pleasure was rehabilitated as a respectable explanation for viewing and listening, and researchers began to credit the audience with a good deal more sophistication than before: they found viewers often sensitive to programme-makers' intentions, able simultaneously to describe what a programme was trying to get them to think and to reject it.[29] Very little of this new work has been taken up by (or emanated from) those researching health and medical programmes.[30] Audience research in this sphere, dominated by broadcasting institutions and health campaigners, remains locked in before/after studies and evaluations of health education campaigns (both broadly part of the 'effects' school), and social–psychological research to determine the most persuasive messages.

Medical programmes' influence: so powerful or so what?

If mass media health education campaigns have proved so inadequate at changing behaviour; if the media reproduce rather than originate ideas; if we abandon the hypodermic needle approach and see the audience as active participants in the production of the media message, sophisticatedly discounting and counter-arguing with the box, need we worry about the media's influence at all? Viewers and listeners obviously bring a developed set of values and beliefs to their viewing and listening. Nevertheless, health and medical programming plays a significant role in shaping public debate and the climate of opinion, both in what it chooses to address and what it doesn't, through its 'symbolic crusades' and moral panics, its sudden creation of social problems, its ongoing obsessions and its routine omissions.

This is the media's agenda-setting role. As one writer said of the Press, it 'may not be successful much of the time in telling people what to think, but it is stunningly successful in telling its readers what to think *about*'.[31] The media play a major role in establishing the salience of different issues in public debate, of defining which aspects are important and which aren't, the terms in which they're discussed and who discusses them. The health agenda set by the media has been criticised for its preoccupation with high-technology, curative medicine, and its individualistic strategies for health. This book has tried to analyse how and why certain limited ways of looking at health and medicine recur in the media, reinforcing the medical and look-after-yourself approaches. The media play a part, especially in the continuities between programmes and advertisements, in normalising particular ways of looking at the world.[32]

Yet it's doubtful whether even the media's agendas are uncritically imbibed by audiences. A subtler process is probably at work. A study of East Londoners' views on health and illness found that they gave substantially different accounts of the same events in their lives on different occasions. It suggested that what people say and how they say it varies according to who they are saying it to and the circumstances they're in. People's public accounts reproduced ideas about health and illness in common currency and known to be socially acceptable, while their private accounts sprang directly from personal experience and the thoughts and feelings accompanying it. Public accounts acknowledged medical authority and drew on scientific concepts, while private theories located the cause of illness in people's personal biographies and environment.[33]

Similarly, a media researcher discussing audience research has distinguished between 'official' and 'unofficial' discourses, the first being a way of talking about the world used in the news media, in contacts with government authorities, in bureaucratic situations, and in talking to researchers who are seen as official, and the second belonging to more personal situations and spontaneous utterances. While he recognised that it would be simplistic to suggest that official discourse was media-inspired, and unofficial discourse pure, unadulterated free speech, he suggests that the official context of most audience research tends to elicit responses compatible with official discourse, while unofficial discourse is relegated to private moments.[34]

Viewers and listeners probably hold contradictory views on health and medicine, simultaneously expressing public or official accounts and private or unofficial ones. When the BBC interviewed 1,000 adults on their attitudes towards health, these contradictions were strikingly displayed. The vast majority – 92 per cent – agreed with the statement that 'staying healthy is an individual's responsibility' (what might be termed the official or public view). At the same time, when asked to rank the most serious health risks (from a list) in order of importance, nuclear waste and pollution emerged as second and third after smoking, with dietary factors like too much fat and too much sugar much lower down the scale (and after stress).[35]

The Corporation judged this a sign of public confusion, rather than an indication of the co-existence of contradictory beliefs, dialectically-related. Certainly, both sets of answers are in part media-inspired (who else has supplied so much evidence of the perils of pollution and the consequences of nuclear waste, especially post-Chernobyl?), but few health and medical programmes or doctors labour the role of pollution and nuclear waste as a cause of illness – diet is considered a much more major risk factor in medical discourse. It seems, then, that we can happily subscribe at the same time to both dominant medical definitions of health *and* lay beliefs, that we both absorb and re-produce the media's medical messages and discount and modify them, in complex and changing ways.

What's more, public accounts are clearly stronger in some groups of viewers and listeners than others, depending on how much they identify with official discourse. So sensitive research on the media and health would need to look not just at how private and public accounts co-exist within individuals or a social group, but how they're distributed differently *between* different groups, and also would need to examine the different factors (both media and non-media) which help create them.[36]

Whose policy?

Those who believe in the media as a supremely powerful social force suggest that programmes can make or change public policy, but such effects, too, are rarely quite so simple. Yorkshire TV's 1983 documentary 'Windscale: Nuclear Laundry', which claimed that the incidence of leukaemia in young children living close to the nuclear reprocessing plant was ten times the national average, is often held up as an example of media power, since it provoked a government-ordered official inquiry within twenty-four hours. Yet when the inquiry reported a year later, it gave a qualified reassurance about the health hazards, though eighteen months later still it emerged that because it had been given incorrect figures, the inquiry had seriously underestimated the levels of radioactive discharge from the plant. The programme had effected no change.

In fact TV rarely forces an issue singlehandedly into public consciousness. When documentaries and TV investigations do cause a furore, precipitating policy reviews and changes, these are often an effective, but final stage in much longer-running campaigns. Perhaps the most powerful British documentary in recent years on health and illness was Yorkshire TV's searing 1982 film 'Alice – A Fight For Life' on mesothelioma (asbestos-induced cancer). It caused the legal limits of asbestos to be changed and illustrates the way in which TV nudges forward issues already in the public domain. Although the programme was outstandingly successful in raising public consciousness about asbestos and would appear to illustrate the power of the media, the campaign against asbestos also demonstrates the media's impotence and is a case-study in TV's variable and complex effects.

Medical knowledge of the terrible health consequences of working with asbestos goes back very far, and there were fully-fledged public outcries about asbestos in the late 1920s, the 1960s, and in the 1970s following the Ombudsman's investigation into the deaths of more than twenty former workers of a Hebden Bridge asbestos factory. In the 1970s and early 1980s, there was a steady stream of articles on asbestos in trades union journals and the national Press (the *Guardian*'s Angela Singer was particularly energetic). There were nine major TV documentaries between 1974 and 1982 alone ('World in Action' was diligent, and even ran a story on the subject in early July 1982, two weeks before 'Alice'), but all with little success – the legally permitted levels were only tinkered with.

'Alice', named after its 'star', a feisty 47-year-old Yorkshire-woman painfully dying of mesothelioma after having worked with asbestos, changed official policy and public consciousness. Employees at a Bradford clutch and brake linings factory who worked with asbestos stopped work for three hours on the day after the broadcast (and two months later, the firm announced the introduction of a new range of asbestos-free brake pads). Five hundred boiler workers in Nottinghamshire went on strike after the programme in protest at the potential dangers of asbestos dust. Union officials launched their own investigations into the health risks. Yorkshire Television got 700 letters, most from people working with asbestos concerned about their own situation or confirming the film's charges. Local environmental health departments all over the country were inundated with inquiries from people worried about asbestos in the home. Nine million pounds was immediately wiped off the shares of Cape Industries and Turner and Newall, the companies featured in the programme. And, after a Commons debate generated by the programme, the Government decided to immediately implement in 1981 new regulations (including lower dust levels) for work with asbestos, rather than wait for EEC directives, and a year later imposed new, stricter controls on the use of asbestos (although trades unionists argued that they didn't go far enough).

Why did 'Alice' succeed where others had failed? As its producer John Willis admitted 'Everyone felt asbestos had been done before. You can imagine going to a commercial TV controller and saying "I want to make a film about asbestos." They'd demote you to the Grimsby office straightaway.'[37] But as one of the film's researchers said,

> John Willis's reputation as a film-maker cannot be discounted. It helped make the film a big event in television terms and it had a good slot in the evening schedule as a result. Secondly, a one-off documentary is always likely to make more ground than a single programme in a running current affairs series.[38]

But television alone can't be credited with the change: almost invariably, the leverage attributed to the media has been preceded and abetted by off-screen campaigning, and years of trades union activity had helped to raise consciousness about the dangers of asbestos, with the General and Municipal Workers Union especially indefatigable. Nonetheless Willis' brilliant use of television's strengths played a major part in hijacking the audience: he cleverly yoked heart-tugging human interest to hard-hitting reportage.

> We started with the thing which makes this kind of thing work – the people, Alice and Georgina. ... We tried to make the film work by locking the investigative material onto the human stories and interweaving them.[39]

Asbestos may have already been creeping onto the map but 'Alice' gave it a very powerful push.

Contrary to belief, 'Alice' type effects are very rare in television. And there's a chastening postscript: asbestos manufacturers Turner and Newall recovered, and in 1985 made profits of £39 million. It's all too easy to overestimate the media's ideological role and underestimate the part played by material conditions in structuring our lives and making us sick. In a sense (and this isn't a novel version of media-bashing), the media themselves have helped us overstate ideology: TV, radio, and the press trade in ideas, images, and words and, weaned on the media, we've come to believe that ideas, images and words are all. Health educators are astounded that we can know something but fail to believe in it or do it. Media-bashers are convinced that if we see it, we subscribe to it or are shaped by it. The media's effects remain far more complex and contradictory.

Conclusion

If this examination of media coverage of health and medicine is largely pessimistic, speculating about the future propels us into the Cassandra mode. This is what the crystal-ball predicts. The medical approach will continue to amaze and spellbind us with medicine's latest developments. Doctors will continue to be marvelled at as they intervene surgically earlier and earlier in the reproductive process, though the high-tech medical approach will be accompanied by more ethical programmes, and health economists offering cost-benefit analyses will be much in demand.

The obsession with health will continue largely unabated. Look-after-yourself programmes will proliferate but their emphasis – in keeping with the new health promotion style – will be fun, fun, fun. All the paraphernalia of marketing – balloons, T-shirts, consumer surveys – will be deployed to sell health and make it glossy and sexy, and TV companies will describe their efforts with pride in their end-of-year reports. Stress will become a big issue, with TV and radio series suggesting all sorts of individual techniques to counter it, while its social and environmental dimensions will be confined to the footnotes. Most people's lives will, meanwhile, continue unaffected, but there'll be plenty of leisure tips on how to while away the unemployed years.

The airwaves will echo with the sound of advice given and information offered. Sex and marital counselling by accredited experts will become commonplace. The telephone will become an adjunct of the TV and radio set, with dial-and-listen or dial-and-tell the essential prologue or postscript to a programme. Courses on how to deal with the media will mushroom, and no doctor or medical worker will contemplate an appearance without advanced skills in unruffable communication. There'll be the mirage of access – push-button voting by viewers, instant polls, 'interactive' media. Phone-ins will creep onto television, and Americanised talk shows reach saturation level: presented by telegenic male doctors with blow-dried hair and immaculately made-up female reporters, they'll offer a medical angle on any personal problem.

Such a vision, Americaphobic and gloomy, may be off-centre. Britain still has an enduring reputation for its public service broadcasting, not all of it left over from the war years. And contradiction and dissent is tolerated if not encouraged in the British media, despite the reintensification in the 1980s of government attempts at control, either directly or through the market. Channel 4 has significantly broadened the range of health and medical programmes, and given a voice to the disenfranchised: psychiatric patients made an articulate and powerful programme about their experiences;[1] NHS workers in a Northern hospital excavated the history of their hospital and its staff;[2] health workers of every rank have made programmes about the effects of the NHS cuts, and the environmental approach has been used for some fresh and innovative documentaries.[3] Moreover, despite the shortcomings of the consumer approach identified in Chapter 3, discussion of health and medicine both on British radio and television and off has become more diverse and critical since the mid-1970s. And off-air, dissenting groups are becoming more organised and sophisticated, and the community development approach has been endorsed and supported by the World Health Organisation.

But present and future changes to the ecology of broadcasting both nationally and internationally – the so-called new information order – augur badly for the health debate. Although satellite and cable television and teletext appear to provide a proliferation of outlets allowing a diversity of opinion, they actually encourage homogeneity. What looks like decentralisation – public service broadcasting organisations in Europe can no longer maintain their monopolies – is actually internationalisation. As huge multi-national media conglomerates secure the channels (local ventures just can't compete), they standardise the output – aptly known as product – for Euroviewing. National regulatory agencies, if they haven't buckled beneath the lunge towards deregulation, are powerless against these blasts of economic power blowing across national boundaries.

It could be argued that the internationalisation of the media itself poses a health threat, colonising the hopes of the citizens of different countries, converting us all into Los Angeloids, and ensuring an unsatisfiable chasm between social values and experiences. Even welcomers of cultural Esperanto concede that it brings problems. In Sweden, for example, where advertising on the country's radio and two TV channels is banned, and the Government has a low-fat, high-fibre food policy, the most popular foreign channel is Rupert Murdoch's satellite station Sky Channel, replete with McDonalds hamburger ads.

In Britain, too, cheap bought-in American material is a staple on cable and satellite TV stations searching for profitability, and with all the competition public service stations' claims for public funding will diminish as their audiences inevitably do. The line of least consensus – the environmental approach to health and medicine – is unlikely to flourish. There may be attempts to innovate or safeguard local media for non-profit organisations, such as the health programming of a German cable TV pilot project,[4] but the experience of the American Cable Health Network whose lofty ideals evanesced as the profits did is instructive.[5] And though satellite owners are earmarking some satellite time for apparently worthy projects, their actual nature may be less benign. 'Worldnet' interactive satellite, managed by the United States Information Agency, arranges for American heart transplant experts in Salt Lake City to answer the questions of foreign doctors. Teletext systems such as Prestel are expensive for residential users (both BBC and ITV versions available to subscribers only), and there's been a general absence of debate about the system's potential social uses, with financial and industrial interests prevailing.[6]

The ironies abound. Today, with more public information about health than ever before, health is more privatised and individual viewer–patients more atomised than ever. The international public health crisis (starvation, coronary heart disease, cancer, AIDS) has been accompanied in the West by what's been called 'a retreat from politics'.[7] Scientists worry about the public understanding of science, but not science's understanding of the public. And marginal, disenfranchised groups remain the objects of professional concern, medical and media, so objectifying and disenfranchising them further.

A real change in the media's coverage of health and medicine requires change in at least some of the major determinants and influences described in this book, and this leads us into the realm of 'if only'. . . . Journalists would need access to alternative sources of information, and would have to consider them legitimate. They'd need training in questioning dominant views, requiring a whole new ideology of journalism. Observers have argued that science and medicine need their critics like music, literature and the arts,[8] that the relationship between journalists and scientists should be adversarial and not symbiotic,[9] and that science as part of the political process requires political reporting.[10] But this would bring journalists into conflict with the medical profession, politicians, and other power blocs, and producers and presenters of medical programmes are in the main dependent on the medical profession for their legitimacy: how far can they risk alienating them?

There have been campaigns to democratise the media – and introduce, for example, a Right of Reply – but to challenge the omissions and to alter reporters' routine dependence on official sources is less straightforward. Some might say that the media have gone as far as they can in challenging medical orthodoxy, without institutional transformations. Can we really expect the media to be tannoys of social change, more progressive than the rest of the culture? Is genuinely pluralistic health and medical programming possible without different forms of ownership and control of the mass media, and therefore major social, political, and economic changes?

Until the broader structural influences are altered, dissenting broadcasting will continue to occupy only the cracks and margins to which committed journalists and persistent groups can lay claim: the environmental approach to health will continue to be squeezed into late-night 'concerned' documentaries, low-budget access slots, the odd crisis-causing current affairs programme and occasional trailblazing exposés, but won't be the media's chief approach. Unless the broader influences are changed, the media will continue to be doctored.

Notes

Introduction

1 Hilary Graham and Lorna McKee, 'Ideologies of motherhood and medicine on radio and television' (unpublished paper given at British Sociological Association conference, University of Sussex, 1978).

2 Mary B. Cassata et al., 'In sickness and in health', *Journal of Communication*, vol. 29, no. 4, 1979.

3 'Plenty to Say About Body Talk' (Broadcast, 18 January 1985).

4 Angie Mason, BBC (personal communication, 24 March 1986).

5 Radio News Study (NBC, 1983).

6 'The BBC's medical programmes and their effects on lay audiences' (BBC, November 1976).

7 Todd Gitlin, *The Whole World is Watching* (University of California Press, 1980), p. 6.

8 Quoted in C. M. Fletcher, *The Medical Profession and the Mass Media* (Royal College of Physicians, no date).

9 William R. Barclay, 'Science reporting to alarm the public', *Journal of the American Medical Association*, vol. 242, no. 8, August 24/31 1979.

10 Irving Page, 'Science writers, physicians and the public – ménage à trois', *Annals of Internal Medicine*, vol. 73, 1970, p. 645.

11 See, for instance, James W. Tankard and Michael Ryan, 'News source perceptions of science coverage', *Journalism Quarterly* 51, 1974, and Susan Cray Borman, 'Communication accuracy in magazine science reporting', *Journalism Quarterly* 55, 1978. Such studies generally treat accuracy as an unproblematic notion, with scientists' perceptions as yardsticks. In this way, and especially when the studies' judges were also the articles' sources, they reproduce medical and scientific values and priorities – something that Tankard and Ryan acknowledge only as an afterthought, and other accuracy researchers not at all.

12   'Medicine on Radio and Television' (British Medical Association, 1960), p. 7.
13   Charles Crawford, 'Broadcasting science and medical news: the responsibilities and obligations', *Journal of Medical Education*, vol. 57, January 1982, p. 12.
14   It's all the more difficult since objectivity is a central tenet of both scientific and journalistic ideology.
15   Al Byrne, 'The doctors and the media', *Journal of the Irish Medical Association*, vol. 73, August 1980, p. 292.
16   Fletcher, op. cit.
17   Quoted by Hedda Heuser, 'Medicine and the mass media', in Manfred Meyer (ed.), *Health Education by Television and Radio* (K. G. Saur, 1981), p. 19.
18   Peter Golding and Sue Middleton, *Images of Welfare: Press and Public Attitudes to Poverty* (Martin Robertson, 1982).

Chapter one

1   Curiously, this Western view of illness as haphazard and unconnected with moral or emotional aspects is considered rational, while Third World cultures' belief that illness has moral explanations is thought of by Western societies as irrational hocus-pocus.
2   'Science now', *Radio Times*, 24–30 July 1982.
3   *Daily Mail* (1977), quoted in David Albury and Joseph Schwartz, *Partial Progress: The Politics of Science and Technology* (Pluto Press, 1982).
4   'Your mental health – depression', Lifetime Cable Network, 13 May 1985. Barbara Beckwith, in a review of popular American magazines, found that genetic and sociobiological explanations of gender differences and male aggression predominated ('He-man, she-woman: Playboy and Cosmo groove on genes', *Columbia Journalism Review*, January/February 1984).
5   Peter Wright and Andrew Treacher, *The Problem of Medical Knowledge* (Edinburgh University Press, 1982).
6   Jeannette Mitchell, *What Is To Be Done About Illness and Health?* (Penguin, 1984).
7   Susan Sontag, *Illness as Metaphor* (Allen Lane, 1979), p. 84.
8   Gordon Best et al., 'Health, the mass media, and the National Health Service' (Unit for the Study of Health Policy, 1977).
9   Ibid.
10   Interview with David Paterson, 17 April 1985.
11   Michael Young, 'The four purposes and the six methods', *Self-*

Health, the Journal of the College of Health, no. 1, November 1983, p. 3.

12 Michael Shanks, Foreword to 'Patients' rights: A guide to the rights and responsibilities of patients and doctors in the NHS' (National Consumer Council, 1982).

13 Gerry and Carol Stimson, *Health Rights Handbook: A Guide to Medical Care* (Penguin, 1980), p. 9.

14 Ivan Illich, *Medical Nemesis* (Calder & Boyars, 1975).

15 Apart from this, like the medical programme, the consumer programme isn't much interested in the causes of illness, seeing it as something befalling the individual without cause.

16 Barbara Castle, Foreword, 'Prevention and health: everybody's business' (HMSO, 1976), p. 6.

17 Thomas McKeown, 'The role of medicine' (Nuffield Provincial Hospitals Trust, 1976), p. 104.

18 'Picture of Health', transmitted by Channel 4, 1983–4.

19 Peter Draper et al., 'The NHS in the next 30 years: a new perspective on the health of the British' (Unit for the Study of Health Policy, 1978).

20 Marc Renaud, 'On the structural constraints to state intervention in health', *International Journal of Health Services*, vol. 5, no. 4, 1975.

21 Karl Figlio, 'Sinister medicine? A critique of left approaches to medicine', *Radical Science Journal* 9, 1979.

22 'Horizon', although it makes programmes *about* the environment, rarely adopts an environmental approach to health and medicine. It woke up to the social causes of illness over seven years after the Black report in the programme 'Death of the Working Classes' (February 1988). Perhaps the most successful recent environmental film was Yorkshire TV's 1982 investigation into asbestos-caused cancer, 'Alice – A Fight for Life', made not by a science or medical producer but by an investigative documentary film-maker – see Chapter 13 for a discussion of it.

23 Quoted in 'The BBC's medical programmes and their effects on lay audiences' (BBC, 1976), p. 5..

24 Catherine Belsey, *Critical Practice* (Methuen, 1980), p. 3.

25 Terry Eagleton, *Literary Theory: An Introduction* (Blackwell, 1983).

26 Chris Anne Raymond, 'Risk in the Press: conflicting journalistic ideologies' in Dorothy Nelkin (ed.) *The Language of Risk* (Sage, 1985).

27 Dr Polykarp Kusch, quoted in David Warren Burkett, *Writing Science News for the Mass Media* (Gulf Publishing, 1965).

28 Dr Philip Abelson, ibid., p. 27.

29 Ruth Garland, 'Images of health and medical science conveyed by television', *Journal of the Royal College of General Practitioners*, June 1984.

30   Gordon Best et al., op. cit.

31   Connie M. Kristiansen and Christina M. Harding, 'Mobilization of health behaviour by the Press in Britain', *Journalism Quarterly*, vol. 61, no. 2, Summer 1984.

32   June Fisher et al., 'The role of popular media in defining sickness and health', in E. McAnany et al. (eds), *Communication and Social Structure* (Praeger, 1981), p. 250. Content analysis isn't unproblematic as a research method: it ignores the audience and purports to find in texts meanings it's already identified.

33   Carol Haslam, 'Health and Channel 4 – new channel, new challenges' (unpublished paper, Channel 4, 29 March 1982).

34   James W. Pichert, 'Diabetes in the national TV news: 1971–1981', *Diabetes Care*, vol. 6, no. 1, January–February 1983.

35   Herbert J. Gans, *Deciding What's News* (Constable, 1980).

36   Raymond, op. cit.

37   Johan Galtung and Mari Ruge, 'Structuring and selecting news' in Stanley Cohen and Jock Young (eds), *The Manufacture of News* (Constable, 1981), p. 55. For a witty cartoon summary of Galtung and Ruge on what makes an event newsworthy or unnewsworthy, see Peter M. Lewis and Corinne Pearlman, *Media and Power – From Marconi to Murdoch* (Camden Press, 1986).

38   Barbara E. Phillips, 'What is news? Novelty without change?', *Journal of Communication* 26, 1976, p. 92, quoted in Gaye Tuchman, *Making News* (Free Press, 1978).

39   Paul Rock, 'News as eternal recurrence' in Stanley Cohen and Jock Young, op. cit.

40   Interview with James Wilkinson, London, 17 December 1986.

41   'Newsnight', BBC 2 (19 July 1982). ITV's 'News at 10' on the same evening also concentrated on the provision of emergency cover.

42   During the junior hospital doctors' dispute of 1975, for instance, though they didn't support the industrial action, the Press were noticeably milder than in their coverage of the ancillary workers' strikes. See Harvey Gordon and Steve Iliffe, *Pickets in White* (MPU Publications, no date).

43   'Staff cuts led to hospital death, court told' (Press Association, 29 January 1987).

44   Only the *Guardian* ('Shortage of nurses blamed for death') and the *Independent* ('Hospital cuts lead to death') carried brief reports (four paragraphs and seven paragraphs respectively, 30 January 1987). The *Observer* ran a major story linked with a new Labour Party report, 'Great bed robbery: doctors say patients are being put at risk as cut-backs force hospitals to send them home too soon' (Annabel Ferriman, 1 February 1987) without referring to the Glasgow death.

45 Reginald Evans, 18 February 1987, adding

> a poor story on a Sunday will get used when it wouldn't stand a
> chance on a more competitive Monday. It's also a story in Scotland.
> To an extent, a story from Scotland has to be stronger than a story
> from England – it's almost a foreign country.

Chapter two

1 Hilda Matheson, *Broadcasting* (Butterworth, 1933), pp. 190–1.
2 Memo, Hilda Matheson, 23 September 1929. This chapter and the
   next are based on unpublished, original material from the invaluable BBC Written Archives Centre, Caversham.
3 Ibid.
4 BBC letter to listener (26 September 1930).
5 'Case for extension of broadcasts of physical exercises' (BBC,
   3 April 1940).
6 If the BBC was right, 750,000 men and 900,000 women were doing
   exercises at the start, though some of the initial enthusiasm was
   attributed to public sympathy for the announcer, assumed to have
   left home at an unearthly hour and to be doing the exercises himself as he announced them. When a rumour started that the whole
   thing was recorded on disc, public enthusiasm began to wane.
7 The fitness craze of the 1930s and the 1940s was in many respects a
   rerun of that of the nineteenth century, when '*mens sana in corpore
   sano*' was a hallowed Victorian concept, and health became a
   metaphor for moral probity.
8 Quoted in Barbara Wooton, Introduction to the second edition of
   Margery Spring Rice, *Working-Class Wives* (Virago, 1981), p. iv.
9 This isn't to suggest that the later preoccupation with medicine
   simply reflected its greater successes, though the arsenal of sophisticated medical therapies did increase enormously in the 1950s. I'm
   arguing instead that in the 1930s and 1940s, popular ideas about
   medicine more closely matched its capabilities, whereas later
   they diverged.
10 BBC Memo from Miss Wace, 'Health talks' (22 March 1932).
11 BBC Memo from Miss Wace, 'Talks on cancer' (14 November
   1932).
12 Quoted in Charmian Kenner, *No Time for Women* (Pandora Press,
   1985), p. 92.
13 Ibid., p. 93.
14 Jane Lewis, *The Politics of Motherhood: Child and Maternal Welfare in
   England 1900–1939* (Croom Helm, 1980).
15 Anstey later speculated (in Elizabeth Sussex, *The Rise and Fall of the*

British Documentary, University of California Press, 1975), that both films' influence derived less from their public showing than through the impact they had on journalists and politicians. He went on to remake *Enough to Eat?* in a more popular form for the news magazine *The March of Time*.

16   Though today the comparable evidence about the connection between poverty and poor diet is rarely taken up by the media.

17   Memo, George Barnes to Janet Quigley (17 February 1937).

18   Memo, Janet Quigley to George Barnes (10 February 1937). (This was Baldwin's Conservative Government.)

19   Written by Joan Greenwood and produced by Olive Shapley in the innovative BBC North Region, it was broadcast in spite of protests from a London BBC mandarin.

20   Paddy Scannell and David Cardiff, 'Serving the nation: public service broadcasting before the war', in Bernard Waites et al. (ed.) *Popular Culture: Past and Present* (Croom Helm, 1982), p. 165.

21   BBC minutes of Controversy Committee (2 May 1928).

22   It was produced by the Talks Department which, as Scannell and Cardiff (op. cit.) point out, was committed to addressing the urgent social issues of the day in a firsthand and accessible way.

23   Quoted in John Stevenson, *British Society 1914–45* (Penguin, 1984), p. 283.

24   Quoted in Kenner, op. cit., p. 35.

25   Ibid, p. 35.

26   Lewis, op. cit.

27   Letter, Sir John Reith to Sir George Newman (25 May 1934).

28   Letter, Sir George Newman to Sir John Reith (28 May 1934).

29   Letter, Sir George Newman to Sir John Reith (12 June 1934).

30   Letter, Wilkinson to George Barnes (17 September 1942).

31   Ibid.

32   Letter, Sir Richard Maconachie to George Barnes (6 October 1942).

33   Maconachie, in common with his medical producers, was quite happy to defer on health programmes to doctors, who were seen as giving impartial professional advice, but didn't want to have to defer to politicians.

34   Letter, Maconachie to Barnes (20 May 1943), his italics.

35   Charles Webster, 'Healthy or hungry thirties?', *History Workshop Journal* 13, 1982.

36   Charles Hill, *Both Sides of the Hill* (Heinemann, 1964), p. 60.

37   The Radio Doctor, 'Wednesday Morning Early' (Hutchinson, no date), p. 15.

38   Letter, Charles Hill to George Barnes (18 November 1941).

39   Letter, Janet Quigley to George Barnes (16 December 1941).

40 Letter, Isa Benzie to Assistant Director of Talks (20 November 1945).
41 Hill 1964, op. cit., p. 119.
42 Ibid., p. 109.
43 The Radio Doctor, op. cit., p. 16.
44 Hill 1964, op. cit., p. 111.
45 Memo, T. W. Chalmers to Isa Benzie (7 November 1945).
46 Barnes to Quigley (17 November 1944).
47 Barnes to Maconachie (4 December 1944).
48 Charles Hill, *The Way to Better Health* (Burke, no date), p. 8.
49 See Chapter 7 for a critical discussion of this term.
50 Quoted in James Curran & Jean Seaton, *Power Without Responsibility: The Press and Broadcasting in Britain* (Fontana, 1981), p. 177.
51 Quoted in Asa Briggs, *The War of Words* (Oxford University Press, 1970), vol. III, p. 40.
52 A Medical Officer of Health, 'The Health Services on Your Doorstep' (Broadcast, 19 February 1943).
53 Asa Briggs, *Sound and Vision* (Oxford University Press, 1979) vol. IV.
54 Benzie to Barnes, 'Influence of the Radio Doctor *vis-a-vis* National Health Services Bill' (10 April 1946).
55 Bill Duncalf to J. Reid (13 April 1961).
56 Martin Armstrong, *Listener*, 7 February 1957.
57 Script of YLITH on polio (transmitted 11 February 1958).
58 Proceedings of the Council of the BMA, Supplement to the *British Medical Journal*, 1 March 1958.
59 Letter, *BMJ*, 8 March 1958.
60 Letter, *BMJ*, 15 March 1958.
61 Ibid. The answer from the 1970s was to be a resounding 'no' – see Chapter 4.
62 See Chapter 13 for a discussion of audience research in general.
63 BBC Audience Research Report on 'Your Life in Their Hands', UR/58/130, 11 March, 1958.
64 The Radio Doctor, of course, was on radio, and YLITH on television – see below for a discussion of the importance of new TV forms. Radio news, current affairs, and documentaries in the 1950s played a much less central cultural role than before: attention had shifted to television.
65 Second draft of 'Your Life in Their Hands' pamphlet, 23 November 1960.
66 John Prince, 'Surgeon to address viewers', *Daily Telegraph*, 11 February 1961.
67 Eliot Friedson, *Profession of Medicine* (Dodd, Mead & Co., 1975).
68 Raymond Williams, *Television, Technology, and Cultural Form*

(Fontana, 1974).

69   Another reason for it was that the BBC had been forced into a highly competitive situation with ITV. The Corporation appeared to be losing its audience to ITV, and under the imaginative leadership of Director-General Hugh Carlton-Greene, they vigorously went out to get the audience. (Peter Lewis drew my attention to this.)

70   Duncalf to Singer (13 December 1960).

71   Singer to Duncalf (14 December 1960).

72   Aubrey Singer, 'Science broadcasting', BBC Lunchtime Lecture, 4th series (BBC, 1966), p. 13.

73   The series' current editor, viewing a 1963 YLITH on the appendix, thought it very instructional, 'as if you're going to have to do it yourself' (interview with David Paterson, 17 April 1985).

74   Charles Fletcher, 'Your life in their labs – the changing face of medicine', *Listener*, 13 November 1975.

75   Quoted in Pat Rowe, 'Operation success', *Radio Times*, 17–23 May 1980

Chapter three

1   Ruth Garland, 'Images of health and medical science conveyed by television', *Journal of the Royal College of General Practitioners*, vol. 34, June 1984.

2   Ivan Illich et al., *Disabling Professions* (Marion Boyars, 1977).

3   Thomas Szasz, *The Manufacture of Madness* (Paladin, 1973).

4   Barbara Ehrenreich, 'The body politic', *Ms Magazine*, May 1984, p. 52.

5   David Armstrong, 'The doctor–patient relationship: 1930–80', in Peter Wright and Andrew Treacher (eds), *The Problem of Medical Knowledge* (Edinburgh University Press, 1982), p. 117. A key discussion of the subject.

6   Not that this is the media's fault: commonly blamed for their powerful social effects, are they now to be found guilty for their *lack* of impact? The point is only that media representations and lived experience are different.

7   William Ray Arney, *Power and the Profession of Obstetrics* (University of Chicago Press, 1982).

8   Wright and Treacher, op. cit., Introduction.

9   A baboon's heart was transplanted into a two-week-old baby.

10 In the first, the parents of a Down's Syndrome baby boy born in Indiana in 1982 refused to consent to corrective surgery. The baby died six days later. The second involved Baby Jane Doe, born in 1983 in Long Island with spina bifida. Her parents also decided against surgery, and the baby survived with severe handicaps. (John Doe is the American equivalent of John Citizen.)

11 A surrogate child whose biological mother refused to give her up and was taken to court in 1987.

12 The doctor could face a conflict between keeping a patient's confidences, for instance, and telling the truth.

13 Interview with David Paterson (17 April 1985).

14 This section is based on Robert Crawford's influential paper, 'You are dangerous to your health: the ideology and politics of victim blaming', *International Journal of Health Services*, vol. 7, no. 4, 1977.

15 Ibid.

16 Michel Foucault, *Discipline and Punish* (Vintage Books, 1979), p. 137.

17 Crawford, op. cit.

18 Politics of Health Women and Food Group, 'Women's health and food' (broadsheet published by Women's Health Information Collective, 1983).

19 It was Edwina Currie, the Conservative junior health minister, who (inadvertantly) put the issue of food and poverty on the media agenda when, in 1986, she told Northerners that their relatively poor health resulted partly from their own ignorance (compared with the more enlightened South) and rejected any direct link between ill-health and poverty. The resulting outcry got huge media coverage.

20 David Widgery ('Quacking out', *New Society*, 27 June 1986) reports hearing a young obstetric registrar in Hackney telling a single Irish woman living in a hostel for the homeless with a six-week-old baby that she was overweight and should join a squash club.

21 Mildred Baxter and Richard Cyster, 'Compliance and risk-taking: the case of alcoholic liver disease', *Sociology of Health and Illness*, vol. 6, no. 3, November 1984.

22 Hilary Graham, 'Smoking in pregnancy: the attitudes of expectant mothers', *Social Science and Medicine*, vol. 10, 1976.

23 For an example of an alternative approach to health promotion, based on redressing inequalities and community participation, see Wendy Farrant, ' "Health For All" In The Inner City' (Paddington and North Kensington Health Authority, 1986), and the discussion in Chapter 13.

24 James Erlichman, 'Muesli eaters, if you thought Mrs T. put you out

in the cold – beware of the freezer', *Guardian*, 20 June 1987. He also cites the example of supermarkets who proudly carry 'full nutritional labelling' on their own-brand lines, and then hide sugar under the listing of carbohydrate.

25 Carl Gardner, 'Out of the frying pan', *New Society*, 17 January 1986.

26 Elaine Farrell, 'Marketing research for local health promotion 1986' (Bath District Health Authority, 1986).

27 The Well Being production team, *Well Being* (Penguin Books, 1982), pp. 13–14. Chapter 13 discusses the ineffectiveness of most mass media health education campaigns.

28 Bobbie Jacobson, *The Ladykillers* (Pluto Press, 1981), p. 74.

29 Hilary Graham, 'Prevention and health: every mother's business: a comment on child health policies in the 1970s' in Chris Harris (ed.), *The Sociology of the Family: New Directions for Britain* (Sociological Review Monograph 28, University of Keele, 1979).

30 See Chapter 9 on media coverage of transplants for abundant evidence.

Chapter four

1 In Britain from 15 per cent in 1927 to 54 per cent in 1946 (see Jane Lewis, *The Politics of Motherhood: Child and Maternal Welfare in England 1900–1939* (Croom Helm, 1980).

2 Charles Hill, *Bringing Up Your Child* (Pheonix House, 1950).

3 In 1948, 67 per cent of British babies were delivered by midwives (*Maternity in Great Britain*, Oxford University Press, 1948).

4 The Medical Press, 21 August 1957.

5 He was chosen because of his iconoclastic beliefs for a 1975 TV profile (which I researched), where he suggested that 'the time has come to question every piece of medical knowledge' ('Does the doctor know best? – a professional opinion', transcript of BBC 2's 'At a Time Like This', *Listener*, 18 December 1975, p. 815).

6 'Tune into a happy event', *Daily Express*, 16 May 1972; 'Hallo world: baby Susan tunes in', *Daily Express*, 30 May 1972; about BBC Radio Nottingham's 'Focus', 31 May 1982.

7 For instance, 'Who Will Deliver Your Baby?' ('Horizon', BBC 2, 16 February 1981) on the obsolescence of the midwife contrasted two labours and bravely tried to suggest that both were equally good, though the pictures showed an alienated high-tech hospital birth next to a gemütlich, midwife-attended, home one.

8 'The Scientist and the Baby' ('Horizon' BBC 2, 8 November 1982), for instance, praised fetal monitoring and ultrasound scans, and

rather than including consumer critics, had doctors answering the criticisms that they themselves had raised.

9   R. Chamberlain et al., *British Births 1970*, vol. 1 (Heinemann, 1973).

10 AIMS was set up when Sally Wilmington wrote a letter to the *Observer* after spending six weeks of her own pregnancy in an antenatal ward, and was deluged with replies from other women.

11 Suzanne Arms, *Immaculate Deception* (Bantam Books, 1975).

12 'I'm Not Ill ... I'm Pregnant' (Channel 4, 14 November 1982).

13 'Birth Reborn' (BBC 2, 11 March 1982).

14 Ann Paul, 'Birth reborn', *Listener*, 11 March 1982.

15 By Ann Oakley, 'Wisewoman and medicine man: changes in the management of childbirth', in Juliet Mitchell and Ann Oakley (eds), *The Rights and Wrongs of Women* (Penguin, 1986); Adrienne Rich, *Of Woman Born* (Virago, 1977); Jean Donnison, *Midwives and Medical Men* (Heinemann, 1977); Barbara Ehrenreich and Deirdre English, *Witches, Midwives, and Nurses: A History of Women Healers* (Compendium, 1974); and Margaret Connor Versluysen, 'Midwives, medical men and "poor women labouring of child": lying-in hospitals in eighteenth-century London', in Helen Roberts (ed.), *Women, Health, and Reproduction* (Routledge & Kegan Paul, 1981).

16 Hilary Graham and Ann Oakley, 'Competing ideologies of reproduction: medical and maternal perspectives on pregnancy', in Helen Roberts, op. cit.

17 Ibid., p. 54.

18 Quoted by David St George, 'Who pulls the strings at the HEC?', *World Medicine*, November 28 1981, p. 52.

19 David St George, ibid.

20 The Social Services Committee Report on Perinatal and Neonatal Mortality, 1980.

21 *Daily Mail*, 17 July 1980.

22 *Guardian* 17 July 1980.

23 *The Times Health Supplement*, 30 October 1981.

24 'No Room at the Inn' (The Spastics Society, 1979).

25 Alison Macfarlane, 'Birth, death, and handicap: saving mothers, spending lives', *Science for People* 48, Spring 1981. Macfarlane also noted that, ironically, TV, radio, and the Press were full of claims that babies born in Britain ran an unacceptably high risk of dying or becoming handicapped at birth just when the perinatal mortality rates were rapidly falling. She also shows how calls for the routine use of fetal monitoring in labour weren't supported by any evidence of benefit, or any examination of the risks it carried.

Elsewhere, the campaign to reduce perinatal mortality rates by identifying 'at risk' mothers and ensuring their attendance at antenatal clinics has been perceived more as an anxiety over the changing position of mothers both inside and outside the family, and the desire to place them under a kind of surveillance. (See Rosalyn Harrison, 'Maternity in the 1970s: the public management of a private issue', unpublished doctoral thesis, University of Bristol Department of Social Administration, March 1985).

26   The National Council for One-Parent Families has shown that the recommended diet for a pregnant woman couldn't possibly be followed by a woman on supplementary benefit. And in Britain today, as in the 1930s, areas with high unemployment also have high perinatal mortality rates. Even in areas renowned for their exemplary maternity services (such as Aberdeen), routine antenatal care hasn't been successful at predicting and detecting obstetric problems like abnormally small babies. See Jill Rakusen and Nick Davidson, *Out of our hands* (Pan, 1982).

27   The Advancement of Maternity Care – set up to challenge natural childbirth – and its founder got wide publicity, featuring in ITV's 'Where There's Life' (1985); debating the subject with the doyenne of natural childbirth Sheila Kitzinger on 'Woman's Hour' (BBC Radio 4, June 1986); and sympathetically interviewed on Channel 4 ('I Laughed And Had A Baby', Diverse Reports, October 1986) and the *Guardian* (in an article unequivocally entitled 'Natural childbirth, a child of the sixties, was and is largely a nutty fad from a noisy group of lentil-eating earth-goddesses', Polly Toynbee, 12 May 1986). Even Odent got criticised (Annabel Ferriman, 'GPs attack pioneer of childbirth au naturel', *Observer*, 19 April 1987).

28   In her account of the case (*A Savage Enquiry: Who Controls Childbirth?*, Virago, 1986), Wendy Savage describes the Press campaign for her reinstatement: more than twenty articles about her suspension appeared in the national and medical Press in the first month alone, with the *Guardian* in particular covering the case regularly.

Chapter five

1   'Woman's Hour' (BBC Radio 4, 7 January 1986).
2   'The Glennie Determination' (BBC Radio 4, 7 January 1986), and 'Wogan' (BBC 1, 24 January 1986).
3   The medical approach often grossly inflates the proportion of congenital abnormalities, detectable by prenatal screening. In reality, most people acquire disabilities later in life, as the result of

an accident or chronic illness like a stroke, where prenatal screening is irrelevant.

4   The spread of the look-after-yourself approach and its emphasis on the perfectability of the body has created a climate in which disability is even more deviant.

5   Allan T. Sutherland, *Disabled We Stand* (Souvenir Press, 1981), p. 15.

6   BBC TV, 'Six O'Clock News' (14 July 1986).

7   Maggie Woolley interviewed by Julienne Dickey, 'Deafness and the media', *Women's Media Action Bulletin*, no. 19, January 1983, p. 3.

8   Keith Armstrong and Wendy Moore, 'Shut out by the media', *Journalist*, October 1985, p. 2. So, 'despite [the fact that she has brittle-bone disease] and the fact that she's broken one or other of her legs nine times, Sharon keeps smiling', or else she wouldn't have got into the *Radio Times*. ('Raising hopes, raising laughs, and raising money', *Radio Times*, November 15–21, 1986.)

9   Tony Macaulay, 'Disability and the Broadcasting Media' (The Volunteer Centre Media Project, December 1985).

10 Maggie Woolley et al., 'That was our year was it?', *The Times Health Supplement*, 22 January 1982, p. 9.

11 Diane Lattin, 'Telethons – a remnant of America's past', *Disabled USA*, vol. 1, no. 4, 1977, p. 19.

12 Woolley et al., op. cit.

13 Nancy Banks-Smith, 'Just a 'Thon at twilight', *Guardian*, 31 October 1985.

14 Quoted by Mark Patterson, 'Children in need', *Media Project News*, September 1984, p. 11.

15 Diane Lattin, 'United Cerebral Palsy: communicating a better image', *Disabled USA*, vol. 2, no. 7, 1979, p. 5, which also describes some innovative UCP TV ads featuring a married couple with cerebral palsy.

16 Armstrong and Moore, op. cit., p. 2.

17 Ibid.

18 Peter Hildrew, 'Lambeth ignores gibes to increase disabled staff to 3 per cent quota', *Guardian*, 18 October 1986.

19 B. D. Leonard, 'Impaired view: television portrayal of handicapped people' (unpublished doctoral thesis, Boston University, 1978), quoted in Timothy R. Elliott and E. Keith Byrd 'Media and disability', *Rehabilitation Literature*, vol. 43, no. 11–12, November–December 1982.

20 Joy Donaldson, 'The visibility and image of handicapped people on television', *Exceptional Children*, vol. 47, no. 6, March 1981. 'A Man Called Ironside' (1967–72) about a cop who happened to be a paraplegic was a rare exception.

21   Allan T. Sutherland and Steve Dwoskin, *Carry on Cripple* (National Film Theatre booklet, February 1981), p. 21.

22   Ibid., p. 19.

23   Woolley interviewed by Dickey, op. cit.

24   Raphael Samuel ('The Elephant Man as a fable of class', *New Society*, 19 November 1981) suggests that the film is an evangelical fable, resembling Sunday School moral stories, with Merrick the incarnation of the deserving poor, grateful to his benefactors and displaying inner grace.

25   Donaldson, op. cit.

26   The cinematographer Haskell Wexler, to avoid conveying a sense of diminishment by photographing the 'vets' from above, devised a special camera dolly to put the camera at the same height as the men in wheelchairs (Martin F. Norden, 'The disabled Vietnam veteran in Hollywood films', *Journal of Popular Film and Television*, vol. 13, no. 1, Spring 1985).

27   The deaf actress Marlee Matlin may have helped: she used sign language when accepting an Oscar for her performance in *Children of a Lesser God*, and her speech was relayed across the world's television to millions.

28   The idea developed out of a meeting between the voluntary group Mencap and Central TV's Controller, himself father of a mentally handicapped child. Mencap was enthusiastic because

> we thought it was about time viewers were able to see a mentally handicapped person in a programme which was not a documentary. Confining them to documentaries seemed rather like confronting them to institutions . . . . Secondly, it seemed likely that the audience of 'Crossroads' would include some of the people Mencap most wanted to reach with information about mental handicap: those who switch off when documentaries come on. It would also be an opportunity to air some of the common prejudices, fears, and misunderstandings about mental handicap, by allowing them to be expressed by characters in the series.

(Brian Rix, 'Mencap at the Crossroads', *Media Project News*, January 1984, p. 28.)

29   'We Won't Go Away', ITV (24 November 1981).

30   'Attitudes – the Second Handicap' (BBC 2, 30 March 1982).

31   'Statement of Intent' (Channel 4, 12 April 1984). 'Dreams Are The Worst' (Channel 4, 26 June 1986) wittily dramatised the problems of access faced by people with disabilities by portraying a Lilliput world where everything is too small for the able-bodied, but they're advised to 'adapt' to it.

32   'The Skin Horse' (Channel 4, 18 December 1983).

33   For instance, 'A Deaf Pride' (BBC TV, 13 October 1983); 'A Language for Ben' (Channel 4, 2 January 1986); and Nigel Evans' superb 'Pictures in the Mind' (Channel 4, 6 April 1987).

34 A deaf competitor and her signing interpreter took part in the ITV game show 'The Price is Right' in December 1986, after the Deaf Broadcasting Campaign (an energetic lobby) made contact with the producer, offered him suggestions and joined the audience, so that he came to feel more confident about using deaf people in the programme. The Deaf Broadcasting Campaign have also lobbied hard, with some success, to have more BBC and ITV programmes subtitled.

35 In 1985, the BBC 'See Hear!' team arranged an experimental studio session to see what problems might arise when a deaf person directed a TV studio. Some hearing members of the 'See Hear!' production team are learning to sign, though the deaf staff have had to work very hard to educate their hearing colleagues.

Chapter six

1   David Elstein, 'Smoking and the media', *Media, Culture, & Society*, vol. 1, no. 3, July 1979, p. 272.

2   Greta Jones et al., *The Presentation of Science by the Media* (Primary Communications Research Centre, University of Leicester, 1978), a valuable paper which this chapter draws on.

3   Anne Karpf, 'Medicine and television' (unpublished M.Sc. dissertation, Polytechnic of the South Bank, 1981), based on a participant–observation study of the making of 'Where There's Life', in which I consider in detail the imperatives of the slot.

4   Ibid, p. 33.

5   Ibid, p. 34.

6   Press release, Cable Health Network (3 May 1982).

7   Interview with Cable Health Network executive, 7 May 1985.

8   Ibid.

9   Roy E. Carter, 'Newspaper "gatekeepers," and the sources of news', *Public Opinion Quarterly*, vol. 12, no. 2, Summer 1958.

10 Chris Anne Raymond, 'Risk in the Press: conflicting journalistic ideologies' in Dorothy Nelkin (ed.), *The Language of Risk* (Sage, 1985). Investigative journalism is a dying genre.

11 Tom Burns, *The BBC: Public Institution and Private World* (Macmillan, 1977), p. 45.

12 Ibid, p. 239.

13 Anthony Smith, 'Internal pressures in broadcasting', *New Outlook*, no. 4, 1972, pp. 4–5, quoted in Burns, op. cit., p. 195.

14 Herbert J. Gans, *Deciding What's News* (Constable, 1979).

15 Caroline Pick, Politics of Health Group conference on medicine and the media (London, 31 October 1982).

16   The Sunday Times Insight Team, *Suffer the Children: The Story of Thalidomide* (Andre Deutsch, 1979), pp. 179–80.

17   June Goodfield, 'Reflections on science and the media', *American Association for the Advancement of Science*, 1981, p. 181.

18   Karpf, op. cit., p. 99.

19   Philip Elliott, *The making of a television series* (Constable, 1972), p. 147.

20   Ibid.

21   June Fisher et al., 'The role of popular media in defining sickness and health' in E. McAnany et al. (eds), *Communication and Social Structure* (Praeger, 1981), although presumably both might have been caused by a third, independent factor.

22   Roger Silverstone, *Framing Science: The Making of a BBC Documentary* (British Film Institute, 1985), p. 44.

23   This further discriminates against people with speech impediments and other disabilities who don't conform to the norms of articulacy.

24   Gaye Tuchman, 'Making news by doing work', *American Journal of Sociology*, vol. 79, no. 1, 1973.

25   Karpf, op. cit., p. 98.

26   Gaye Tuchman, *Making News* (Free Press, 1978).

27   For instance, in 'A Question of Life and Death', the 1981 follow-up to the Panorama on brain-death – see Chapter 10. And see Stuart Hood, *On Television* (Pluto, 1980) on the meaning of direct TV address. A rare exception was BBC 1's innovative late-night series 'Well Woman' in April 1983.

28   Interestingly, women rarely narrate science and medical programmes, partly perhaps because they're thought to lack cultural authority, or might – by association – personalise the issues, but also because science and technology are considered objective, male subjects.

29   Roger Graef et al., 'Decision' (Granada 1976 and 1978).

30   See, for instance, Norman Swallow, 'Fly-on-the-wall TV documentaries: what is the relationship between truth and life?', *Listener*, 12 May 1983, and the subsequent correspondence: Roger Graef, 'The meaning of verité' (19 May 1985), and Norman Swallow (26 May 1985).

31   Mike Poole, *City Limits*, 26 February 1982.

32   See, for instance, Roger Silverstone, 'Narrative strategies in television science – a case study', *Media, Culture, and Society*, vol. 6, no. 4, October 1984, and Carl Gardner and Robert Young's useful 'Science on TV: a Critique' in Tony Bennett et al. (eds), *Popular Television and Film* (British Film Institute, 1981), drawn on here.

Chapter seven

1   David M. Rubin and Val Hendy, 'Swine influenza and the news media', *Annals of Internal Medicine*, vol. 87, no. 6, 1977.

2   Arthur Herzog, 'Faking it', *Saturday Review of Society* 1, April 1973, p. 36–37, quoted in Rae Goodell, *The Visible Scientists* Little, Brown & Co, 1977, p. 202.

3   R. Gordon Shepherd, 'Selectivity of sources: reporting the Marijuana controversy', *Journal of Communication*, Spring 1981.

4   The Medical Journalists' Association unanimously passed a motion in 1984 decrying Health Ministers' attempts to manage news by announcing stories late (which prevents critical analysis); selectively; or not at all (Medical Journalists' Association newsletter, 1984).

5   Carol Tavris, 'How to publicize science: a case study', in Jeffrey H. Goldstein (ed.), *Reporting Science: The Case of Aggression* (Lawrence Erlbaum Associates, 1986).

6   Greta Jones et al., *The Presentation of Science by the Media* (Primary Communications Research Centre, University of Leicester, 1978).

7   Interview with Art Ulene, 27 July 1986.

8   Nicki Household, 'What's up Doc?', *Radio Times*, June 27–July 3, 1981.

9   Richard Smith, 'Fit for what?', *Observer Colour Magazine*, 5 June 1983, p. 35.

10 Nicholas Hildyard, *Cover Up* (New English Library, 1983).

11 Betty Medsger, 'Asbestos: the California story', *Columbia Journalism Review*, vol. 16, no. 3, September/October 1977.

12 Frank Mortenson and Erik Nordahl Svendsen, 'Creativity and control: the journalist betwixt his readers and editors', *Critical Sociology* no. 7, 1980, quoted in Chris Anne Raymond, 'Risk in the Press: conflicting journalistic ideologies' in Dorothy Nelkin (ed.), *The Language of Risk* (Sage, 1985).

13 June Goodfield, 'Reflections on science and the media', *American Association for the Advancement of Science*, 1981.

14 Jones et al., op. cit., p. 58. Some reasons for this are advanced later in this chapter.

15 'The BBC's medical programmes and their effects on lay audiences' (BBC, 1976, p. 6).

16 Willis J. Elwood et al., 'The Bolton Television – Hospital Series', *Social Action and the Media*, case study no. 3, The Volunteer Centre, July 1978, p. 5.

17 Interview with Ian McColl, London, 25 July 1985.

18 Ibid.

19 Ibid.
20 Interview with Edward Lincoln, General Manager MEPR Health and Medical Division, 18 January 1985.
21 A practice which Current Affairs staff frown on.
22 A recent attempt to sever the MJA's financial dependence on drug companies in the interests of professional integrity was narrowly defeated. Some members confessed they'd been unduly influenced by the receipt of an award; others maintained that the awards helped foster good relations with the pharmaceutical industry (MJA minutes of AGM, 15 May 1985).
23 *PR and the Media Survey 1986* (The Quentin Bell Organisation, 1986).
24 Oscar H. Gandy, *Beyond Agenda Setting: Information Subsidies and Public Policy* (Ablex, 1982). See also Barbara Stocking and Stuart L. Morrison, *The Image and the Reality* (Oxford University Press, 1978) for a fascinating case study on the way in which the costs and benefits of the body scanner could have been, but weren't, evaluated.
25 *Observer*, 13 April 1986.
26 14 April 1986. It may, of course, be a valuable piece of equipment – that isn't the issue; the point is, its usefulness is never questioned. And see Chapter 4 for a discussion of the media's predilection for technological solutions to obstetric risk.
27 Sharon M. Friedman, 'Blueprint for breakdown: Three Mile Island and the media before the accident', *Journal of Communication* 31, no. 2, Spring 1981.
28 Carol Haslam, 'North America – the role of the media in health promotion' (unpublished paper, King's Fund Centre, 1986).
29 James Erlichman, 'Food firms put bite on 'faddists' who are ruining their figures' (*Guardian*, 4 July 1986, p. 23).
30 Haslam, op. cit.
31 Helen Chislett, 'The hidden film persuaders', *Guardian*, 3 December 1986.
32 Ibid.
33 Interview with David Cordingley, 11 July 1986.
34 Angie Mason, Health Education Council/King's Fund Conference on Health Promotion, London (24 March 1986).
35 Peter Taylor, *Smoke Ring: The Politics of Tobacco* (Bodley Head, 1984). British colour supplements have a policy of forewarning advertisers of a looming clash between editorial and advertising, but when the *Sunday Times* in 1980 ran a feature on seven heavy smokers undergoing heart transplants and mentioned which brands they'd smoked, two references to Embassy were removed at the last minute. Embassy was being advertised on the opposite page (ibid.).

36 Des Wilson, *Pressure: The A to Z of Campaigning in Britain* (Heinemann, 1984).

37 'Nurses', BBC 2, 10 November 1986 and the following five weeks.

38 A. Amos, 'British women's magazines – a healthy read?', in D. S. Leathar et al (eds), *Health Education and the Media 2* (Pergamon Press, 1986).

39 Fred Jerome, 'Gee Whiz! Is that all there is?' in Sharon M. Friedman et al. (eds), *Scientists and Journalists* (Free Press, 1986).

40 Michael Ryan, 'Attitudes towards media coverage of science news', *Journalism Quarterly*, vol. 56, no. 1, Spring 1979.

41 Interview with Maura Lerner, New York, 6 May 1985.

42 Quoted in Anne Karpf, 'Medicine and television' (unpublished M.Sc. dissertation, Polytechnic of the South Bank, 1981), p. 47.

43 Alan Dalton, 'Asbestos – TV succeeds where others fail', *Science for People* 53, Winter 1982.

44 Quoted in Medsger, op. cit., p. 43.

45 Quoted in Raymond, op. cit., pp. 124–5.

46 Ben G. Frank, 'Using talk show interviews as effective practice builders', *New York State Dental Journal*, vol. 49, no. 3, March 1983.

47 Ibid., pp. 164–5.

48 Sharon Dunwoody and Michael Ryan, 'Scientific barriers to the popularization of science in the mass media', *Journal of Communication* 35, Winter 1985.

49 Quoted by Glyn Jones, 'Something good on the other side?', *New Scientist*, 2 August 1979, p. 378.

50 Luc Boltanski and Pascale Maldidier, 'Carrièe scientifique, morale scientifique et vulgarisation', *Information sur les sciences sociales*, vol. 9, no. 3, 1970.

51 Dunwoody and Ryan, op. cit., p. 28.

52 Goodell, op. cit., p. 121.

53 Thomas S. Kuhn, *The Structure of Scientific Revolutions* (University of Chicago Press, 1962). Kuhn has been accused of circularity and of overstating the unanimity of scientists. But as an account of science as a social practice, he's still valuable.

54 See M. R. Bury, 'Social constructionism and the development of medical sociology', *Sociology of Health and Illness*, vol. 8, no. 2, June 1986. A succinct discussion of the claims of and difficulties with the social constructionist account of medicine.

55 Ivan Waddington, 'The role of the hospital in the development of modern medicine: a sociological analysis', *Sociology*, vol. 7, no. 2, 1973, p. 217.

56 Eliot Freidson, *Profession of Medicine* (Dodd, Mead & Co., 1975).

57 Irving Kenneth Zola, 'Medicine as an institution of social control',

in John Ehrenreich (ed.), *The Cultural Crisis of Modern Medicine* (Monthly Review Press, 1978).

58 Ibid., pp. 90–1.
59 Freidson, op. cit., p. 251.
60 Peter Conrad, 'On the medicalization of deviance and social control', in David Ingleby (ed.), *Critical Psychiatry* (Penguin, 1981).
61 P. M. Strong, 'Sociological imperialism and the profession of medicine', *Social Science and Medicine*, vol. 13A, 1979.
62 Jocelyn Cornwell, *Hard-Earned Lives* (Tavistock, 1984).
63 Ibid., p. 22.
64 Editor of 'Where There's Life' quoted in Karpf, op. cit., p. 87.
65 Ulene, op. cit.

Chapter eight

1 BBC, 'Principles and Practice in News and Current Affairs' (1971), quoted in Philip Schlesinger, *Putting 'Reality' Together* (Constable, 1978), p. 165.
2 Stanley Cohen, *Folk Devils and Moral Panics* (Martin Robertson, 1980), p. 9.
3 Vicki S. Freimuth et al., 'Covering Cancer: newspapers and the public interest', *Journal of Communication*, vol. 34, no. 1, Winter 1984. Interestingly, the proportion of stories about lung and breast cancer was more commensurate with their incidence. But cancers of the male reproductive system, in 1980 more common than those of the female reproductive system, received much less coverage. This presumably originates from the idea of the female reproductive system as in some way pathological, and the normality of the male system; see Naomi Pfeffer, 'The hidden pathology of the male reproductive system' in Hilary Homans (ed.), *The Sexual Politics of Reproduction* (Gower, 1985).
4 *Daily Mirror*, 11 November 1981, p. 1.
5 *Sun*, 11 November 1985, p. 5.
6 Anne Robinson (*Daily Mirror*, 25 July 1984). Quoted in Kim Cotton and Denise Winn, *Baby Cotton: For Love And Money* (Dorling Kindersley, 1985), p. 90.
7 Karl Sabbagh, 'Use and abuse of Radio and TV by voluntary organisations', *Journal of the Royal College of Physicians of London*, vol. 13, no. 4, October 1979, p. 250.
8 *The Times, Daily Telegraph, Daily Express, Sun* (25 February 1970).
9 The birth of the first test-tube baby was even filmed by the Government's Central Office of Information.

10   Annette Kuhn, *The Power of the Image* (Routledge & Kegan Paul, 1985).

11   'The Real World', ITV, 13 December 1982.

12   Kaye Wellings, 'Sickness and sin: the case of genital herpes' (Paper presented to the British Sociological Association Medical Sociology Group Annual Conference, 1983).

13   Ibid., pp. 28–29.

14   *Sun*, 1 February 1985. AIDS is also discussed in Chapter 10 as a controversy over language, and in Chapter 13 as a mass media health education campaign.

15   *Sun*, 21 November 1986.

16   *The Times*, 21 November 1984.

17   See for instance 'AIDS: A Strange and Deadly Virus', 'Horizon' (BBC 2, 24 March 1986).

18   TV Eye, ITV, 8 November 1985.

19   '20/20' (ABC, 26 May 1983), quoted in Jay Winsten, 'Science and the media: the boundaries of truth', *Health Affairs*, vol. 4, no. 1, Spring 1985, p. 11.

20   'This Week', 'AIDS – The Last Chance', 23 October 1986.

21   *Evening Standard*, 20 March 1986.

22   Oliver Gillie et al., 'Panic', *Sunday Times*, 24 February 1985.

23   *Star*, 5 January 1985.

24   'This Week', op. cit.

25   Andrew Britton, 'AIDS – apocalyptic metaphor', *New Statesman*, 15 March 1985.

26   *Sun*, 3 October 1985.

27   *Star*, 3 October 1985.

28   *Daily Mail*, 3 October 1985. And in the *Observer*'s end-of-year pictorial obituary of forty-two famous people who died in 1985, Hudson was the only one whose cause of death was mentioned, as if all the others died of natural (or more natural) causes. (*Observer*, 29 December 1985.)

29   The death in 1987 of singer Liberace received similar tabloid treatment.

30   'AIDS', *Newsweek*, 12 August 1985.

31   See, for instance, Andrew Veitch, 'The spread of AIDS blamed on blood trade', *Guardian*, 22 March 1985.

32   But recent researchers have found the claim that Africa was the source of AIDS seriously flawed and racist.

33   Quoted in David Talbot and Larry Bush, 'At risk', *Mother Jones*, April 1985.

34   Jonathan Dimbleby, 'AIDS – The Last Chance', 'This Week', ITV, 23 October 1986.

35   Nicholas Wapshott, 'New morality and the sexual time bomb', *Observer*, 28 December 1986.

36 'The social fallout from an epidemic', *Newsweek*, 12 August 1985, p. 46. Norman Fowler, Secretary of State for Social Services, shared this classification when he talked of 'the tragic cases of haemophiliacs . . . and worst of all of small babies' (DHSS Press Release 86/367, 21 November 1986.) No such epithet was attached to homosexual sufferers. The media made the same distinction between innocent and guilty victims in the case of prostitutes and other women murdered by the 'Yorkshire Ripper'.

37 'Cervical Cancer – And Men', 'Panorama' (BBC 1, 3 November 1986).

38 'AIDS and You', 'TV Eye' (ITV, 8 November 1985).

39 Stuart Hall, quoted in Marl Lilly, 'Are we being served?', *Free Press*, no. 34, April 1986.

40 This book went to press before the publication of Simon Watney's engaged book *Policing Desire: Pornography, AIDS and the Media* (Comedia, 1987), with its interesting critique of the concept of moral panics.

41 'Living with AIDS' (Panorama, BBC 1), 26 January 1987). On the other hand, by Summer 1987 the programme was examining the ways in which different countries tackled the disease, and was implicitly critical of those which drove people with AIDS underground and sympathetic to those advancing a consensual rather than a punitive approach (AIDS – The Fight For Control', 'Panorama', BBC 1, 29 June 1987).

Chapter nine

1 Promotional material for '40 Minutes' – 'Heart Transplants' (BBC, 1982).

2 Press release, '40 Minutes – Heart Transplant' (BBC, 1982).

3 See, for instance, 'Bruce Anderson's Heart', fourth programme in the '40 Minutes' series (BBC 2, 15 April, 1982), and Annabel Ferriman, 'Price of a Chance to Live', *Observer*, 26 September 1986.

4 Interview with James Wilkinson, London, 17 December 1986.

5 Robert Bazell, 'Hearts of gold', *The New Republic*, 18 February 1985, p. 17.

6 'And Now the Bill Schroeder Show', *Life*, May 1985, p. 37.

7 NBC Memorandum, Bazell to Schatz (1984).

8 Bazell (1985), op. cit.

9 De Vries quoted in *Life*, op. cit., p. 41.

10 See Nancy Pfund and Laura Hofstadter, 'Biomedical innovation and the Press', *Journal of Communication* 31, no. 2, Spring 1981.

Pfund and Hofstadter found questioning articles on the artifical heart only in opinion pieces in small-circulation publications and, interestingly, the business press.

11 Jennie Popay et al., 'Transplanting priorities', *New Scientist*, 17 April 1980).

12 For instance, Ferriman, op. cit.

13 Pfund and Hofstadter, op. cit.

14 Judged in part by the impact it would make on his print colleagues: 'The whole of Fleet Street is likely to be after this story . . . [it] will make a page lead in the papers tomorrow, maybe front page. It's an obvious story, because it's the first time it's happened.' (Interview with James Wilkinson, London, 17 December 1986.)

15 Interview with James Wilkinson, 19 December 1986. The rest of the quotes from Wilkinson in this section come from this interview.

16 Subsequent BBC coverage of the story, in the absence of any new medical information, took an entirely human interest line with, first, the husband's press conference talking about her courage ('She's a fighter', BBC 'Nine O'Clock News', 18 December 1986), and then the photo-call when the patient left hospital to go home (BBC 'Nine O'Clock News', 20 February 1987). This last stressed the almost miraculous nature of the cure: 'Up to two months ago, a stroll with her husband and daughter would have been impossible . . . . All that changed last December . . . . She said that those few hours had given her a whole new chance of life.' As for ITV, 'News at Ten' (17 December 1986) ran the story ten minutes into the bulletin, shorter and slightly less celebratory in tone than the BBC, but otherwise substantially similar to the BBC's Nine O'Clock bulletin story. 'Channel 4 News' carried nothing at all. Press coverage was almost identical to the later BBC reports.

17 'The World at One' (BBC Radio 4, 17 December 1986). And see below TV's even more explicit role with liver transplants.

18 Andrew Veitch, 'Heart study cost highlights plight', *Guardian*, 22 May 1982. Presumably, Harefield and Papworth Hospitals revealed it.

19 Ralph Heussner, quoted in Phil Gunby, 'Media-abetted liver transplants raise questions of "equity and decency" ', *Journal of American Medical Association*, vol. 249, no. 15, 15 April 1983, p. 1973.

20 Dr John Najarian, quoted in ibid., p. 1973.

21 Quoted in Esther Rantzen and Shaun Woodward, *Ben* (BBC Publications, 1985), p. 17.

22 Ibid., p. 22.

23 *Daily Mail* and the *Sun* 24 January 1984. 'That's Life Boy in Hospital Drama' reported the *Daily Mirror*, and 'That's Life Boy Has Liver

Swop Operation' said the *Star*. Even *The Times* and the *Guardian* carried front-page stories.

24   One paper claimed that the donor's parents were disappointed that Ben's parents hadn't sent a wreath to their child's funeral (Rantzen and Woodward, op. cit.).

25   'Transplant', *Evening Standard*, 24 January 1984.

26   Celia Wright, quoted in Rantzen and Woodward, op. cit., p. 71, and on 'That's Life' (BBC 1, 22 January 1984).

27   John Patten, quoted in Rantzen and Woodward, op. cit., p. 141.

28   The programme also donated £70,000 to set it up (Diary, the *Guardian*, 26 April 1984). There are many examples of charities (after a public appeal) gifting a health authority an expensive piece of equipment whose running-costs match or even exceed the original donation. In the 1970s, gifts (after emotional media appeals) of body-scanners often had this result.

29   DHSS Press Release, 'Additional Funds For Transplant Programme' (84/425, 17 December 1984) which also reminded journalists, just in case they'd forgotten, that 'it was at this hospital that Ben Hardwick received his liver transplant earlier this year'.

30   'That's Life' (15 January 1984, quoted in Rantzen and Woodward, op. cit., p. 31).

31   Rantzen and Woodward, op. cit., p. 13.

32   Ibid., p. 19. Compare this with television's profligate, almost pornographic, use of pictures of people dying of AIDS.

33   Ibid., pp. 19–20.

34   Daniel Callahan, quoted in Gunby, op. cit., p. 1982.

35   Robert Veatch, ibid., p. 1982.

36   Dr John Najarian, quoted in Gunby, op. cit., p. 1974.

37   See, for instance, Rantzen and Woodward, op. cit., p. 40.

38   Programmes on transplants are generally unwilling to dwell on the donor, since this brings up again the troublesome subject of death, which the miracle cure purports to erase. So they resort to impersonal categories ('a donor'), or disembodied organs ('a heart'), magicked out of nowhere ('became available'). A rare exception was 'Wogan' (BBC 1, 13 January 1988) where a noted transplant critic talked of donors' deaths and of transplants' small potential impact on heart disease. But the producer still deliberately gave more time in the programme to a transplant patient and her doctor.

39   See, for instance, a story headed 'Boy's Death Helps Three', *Guardian*, 28 February 1984.

Chapter ten

1 Interview with James Wilkinson, 19 December 1986 (from where all the other Wilkinson quotes in this section also come). In a circular argument, Wilkinson devalues dissenting opinion ('stage army', 'wheeled out'), in order to dismiss it, though the doctor he brought in to defend the triple transplant and whom he'd used before, could be similarly described as 'wheeled out'.

2 'Policy Notes' (BBC, 18 December 1944). A previous memo suggested that there might be times when doctors could express views different from 'or even in advance of accepted opinion', provided this was made clear to listeners (Janet Quigley, 'Health talks', 6 October 1944) – presumably the 1940s equivalent of today's warning that a speaker will be giving a 'personal view', thus distancing the network from departures from orthodoxy.

3 'Discussion on vaccination', BBC Controversy Committee Minutes (4 January 1929).

4 Letter from the National Anti-Vaccination League to BBC Director of Talks (4 October 1951), and letter from Sir Henry Dale of the Medical Research Council to Miss Mary Somerville, Controller of Talks (23 January 1952).

5 Letter from R. A. Rendall, Controller of Talks, to Alice Jenkins, Honorary Secretary of the Abortion Law Reform Association (29 July 1948).

6 Minute 146 of a meeting of the BBC Board of Governors, 30 October 1935, quoted in 'Note of the Corporation's Policy and Practice with regard to mention at the microphone of such subjects as Veneral Disease' (BBC Secretariat, 16 October 1942).

7 Paddy Scannell, 'Broadcasting and the politics of unemployment 1930–1935', *Media, Culture and Society*, vol. 2, no. 1, January 1980.

8 Letter, Deputy Director-General to Lord Horder (22 October 1935).

9 Information Note no. 6, issued by BBC Secretariat (November 1942), quoting letter to the General Secretary of the National Council of Civil Liberties. Marie Stopes finally gained airtime on 24 July 1956, giving a talk on birth control for the World Service in a series called 'What I Believe'.

10 See Jane Lewis, 'The ideology and politics of birth control in inter-war England', *Women's Studies International Quarterly*, vol. 2, no. 1, 1979.

11 Elizabeth Wilson, *Only Halfway to Paradise: Women in Post-war Britain 1945–68* (Tavistock, 1980).

12   Quoted in 'BBC prudery', *World Medicine*, vol. 12, no. 17, editorial, 1 June 1977).

13   Alton Blakeslee, 'The role and responsibility, 1975, of the mass media in the USA', in R. D. Caterall and C. S. Nicol (eds), *Sexually Transmitted Diseases* (Academic Press, 1976), p. 252.

14   For an account of Parran's campaign, see Allan M. Brandt's fascinating book *No Magic Bullet: A Social History of Venereal Disease in the United States Since 1880* (Oxford University Press, 1987).

15   BBC Policy in 1937 ('Note of the Corporation's policy and practice', op. cit.). The experience of the First World War hadn't been very encouraging: VD propaganda films made by the social purity organisations did remarkably well in the cinemas, 'sex-exciting' audiences in an era when other public depictions of sex weren't available (see Annette Kuhn, *The Power of the Image*, Routledge & Kegan Paul, 1985).

16   'Disgrace of flaunted vice at Piccadilly Circus', *News Chronicle*, 21 October 1943.

17   Sir Wilson Jameson, 'The Nation's Health', Home Service talk reprinted in the *Listener*, 9 November 1944.

18   'AIDS and the Prime Minister', *New Society*, 31 October 1986.

19   CBS's Vice-President of Communications George Schweitzer, quoted in Sue Woodman, 'AIDS and the Media with no Message', *Guardian*, 26 January 1987.

20   'AIDS Open Air' (BBC TV, 3 March 1987).

21   Bruce J. Cole, 'Trends in science and conflict coverage in four metropolitan newspapers', *Journalism Quarterly* 52, Autumn 1975.

22   Letter from Michael O'Donnell, *British Medical Journal*, 25 February 1978.

23   Letter from Paul Bonner, *British Medical Journal*, 25 February 1978, p. 503.

24   Letter from John Garfield, *British Medical Journal*, vol. 281, 25 October 1980, p. 1140.

25   Letter from Professor R. Y. Calne, 'BBC presentation of transplant dilemma', *The Times*, 16 October 1980.

26   Letter from J. F. K. Mason, ibid.

27   Letter from Robert Sells, *British Medical Journal*, vol. 281, 1 November 1980, p. 1212.

28   Calne, op. cit. Ironically, this was the same transplant surgeon who encouraged the mother of Ben, seeking a liver transplant, to find a friendly TV producer (see Chapter 9), and seemed quite happy for Ben's case to feature weekly on an entertaining programme.

29   Letter from Bryan Jennett, *British Medical Journal*, vol. 281, 25 October 1981, p. 1139.

30   Quoted in Alan Rusbridger, 'Doctors withdraw from Panorama', *Guardian* 21 November 1980.

31 'A Question of Life and Death' (BBC TV, 19 February 1981).
32 Professor Roy Calne, quoted in Pat Blair, ' "Disastrous" year for transplants', *Times Health Supplement*, 25 December 1981.
33 John Gau, 'The doctors and 'Panorama' ', *Listener*, 4 December 1980.
34 Indeed, the reason for the accusation was that the doctor had made 'a statement like that here, on the media' and not by 'publishing among your peers' ('A Question of Life and Death', BBC TV, 19 February 1981).
35 'A Gentle Way With Cancer?', transmitted on BBC 2 from 17 March 1983.
36 'A Whole New Medicine' (BBC 2, 12 January 1981). And by 1983, even *The Times* was running an enthusiastic series on alternative therapies.
37 James Wilkinson, 'Six O'Clock News' (BBC 1, 12 May 1986).
38 Robert Eagle, 'Alternative medicine', *Listener*, 25 September 1980.
39 Roger Mills, 'Cancer: a cautious approach to "holistic" treatment', *Listener*, 14 April 1983.
40 'And conquering cynicism along the way', *The Times*, 16 March 1983.
41 Mills, op. cit.
42 So a TV programme on alternative medicine cited a cancer specialist who is 'concerned about the diversion of patients towards therapies for which there is no evidence of success' ('Brass Tacks – A Patient's Dilemma', BBC 2, 27 February 1985) without pointing out that same is true for many allopathic cancer treatments. By contrast, the BBC's Director-General insisted on cutting a sequence from a programme on breast cancer which pointed out that, despite advances in surgery and medicine in general, the survival rates of women with breast cancer hadn't increased over the last four decades. ('Man Alive – Breast Cancer', BBC 2, 19 June 1979.)
43 'Mind Over Cancer' (BBC 1, 2 August 1983).
44 Fourth Programme of 'Herbs, Useful Plants' (BBC Radio 4, 4 December 1981).

Chapter eleven

1 George Gerbner et al., 'Programming health portrayals: what viewers see, say, and do', in D. Pearl et al. (eds), *Television and Social Behaviour: Ten Years of Scientific Progress and Implications for the Eighties* (National Institute of Mental Health, 1982).

2   Muriel G. Cantor and Suzanne Pingrec, *The Soap Opera* (Sage, 1983).

3   Anthony Kearey, speaking at the National Film Theatre (15 February 1984).

4   Dr Kildare had actually originated in a series of 1930s MGM movies.

5   'Tell Me If It Hurts' was the first film made by Dr Richard Massingham (later a maker of shorts and propaganda films). And when in 1938, MGM filmed the 1937 novel, *The Citadel* (by another doctor, A. J. Cronin) which showed the best and worst of medicine, they changed his standard disclaimer ('Every character, place and institution in the book is entirely fictitious and no reference whatsoever is intended to any living person') to the rather more rhapsodic

> This motion picture is a story of individual characterizations and is in no way intended as a reflection on the great medical profession which has done so much towards beating back those forces of nature that retard the physical progress of the human race.

6   Anthony Kearey, op. cit. At the time, this was a liberal position.

7   BMA, 'Medicine on radio and television' (evidence submitted to the Pilkington Committee, 1960), and see also ITA Annual Report and Accounts (1959–60).

8   Kearey, op. cit.

9   Polly Toynbee, 'Richard Gordon: Doctor at Heart', *Guardian*, 23 May 1983.

10 Like Dr Joe Gannon in the American series 'Medical Center' (1969–76, one of CBS's four top-rated shows), whom, a writer suggested, seemed qualified in all twenty of the medical specialities recognised by the American Medical Association (Michael Real, *Mass Mediated Culture*, Prentice-Hall, 1977).

11 'Maybury', broadcast on BBC 2 in 1981 and 1983.

12 Gerbner et al., op. cit.

13 Joan Liebmann-Smith and Sharon L. Rosen, 'The presentation of illness on television' in Charles Winick (ed.), *Deviance and Mass Media* (Sage 1978).

14 Ibid.

15 Michael Halberstam, 'An MD reviews Dr Welby of TV', *New York Times Magazine*, 16 January 1972.

16 Liebmann-Smith and Rosen, op. cit. Real, op. cit., sampling nine episodes of the series, found seven out of the nine patients were wealthy.

17 Mary B. Cassata et al., 'In sickness and in health', *Journal of Communication*, August 1979, 29 (4). But see later in this chapter for recent changes.

18 Manuela Soares, *The Soap Opera Book* (Harmony, 1978).
19 Cassata, op. cit.
20 Donna Woolfolk Cross, *Mediaspeak* (Mentor, 1983).
21 James McLaughlin, 'The doctor shows', *Journal of Communication* 25 (3), 1975.
22 Liebmann-Smith and Rosen, op. cit.
23 Though these, too, have been changing since the advent of 'Hill Street Blues' and 'Cagney and Lacey'.
24 Charlotte Brunsdon, ' "Crossroads": notes on soap opera', *Screen*, vol. 22, no. 4, 1981, p. 34.
25 'Marcus Welby, MD' (pilot episode, transmitted 26 March 1969).
26 Richard Dyer, 'Entertainment and Utopia' in Rick Altman (ed.), *Genre: The Musical* (Routledge & Kegan Paul, 1981), p. 177.
27 Quoted in Horace Newcomb and Robert S. Alley, *The Producer's Medium* (Oxford University Press, 1983), who comment 'The TV doctors and lawyers have become metaphors for social dreams, personifications of social spirit' (p. 80).
28 Barbara M. Korsch and Vida Francis Negreta, 'Doctor–patient communication', *Scientific American*, 227 (5), 1972.
29 D. Tagliacozzo and H. Mauksch, 'The patient's view of the patient's role' in G. Jaco (ed.), *Patients, Physicians, and Illness* (Free Press, 1972).
30 Michael Balint, *The Doctor, His Patient, and the Illness* (Tavistock, 1957). Enid Balint and J. S. Norell ((eds) *Six Minutes for the Patient*, Tavistock, 1973) later suggested that this didn't necessarily require a long interview with the patient, but could be based on the 'flash' technique, whereby the doctor – in a personal flash of insight – uses their intuition to connect with the patient and gauge what's really troubling them. The TV doctors do it all the time.
31 Even the episode's ironic title – 'Behold the Great Man' – made plain its critique ('Dr Kildare', second season, NBC, 1962).
32 Liebmann-Smith and Rosen, op. cit.
33 Raymond Massey, *A Hundred Different Lives* (Robson Books, 1979, p. 392).
34 Quoted by Halberstam, op. cit., p. 30.
35 Newcomb and Alley, op. cit. David Victor countered, 'I helped the image, the positive image, of medicine' (p. 88).
36 Liebmann-Smith and Rosen, op. cit.
37 C. Murray Parkes, 'Psycho-social transitions: a field for study' *Social Science and Medicine*, vol. 5. 1971, p. 102.
38 Harris Dienstfrey, 'Doctors, Lawyers and other TV heroes', *Commentary*, 35 (6), June 1963, p. 524.
39 John Carvel and Dennis Barker, 'Cabinet overruled Tebbit on Ministerial link for BBC attack', *Guardian*, 3 October, 1986.

40   Richard Brooks, 'BBC faces new Tory broadside', *Observer*, 2 November 1986.

41   'Class and Trash', *Self*, September 1984, p. 104.

42   'St Elsewhere' actually introduced corridors because the series was set in a Boston hospital but filmed in Los Angeles, so almost no outside shots were possible: the long corridors allowed a wide-angled camera to make long, tracking shots and move to different scenes, providing visual variety.

43   The doctor shows also became, in a sense, redundant. It was no longer necessary to depict ideal fictional doctors in order to fault real ones: their failings could now be more directly addressed in documentaries.

44   Cronin, of course, invented ideal doctors too: he wrote *Adventures of a Black Bag*, on which the TV and radio series 'Dr Finlay's Casebook' was based.

45   Roderick Gilchrist, 'Why there are too many suitable cases for treatment', *Daily Mail*, 18 June 1977.

46   'The Quality of Mercy' ('Medical Story', NBC, 8 January 1976.

47   Quoted in Mike Poole and John Wyver, *Powerplays: Trevor Griffiths in Television* (BFI, 1984, pp. 117–8).

48   Trevor Griffiths, *Through the Night and Such Impossibilities* (Faber, 1977), p. 61.

49   Ibid., p. 63.

50   Author's Preface, ibid.

51   Griffiths, op. cit., p. 63.

52   Quoted in an interview with Ralph Appelbaum, 'Genetic genocide', *Films and Filming* 280, vol. 24, no. 4, January 1978, p. 16).

53   'Minor Complications' was transmitted by BBC 1 (18 November 1980), just around the time of the 'Panorama' programme on brain-death (see Chapter 10).

54   Quoted in an interview with Anne Karpf, 'The NHS: a terminal case', *Guardian*, 5 October 1983.

55   Chris Dunkley, *Financial Times*, 7 October 1983.

56   Darrell Maddox, 'How they keep TV medical shows honest', *Modern Healthcare*, November 1975, p. 38.

57   'The BBC's medical programmes and their effects onlay audiences' (BBC, 1976).

58   Lois Kaufman, 'Prime-Time Nutrition', *Journal of Communication* no. 30, 1980. See also Wendy L. Way, 'Food-Related behaviours on prime-time television', *Journal of Nutrition Education*, vol. 15, no. 3, 1983, and Gerbner et al., op. cit.

59   Warren Breed and James R. De Foe, 'The portrayal of the drinking process on prime-time television', *Journal of Communication*, vol. 31, no. 1, 1981. J. M. Wober, interestingly, found British viewers

thought that drinking – both as a positive and negative experience – occurred more often in real-life than on television ('Alcohol on television and in viewers' experience', paper given at the 21st International Congress of Applied Psychology, Jerusalem, July 1986).

60 Lilian Nowak, 'Alcohol in television fiction in Sweden – some theoretical and methodological reflections' (unpublished paper, Audience and Programme Research Department, Swedish Broadcasting Corporation, July 1985). See also Anders Hansen, 'The portrayal of alcohol on television', *Health Education Journal*, vol. 45, no. 3, 1986, and Shearon A. Lowery, 'Soap and booze in the afternoon: an analysis of the portrayal of alcohol use in daytime serials', *Journal of Studies on Alcohol*, vol. 41, no. 9, 1980.

61 Lawrence Wallack and Warren Breed, 'Mass media and alcohol: some opportunities for change' (unpublished paper, Pacific Institute for Research and Evaluation, no date). The campaigners were inspired by the case of cigarettes, whose use by prime-time characters steadily declined after the first Surgeon-General's report in 1964 linking smoking and lung cancer. While cigarette use was 4.52 per hour in dramas in the early 1950s, it had dropped to 0.35 by 1981–2.

62 Alice Kubiaczyk, quoted in Mindy Beck, 'Public interest groups tap into entertainment TV', *Access*, no. 18, September 1975, p. 9.

63 Ibid., pp. 9, 10.

Chapter twelve

1 Philip A. Kalisch et al., 'Images of Nurses on Television' (Springer 1983).

2 Ibid.

3 'St Elsewhere' (transmitted NBC, 26 February 1986).

4 'Angels', transmitted on BBC 1 between 1975 and 1984, gathered a sizeable audience, almost 5½ million.

5 Margaret Gallagher, 'Television content and gender: what it portrays and how it is perceived' (paper presented at the conference of the International Association of Mass Communication Researchers, Paris, 1982).

6 *Carry on Nurse* (1959); *Carry on Doctor* (1967); *Carry on Again Doctor* (1969); and *Carry on Matron* (1972).

7 *Doctor in the House* (1954); *Doctor at Sea* (1955); *Doctor at Large* (1957); *Doctor in Love* (1960); *Doctor in Distress* (1963); *Doctor in Clover* (1966); and *Doctor in Trouble* (1970).

8 Roslyn Wallach Bologh, 'Alienation in the patient role: source of ambivalence and humor in comic get well cards', *Sociology of Health and Illness*, vol. 1, no. 2, September 1979.

9 Acknowledged when the raunchy physician in *Carry on Doctor* declares: 'the only thing I'm good at you get struck off for'.

10 'The Singing Detective', transmitted on BBC 1 from November 1986. In a nod to the doctor shows and their idealisations of medicine, one of the doctors was called Dr Finlay.

Chapter thirteen

1 Albert Bandura, *Principles of Behaviour Modification* (Holt, Rinehart & Winston, 1971).

2 Michael Adler, 'Medicine and the media', *British Medical Journal*, vol. 283, 21 November 1981 and 'Consulting patterns after a television programme on sexually transmitted diseases', *British Journal of Venereal Disease*, vol. 58, 1982. The programme was a 50-minute 'Man Alive' (BBC 2, April 1981).

3 Charles E. Irwin and Susan G. Millstein, 'Predictors of tampon use in adolescents after media coverage of Toxic Shock Syndrome', *Annals of Internal Medicine*, vol. 96, Part 2, 1982.

4 Stephen Platt, 'The aftermath of Angie's overdose: is soap (opera) damaging to your health?', *British Medical Journal*, vol. 294, 11 April 1987.

5 'Trouble and Strife', *New Society*, 2 May 1986.

6 This section specifically addresses mass media look-after-yourself compaigns in Western countries. Third World versions, such as Tanzania's radio campaigns, are conducted in very different circumstances and are beyond the scope of this book, but have been well documented. See, for example, Bertram A. P. Mahai, 'Health and nutrition education through radio study groups: the Tanzanian experience' in Manfred Meyer, (ed.) *Health Education by Television and Radio* (K. G. Saur, 1981).

7 Leon S. Robertson et al., 'A controlled study of the effect of television messages on safety belt use', *American Journal of Public Health*, vol. 32, April 1982.

8 P. S. Mukherji et al., 'Consultation behaviour and the influence of the media', *Journal of the Royal College of General Practitioners*, vol. 32, April 1982.

9 A. Gatherer et al., 'Is Health Education Effective?' (Health Education Council 1979).

10 H. J. Barnum, 'Mass media and health communications', *Journal of Medical Education*, vol. 50, January 1975, p. 24.

11 Robin McCron and Judith Budd, 'Mass communication and health education' in Ian Sutherland (ed.), *Health Education: Perspectives and Choices* (Allen & Unwin, 1979).

12 Pekka Puska and Kai Koskela, 'Community-based strategies to fight smoking', *New York State Journal of Medicine*, December 1983, and Pekka Puska et al., 'A comprehensive television smoking cessation programme in Finland', *International Journal of Health Education*, supplement to vol. 22, issue no. 4, Oct–Dec, 1979.

13 Nathan Maccoby and Douglas Soloman, 'Experiments in risk reduction through community health education' in Meyer, op. cit., p. 154. In the same work, Brian Flay also concluded that mass media with social support or printed material was more effective than just viewing.

14 A study of a local radio medical phone-in (on Plymouth Sound, Devon) found that 96 out of 158 callers were referred directly back to their GP (Adrian Rogers, 'Doctor on the Air', *Journal of the Royal College of General Practitioners*, October 1980).

15 See, for instance, the interviews in Wendy Farrant and Jill Russell, 'The politics of health information', *Bedford Way Papers* 28, University of London Institute of Education 1986. And see Chapter 3 for a critique of individualistic health education.

16 J. M. Wober, 'Informing the public about AIDS' (IBA, April 1987); see also 'Public attitudes to AIDS: the report of a follow-up BBC/Gallup survey (BBC,. April 1987).

17 John McKnight, 'Power, not poverty, for a healthy public', *Radical Community Medicine*, no. 22, Summer 1985, p. 35. Nicholas Dorn and Nigel South, *Message in a Bottle* (Gower, 1983) note that look-after-yourself programmes, far from encouraging 'informed autonomy' in the audience, may be trying to foster greater public dependency on the media – albeit through their 'good' rather than 'bad' messages.

18 J. Lo and C. Pinto, 'Multilingual health announcements on television: an effective way to communicate with ethnic minorities?' in D. S. Leathar et al., *Health Education and the Media II* (Pergamon Press, 1986).

19 BBC Radio London's 1979 Ethnic Health project tried to do this. For an account see Penny Webb and Keith Yeomans, 'A delicate balance – health education and local radio' (unpublished paper given at the First Internation Conference on Health Education and the Media, Edinburgh, 1981) and Penny Webb, 'Health education', *Media Project News*, October 1979).

20 McKnight, op. cit., pp. 34, 37.

21 'An audience research inquiry into some of the reactions to, and effects of, the television series "The Changing Face of Medicine", broadcast in November 1975', in 'The BBC's medical programmes

and their effects on lay audiences' (BBC, 1976).

22   Irene Shaw, 'Horizon: alcohol programme' (BBC Broadcasting Research 1983, p. 19)

23   Karen Day, 'Attitudes towards health and health education' (BBC Broadcasting Research, 1987), p. 22.

24   Interview with Maura Lerner, May 1985, New York.

25   Interview with David Paterson, April 1985.

26   Both quotations from Anne Karpf, 'Medicine and television' (unpublished M.Sc. dissertation, Polytechnic of the South Bank 1981, pp. 129–30).

27   Jay Blumler and Denis McQuail, *Television in Politics* (Faber, 1968, pp. 11–12). These were the kind of questions which health educators were also pondering in their attempt to reach the public, but among social scientists, 'uses and grats' formed the basis of relatively little empirical audience research, with great difference of emphasis in what research there was.

28   Stuart Hall, 'Encoding/decoding', in Stuart Hall et al. (eds), *Culture, Media, Language* (Hutchinson 1980), and David Morley who, in 'The "Nationwide" Audience' (British Film Institute, 1980) showed two 'Nationwide' programmes to twenty-nine groups of different social, cultural, and educational backgrounds, and found radically different readings. For a criticism of Morley's work, see Justin Wren-Lewis, 'The encoding/decoding model: criticisms and redevelopments for research on decoding', *Media, Culture & Society*, vol. 5, no. 2, April 1983.

29   Kay Richardson and John Corner, 'Reading reception: mediation and transparency in viewers' accounts of a TV programme', *Media, Culture & Society*, vol. 8, no. 4, October 1986.

30   Except for the work of Robin McCron and Judith Budd, op. cit., and Dorn and South, op. cit.

31   Bernard C. Cohen, *The Press and Foreign Policy* (Princeton University Press, 1963), p. 120, quoted in Maxwell E. McCombs and Donald L. Shaw, 'The agenda-setting function of mass media', *Public Opinion Quarterly*, vol. 36, Summer 1972, p. 177.

32   An American study into the relationship between children's exposure to TV drug advertising and attitudes towards medicine found that heavy viewing children believe that people are frequently sick and frequently take medicine; relief after taking medicine is quick; and the feeling of recovery is greater after taking medicine (Charles Atkin, 'Effects of television advertising on children: survey of preadolescent's response to television commercials', Report no. 6, Michigan State University). In other words, just the view you'd get from watching a lot of medical documentaries. TV drug ads also encourage us to try this or that proprietary drug to cure our headache so that we can get on with our lives, as if our ailments had nothing to do with our lives.

33　Jocelyn Cornwell, *Hard-Earned Lives: Accounts of Health and Illness from East London* (Tavistock, 1984).

34　Peter Dahlgren, 'Media, meaning and method: a 'post-rational' perspective', *Nordicom Review of Nordic Mass Communication Research*, no. 2, 1985. There is a problem in using a public/private or official/unofficial typology similar to that with the 'preferred reading' (note 28). How are official accounts to be identified except by the researcher allocating certain beliefs in advance to the official category? The very allocation of views into official and unofficial categories is itself an ideological process. Nevertheless, since all categorisations are subjective and partly derive from the researcher's assumptions rather than emerging spontaneously from the data, I still think the public/private typology is useful in distinguishing between medically-sanctioned views in wide currency and contrasting lay beliefs.

35　Day, op. cit.

36　Dorn and South, op. cit., do something like this in their 'class cultural' approach.

37　John Willis, speaking at Thames TV's 'Social action through television' conference, London (4 November 1983).

38　Quoted in Alan Dalton, 'Asbestos – TV succeeds where others fail', *Science for People* no. 53, Winter 1982.

39　Ibid.

Conclusion

1　'We're Not Mad . . . We're Angry' (Channel 4, 17 November 1986), part of Channel 4's 'Mind's Eye' season on mental health, which included a three-part series on schizophrenia, with schizophrenics talking about their experiences. Channel 4 has also broadcast some innovative programmes on disability (see Chapter 5).

2　'City General' (Channel 4, 16 December 1984), repeated in 1985 as part of a six-part series.

3　For example, 'Picture of Health', eight 45-minute documentaries on Channel 4 from 18 November 1983, and 'Under the Health Surface' about the origins of ill-health in Northern Ireland on Channel 4, 15 June 1986.

4　See K. Klein et al., 'The health education concept in the cable television pilot project in Ludwigshafen, Rhineland-Palatinate, Federal Republic of Germany', in D. S. Leathar et al., *Health Education and the Media II* (Pergamon Press, 1986).

5　See Chapter 6.

6　See Philip Schlesinger, 'From public service to commodity: the political economy of teletext in the UK', *Media, Culture & Society*, vol. 7, no. 4, October 1985.

7   Christopher Lasch, *The Culture of Narcissism* (Abacus, 1980), p. 5.

8   June Goodfield, 'Reflections on science and the media', *American Association for the Advancement of Science*, 1981.

9   Tabitha M. Powledge, 'What is "The Media" and why is it saying these terrible things about aggression research?' in Jeffrey H. Goldstein (ed.) *Reporting Science: The Case of Aggression* (Lawrence Erlbaum Associates, 1986).

10 Rae Goodell, 'How to kill a controversy: the case of recombinant DNA' in Sharon M. Friedman et al. (eds), *Scientists and Journalists* (Free Press, 1986).

Index